THE HEALTH OF THE PRESIDENTS

The Health
of The Presidents

RUDOLPH MARX, M.D.

G. P. Putnam's Sons   NEW YORK

To Agnes

ACKNOWLEDGMENTS

To my regret I cannot enumerate the names of all the friends who encouraged and advised me in writing this book, particularly my colleagues in the various medical specialties whom I buttonholed for dozens of curbstone consultations.

A particular debt of gratitude I owe to Mr. Stephen Longstreet who gave me the idea for this book, and Doctor Julius Kahn who read the copy for me.

I also want to acknowledge that among the hundreds of books used for reference, I derived the most valuable information from Doctor Philip Marshall Dale's *Medical Biographies; Mr. President—How Is Your Health?* by Karl C. Wold, M.D.; and *Lincoln and the Doctors* by Milton H. Shutes, M.D.

I also want to express my gratitude to John M. Conner, Chief Librarian of the Los Angeles County Medical Association Library and his staff for their interest and support.

THE AUTHOR

CONTENTS

FOREWORD

JUST as darkness and light are inseparable parts of day, sickness and health are indivisible essentials of life, and of history —life's flow and record.

The borderlines between the realms of sickness and health are indefinite and fluid, subject to arbitrary interpretation, particularly in the field of psychology. Hence, the description of the medical aspect of history is hampered even more than the writing of history in general by a dearth of unequivocal data and standards.

These medical portraits of the Presidents are concerned with the role sickness and health played in molding their character and in influencing their actions and decisions, especially during their terms in office. In the same way that the health of any leader affects the lives of other members of his group, so the health of the President of the United States concerns all of us, and often has far-reaching effect on world events.

Years of ill health gave George Washington the fortitude to win the Revolutionary War against hopeless odds. A mental depression of his successor, John Adams, jeopardized peace negotiations with France. Woodrow Wilson, during his struggle for the League of Nations, was afflicted with arteriosclerotic vascular insufficiency of the brain that deprived his mind of the resilience to make the necessary compromises. Franklin Delano Roosevelt might never have become the master politician and courageous leader he was, but for the attack of poliomyelitis in his thirty-ninth year.

11

The health of the Presidents of the United States automatically highlights the history of medicine over the past two centuries, during which time diagnostic, preventive, and therapeutic medicine, keeping abreast of the progress in allied sciences, has been completely transformed.

A doctor today must interpret from meager, incomplete records the symptoms and ailments of our early Presidents. Diagnostic methods then were in their infancy. Up to the beginning of the nineteenth century even percussion, tapping, to discover the location and extent of an abnormal density was unfamiliar to American medicine. The stethoscope was introduced some twenty-five years later. The first experiments in bacteriology— which led to the discovery that most diseases are caused by specific microorganisms—were made by Pasteur at the time of our Civil War. The X-ray, which revolutionized the art of diagnosis, was not discovered until 1895 in Germany; the first electrocardiograph, as recently as 1903 in Holland.

For our forefathers, pain and death from infection were the concomitants of surgery. Anesthesia and antiseptics were still far off. The first operation under ether was performed in Boston in 1846. Antisepsis in surgery, introduced in Europe in 1867 by Lister, was not generally accepted in America for another twenty years.

Up to the second half of the nineteenth century, a high rate of infant mortality was taken for granted. In London, between 1719 and 1809, 41.3 per cent of the children died before the age of five. Child mortality in the thirteen colonies was certainly no less. A high percentage of babies died from nutritional deficiencies and diarrhea. Those that survived faced the prevalent contagious diseases of childhood—measles, scarlet fever, whooping cough, and diphtheria. If a person living in the eighteenth century survived these trials of infancy and childhood, he had still to run the gauntlet of countless other diseases.

The "White Plague," tuberculosis, was the number one killer of the time, easily transmitted by close contact. Malarial mosquitoes were breeding in the swamps everywhere. Ever present were the various strains of dysentery and the enteric fevers, typhoid and paratyphoid, harbored in human carriers, transmitted by food, drink, and the ubiquitous flies. Different types of pneumonia were a constant menace. Smallpox took its steady toll. The shock troops of death, staphylococci and streptococci, feasted in every wound. Lurking in the background of this Odyssey of monsters were the sirens of venereal diseases whose island was littered with their victims.

The medical concepts of the colonists were based for the most part on a hodgepodge of ancient superstitions and traditions. Contamination of the air by a miasma was blamed for the spread of most diseases. These miasmata were believed to emanate from putrescent water and from swamps, and to float in the air. The word "malaria" literally means "bad air." Some diseases were supposedly transmitted by polluted water, a theory that came close to the truth for typhoid and dysentery.

Specific remedies against most infections were unknown, except quinine, effective against malaria, and mercury, for the sores of syphilis. The prevalent methods of therapy, instead of assisting the body's defenses against the invading foe, often betrayed and weakened them. It seemed all too true, as Molière had written in Le Malade Imaginaire in 1673, that "nearly all men die of their remedies and not of their illnesses."

One of the most barbarous of customs was "bleeding," a holdover from prehistoric times when it was supposed to let demons escape from the body. The average amount removed in one bloodletting was a pint, and the more serious the illness, the more "bad" blood was taken. The theory was that some glandular secretion in the body could replace the drained blood within a few hours; actually it takes weeks. This indiscriminate practice of venesection, or bleeding, continued until a hundred years ago.

The use of purgatives and emetics—practiced by the ancient Egyptians, whose higher caste purged themselves every ten days —was still the treatment for sickness in the eighteenth century. Usually they did more harm than good. Laxatives have killed thousands of appendicitis victims by distending and bursting an inflamed and brittle appendix. Enemas were somewhat less dangerous, though repeated colonic flushings as practiced by seventeenth and eighteenth century physicians weakened and exhausted the patient.

Another common practice of colonial doctors was the raising of blisters on the skin close to the focus of the ailment. This was based on the belief that the inflammation could be "drawn" from the inside to the outside of the body by counterirritation. As it was usually done with caustic substances, it often produced severe and painful chemical burns.

Preventive medicine was practically unknown up to the first breakthrough of the barrier of ignorance, toward the end of the eighteenth century, when the English physician Janner advocated vaccination with cowpox against smallpox. Previously the more dangerous method of inoculation, using pus of human pox, had been sporadically practiced throughout the world. Jenner's method consisted in transferring cowpox infection by scratching the patient with a needle bathed in the contents of the cow blister. The result was an abortive form of cowpox, immunizing the vaccinated patient against the dangers of the smallpox.

Doctors during Washington's time were incapable of giving a rational explanation of most disease phenomena. In place of facts, they would offer only hoary philosophical theories for the bewildering kaleidoscope of symptoms and for their traditional methods of treatment. Little wonder that only a few people survived to the "cancer age." In 1789, the oldest vital statistics in America, compiled for Massachusetts and New Hampshire by one Reverend Edward Wigglesworth, gave a life expectancy of 28.15 years, a figure comparable to European statistics at that time.

It is not only the short life expectancy that startles us. Just as shocking is the thought of the needless pain and suffering, the long months of incapacitating illness which were the lot even of those whose constitutions permitted them a longer and fuller life. To this category belonged the first President of the United States, who was penalized all his life by the ignorance of his time.

THE HEALTH OF THE PRESIDENTS

George Washington

(1732 – 1799)

IF YOU look closely at the best-known portrait of George Washington by Gilbert Stuart, you will observe a bulging of the cheeks, as if they had been stuffed with cotton. It has been reported that Gilbert Stuart actually did use cotton to fill out the sunken cheeks of the illustrious sitter of this portrait, who at the time was wearing a set of ill-fitting dentures. In 1795, when the portrait was painted, Washington was the proud possessor of two sets of these awkward and noisy contraptions made of hippopotamus ivory.

Up to the nineteenth century, dentistry in the modern sense was unknown. If something was wrong with a tooth, it was pulled out. At the age of twenty-two, Washington had a toothache which was relieved by having the tooth pulled. The same treatment was used for every aching tooth over the years, so that by the age of fifty-seven he had hardly any teeth left and had to wear dentures. Six years later his one remaining tooth was pulled.

The blue eyes of the Father of our Country look down from the portrait with his proverbial Olympian serenity. Yet these eyes had flashed angry lightning at Brandywine and Germantown when they saw the Continental Army break and flee.

What appears to be a white wig in the picture, is reported to have been Washington's own hair, well powdered. It had been reddish in his youth, turning, as he had said, an early gray in the service of his country. In the picture the face of the President is covered with a rosy glaze. His real complexion was described by his contemporaries as sallow.

17

The painter also carefully left out the pockmarks which deeply pitted Washington's features. These blemishes he had acquired at the age of nineteen during an ill-fated journey to the Barbados. He was then accompanying Lawrence, his brother and guardian, who was suffering from tuberculosis of the lungs and was vainly looking for salvation in the balmy climate of the West Indies.

In his diary, Washington notes that he was "strongly attacked" by smallpox and was in bed for three weeks. He carried the marks of the disease to his grave.

In most portraits, the Father of his Country is shown with chest bulging with well-deserved pride. The chest, too, must have been tailor-made. Actually, Washington's chest was flat and somewhat hollow in the center, probably from early rickets.

Other physical characteristics of the President are more realistically painted in the Gilbert Stuart pictures. They are the strong nose, jutting chin, and the large strong hands. Many are the tales of his athletic prowess. Every child knows the story of how young George once threw a silver dollar across the Rappahannock River, which seems incredible in view of the great width of the river at the point described, and also because Washington was not one to throw silver dollars around.

Like Lincoln, with whom he had many physical characteristics in common, Washington in his youth was a champion wrestler and rail-splitter. It is curious that the two greatest Presidents of the United States were also physical giants. During the times of both, the average man was considerably smaller.

In spite of great physical strength and endurance, Washington was subjected to a host of diseases in his lifetime. He suffered at least ten attacks of serious illness which on several occasions brought him to the brink of death. The question is whether Washington had more than his share of sickness in a period of history when a number of diseases were taken for granted, diseases which modern science has practically conquered and which we have almost forgotten.

Concerning the medical history of Washington's progenitors,

we know that his grandfather died at thirty-seven, his father at forty-nine, probably from infectious diseases; on his maternal side we only know that his mother reached the age of eighty-two, to die from cancer of the breast a year before Washington's death. From her, George, her first-born son, inherited not only his physical features but also his unusually strong constitution and power of endurance. However, he was born with little natural immunity against most of the diseases to which he was exposed. And if we consider his medical history, we marvel that he ever reached the age of sixty-seven, when he succumbed to a streptococcic throat infection—and to the medical mistreatment he received.

We know nothing about Washington's childhood diseases. They were taken for granted and no one bothered to record them. From the diaries and letters of Washington and from the reports of his doctors and friends, we have an exact knowledge of the illnesses which attacked him after his sixteenth year. At seventeen Washington was licensed from William and Mary College in Virginia as a public surveyor, a profession he practiced for several years in Fairfax County. At that time great stretches of Virginia were dotted with swamps infested with malaria-carrying mosquitoes. Of the original thirteen colonies, the southernmost, Virginia, had the largest population, the majority of which was infected with malaria. Camping outdoors as a surveyor, Washington was bitten by mosquitoes and suffered his first attack of malaria, called "ague." During his later life Washington had numerous additional bouts of this intermittent fever.

We have already mentioned the severe case of smallpox which he contracted at nineteen during a visit to the Barbados. This calamitous trip not only failed to cure his brother, who died a few months later, but, nursing his sick brother, George came in close contact with the tuberculosis bacilli and they promptly invaded his body. He had barely recovered from his smallpox attack and returned to Mt. Vernon when the tuberculosis flared up in the form of acute pleurisy. He recovered slowly and was in poor health for two years. By that time the disease must have been arrested, as Washington felt strong enough to enter military service. In October 1753, he received a commission as major in the Virginia militia and was immediately ordered on a fruitless mission to the French commander of the Ohio Territory. During the next year he led a military expedition against the French at Fort Duquesne and was badly defeated. He had hardly returned when he was stricken with a severe attack of malaria.

In 1755, the English general Edward Braddock arrived in Virginia with several battalions of British troops. Braddock was told of Washington's experience in frontier fighting and of his intimate knowledge of the terrain, and asked him to join his expedition against the French and Indians as his personal aide-de-camp and leader of the Virginia Auxiliaries. The campaign had not progressed far when Washington fell ill, apparently of influenza.

On the day before the battle of Monongahela, Washington rose from his sickbed, still weak and barely able to sit on his horse. The leading column under Braddock fell into a French-Indian ambush and was almost annihilated. Trying to rally his troops, Braddock received a mortal wound. Washington managed to extricate the remainder of the detachment after two horses had been killed under him and his uniform pierced by four balls. He returned to Mt. Vernon exhausted, and wrote to one of his half-brothers: "I am not able were I ever so willing, to meet you in town for I assure you that it is with some difficulty and much fatigue that I visit my plantations in the Neck; so much has a sickness of five weeks duration reduced me." Two years later Washington contracted a severe type of dysentery accompanied by high fever and deep prostration which lasted several months. Recovery was slow and Washington was worried about his condition.

In the meantime the British government had sent a new general, John Forbes, with considerable reinforcements for a new campaign against the French and Indians in the Ohio Basin. The twenty-six-year-old Colonel Washington was roused from his "apprehensions of decay" by the drums of war. The tonic of excitement invigorated him enough to accompany Forbes as commander of the advance guard. Washington had the great satisfaction that this, the third attempt to defeat the French in which he participated, was successful. Fort Duquesne was taken and renamed Fort Pitt, later Pittsburgh.

After this campaign Washington resigned his commission, returned, and in January 1759 married the widow Martha Custis. Martha brought to Mt. Vernon the two surviving children from her first marriage. The marriage was happy though childless. Apparently it had a beneficial influence on Washington's health. No sickness is recorded in his diaries until 1761, when he had another attack which he believed to be malaria, though it may have been typhoid fever. He was in bed for several weeks with pain and great prostration. Barely recovered, he had a relapse of fever which made him quite despondent and fearful that he was very near his "last gasp."

Scanning the diaries of Washington, one is astonished by his gloomy outlook each time he was stricken with serious illness, and by his readiness to anticipate a fatal outcome. A superficial reader might suspect that Washington was a hypochondriac, but the medical history of Washington's family makes it clear that Washington's apprehensions were justified. He saw the toll that disease took of his own generation in his family. Of his nine brothers, half-brothers and sisters, two died in infancy, the other seven between the ages of thirteen and sixty-four. George survived them all, as well as his two adopted children. How could he expect to outlive all his near relatives, except his wife, Martha?

Sickness affects different people in different ways. Long periods of disease accompanied by disability, pain and danger, such as Washington had to endure, exert a profound influence in molding a person's character. They are times of trial which soften the weak and temper the strong. Suffering and heartache bring out in small men selfishness and self-pity, in great souls humanity and compassion.

The loneliness of the sickbed gives the patient an opportunity to know himself, take stock of his capabilities, and to crystallize his dreams and ambitions. Long periods of physical disability gave Washington the time to find himself, and to plan his role in life.

Men's virtues are not born with them; they must be attained with great effort. Much has been written about the self-control and patience of Washington as a leader. Self-control and patience are masks which are acquired by long and painstaking practice in suppressing natural outbursts of emotion and impatience. The sickbed is the best school in which to learn patience. Knowing that healthy people do not like to hear others complain and moan, the sick man tries to hide his resentment and pain under a forced smile, and to play the good sport. In time he learns self-control.

It can be assumed that other qualities which the mature Washington exhibited, his courage and unyielding determination, were also conditioned by his state of health. A man who has repeatedly faced death from mysterious diseases is relieved to encounter enemies he can see and fight. Washington's singleness of purpose may have derived its force from the store of energy dammed up by the frustrations of sickness.

There exists only one report that Washington was incapacitated by sickness during the Revolutionary War. At Valley Forge there was not a day when Washington was not at his post, keeping together and encouraging his ill-armed, ill-clothed, ill-fed little army, far outnumbered by the well-nourished and well-equipped British troops. His sense of responsibility and the consciousness of his mission gave stimulation to his adrenal glands, raised his normal powers of endurance, resistance and immunity. Destiny kept alive and well the only man of his time who could lead the American Revolution to victory. The General's life seemed charmed. He was never touched by a bullet though he was exposed at all times to enemy fire, leading and rallying his troops.

Washington remained free of disabling disease until 1786. Then, after the war and his election to the Presidency, came a letdown. Once more he fell ill with "ague and fever." He was treated by Dr. James Craik, his physician and close personal friend for thirty-two years. Craik was born in Scotland and had graduated from the University of Edinburgh, the most renowned medical school of the time. After his graduation, he had migrated to the New World. He had accompanied Washington on the Braddock expedition and all during the War of Independence had been connected with the Continental Army, serving as second in command to the medical director general. Through Craik's agency, the Conway Cabal, a conspiracy to replace Washington with General Horatio Gates, had been exposed.

In 1786 Dr. Craik for the first time employed "the bark" on Washington for malaria, with excellent results. This was quinine, from the bark of the cinchona tree, used for a hundred and fifty years against malaria in South America and Europe, but apparently it had not yet been introduced in North America. It was given in the form of a powder, decoction or extract, and was one of the first specific remedies employed for any disease.

During his first year as President, there developed what the doctors called "a malignant carbuncle" on Washington's left hip, probably of staphylococcic origin. For several weeks he was desperately ill. He was cared for by Dr. Samuel Bard, a well-known New York physician, who watched over the patient constantly for many days and nights.

Finally Dr. Bard summoned all his courage, incised the carbuncle and drained the pus, with immediate improvement. When the President was able to go out after six weeks, his coach had to be rebuilt to enable him to lie at full length.

In 1789 Washington went on an official visit to New England. At the outskirts of Boston he was delayed a considerable time in rain and stormy weather; it seemed the city and state authorities were unable to decide on the etiquette of receiving the Chief of State, for which there was no precedent. As a result of the delay, Washington developed a bad cold, with inflammation of the eyes. Following this visit, an epidemic of respiratory infections spread through the city. The die-hard Loyalists of Boston promptly named it "the Washington Influenza."

Numerous colds and the large doses of quinine taken for his malaria affected Washington's hearing noticeably during the last decade of his life. The deafness made it difficult for him to carry on conversations at public affairs, and increased his native diffidence. Thus he acquired a reputation of being cold and aloof.

After reaching middle age, Washington had to wear glasses for reading. In those days, glasses were just as unfashionable as wearing hearing aids has been until quite recently. People were ashamed to wear glasses, considering them a humiliating disfigurement like a clubfoot or hunchback. Washington used his reading glasses only in the privacy of his family or among intimate friends.

In 1790 the federal government was removed from New York to Philadelphia. In the spring of the same year Washington was brought down with pneumonia followed by a relapse which almost proved fatal. He wrote: "I have already within less than a year had two severe attacks, the last worse than the first. A third probably will put me to sleep with my fathers."

No doubt the pressures and frictions of the Presidency were a great drain on the health of the aging Washington, as on most other Presidents since. He was galled by the ingratitude of the people and the press, who assailed him bitterly during his second term.

Sixty-five years old, sick, and tired of public service, Washington declined to be nominated for a third term and retired to the seclusion of Mt. Vernon in the spring of 1797. There he was allowed only two and a half years of well-deserved rest. In 1798 his old nemesis malaria recurred, and responded only tardily to "the bark."

On December 12, 1799, as was his custom, Washington was riding about his farm from 10 A.M. until 3 P.M. The weather was bad, with rain, hail and snow falling alternately, driven by an icy wind. Washington was a stickler for punctuality in all his activities, including meal hours. But on this day, Washington was late for dinner. Served promptly at three o'clock, the meal was on the table when he entered the house. Colonel Lear, his faithful friend and secretary, observed that the collar of the General's jacket appeared wet and that snow was sticking to his hair, but Washington refused to change his clothes and sat down to dinner. The next day he complained of a cold and sore throat and did not go out in the morning as usual. During the afternoon, in spite of his cold, he went outside to mark some trees he wanted cut down. In the evening a severe hoarseness developed, but he made light of it. Upon retiring, Colonel Lear suggested that the General take something for his cold, but Washington answered, "No, you know I never take anything for a cold; let it go as it came."

Next day at 3 o'clock in the morning, Washington told Martha that he was very unwell, that he had the ague. He could hardly speak, and he breathed with difficulty. Martha begged him to let her awaken the servants and fetch him a home remedy. But Washington sternly refused to let her get up for fear she, too, would catch cold. At daybreak a servant lighted the fire. Colonel Lear presently arrived and found the General unable to speak. A loathsome mixture of molasses, vinegar and butter was offered to him but Washington could not swallow a drop. In trying to get it down, he started to cough convulsively, and almost suffocated.

Rawlins, the overseer of the farm, was sent for to bleed the President. The overseer had acquired his surgical acumen in the practice of veterinary medicine on the farm. He took a pint of blood from Washington, but there was no relief. Colonel Lear next applied "sal volatile," the menthol rub of the time, to the sick man's throat, upon which the patient complained that his throat was very sore. A piece of flannel saturated with the same evil-smelling salve was wound around his neck, and the feet immersed in warm water—all to no avail. At about eight o'clock Washington got up for two hours, but obtained no relief from the changed position. Dr. Craik arrived shortly after nine o'clock.

He applied a blister of Spanish flies (derived from dried and powdered blister beetles) to the throat, took some more blood, and prescribed a gargle of vinegar and sage tea. He also ordered vinegar and hot water for steam inhalation. In attempting to gargle, the patient choked and regurgitated the liquid. At eleven o'clock the bleeding was repeated but the difficulty in swallowing and breathing was not eased. In the meantime Dr. Gustave Richard Brown of Fort Tobacco, and Dr. Elisha Cullen Dick of Alexandria, had been summoned as consultants.

Dr. Brown, the son of a doctor, had been born in Maryland and, like Dr. Craik, had been graduated from the University of Edinburgh. Dr. Dick, the youngest of the attending physicians, was born in Pennsylvania and graduated from the recently founded Medical School of Pennsylvania at Philadelphia.

Both consultants arrived around three o'clock and sat down at the patient's bedside. The most elementary diagnostic methods were not practiced at the time. There is not even a record that the interior of Washington's throat was ever inspected by the physicians. A diagnosis was arrived at by watching the patient, taking his pulse, and observing his external symptoms. The three doctors attending Washington sat helpless while their patient struggled for breath, each inspiration producing a shrill, harsh sound as the air was painfully forced through the obstructed air passage. His skin was blue and the nostrils dilated and contracted with the effort of breathing. He also had great difficulty in swallowing.

The first diagnosis thought of was quinsy, which meant peritonsillar abscess. Later on the diagnosis was changed to "cynanche trachealis," a vague medical term of the time for a severe sore throat involving the voice box, in which the inflammatory swelling of the vocal cords encroaches upon the breathing space. Dr. Brown suggested using the standard treatment recommended by the bloodthirsty medical school of Edinburgh for this condition —additional copious bleeding. The young American doctor, Dick, objected. He argued, "He needs all his strength—bleeding will diminish it." He was overruled by his two senior colleagues, who were supported by the good soldier Washington. A whole quart of blood was taken this time and it was observed that the blood came "slow and thick," the effect of dehydration.

To add insult to injury, the laxative calomel, and the emetic antimony tartrate, were administered, weakening the patient still further by producing vomiting and diarrhea, increasing his dehydration. About half past four Washington gave instructions about his will, and about five o'clock he tried to sit up but was too weak to remain upright for more than half an hour. In the course of the afternoon he appeared in great distress and pain, and frequently changed his position in bed, struggling for breath.

As a last resort Dr. Dick suggested the use of a daring surgical method, the only one available which could have saved the patient from slow suffocation caused by the obstruction of the larynx, tracheotomy—the surgical cutting of an opening into the windpipe below the point of obstruction. In a communication several years later Dr. Dick reasoned, "I proposed to perforate the trachea as means of prolonging life and of affording time for the removal of the obstruction to respiration in the larynx which manifestly threatened immediate dissolution." He argued that the method recommended was imperative at this crucial moment because there was not yet any evidence of involvement of the lower air passages, in which case it would have been too late. He even offered to take personal responsibility for failure.

The older colleagues refused to take a chance on their illustrious patient by using such an unproved and risky procedure which had been successfully employed in only a few instances up to that time. The urgent entreaties of Dr. Dick were in vain. Instead, the senior physicians continued their futile measures by applying blisters and poultices of wheat bran to the legs and feet of the dying patient. The process of gradual suffocation progressed inexorably until about ten minutes before the General expired; then the breathing became easier. The exhausted heart stopped beating between ten and eleven o'clock on the night of December 14, 1799.

From the first, Washington as usual had been exceedingly pessimistic about his illness. He had made up his mind that he was going to die and did what he could to dissuade his doctors from making special efforts for him, begging them only to let him die in peace. "I find I am going," he whispered to Colonel Lear. "My breath cannot last long. I believed from the first that the disorder would prove fatal." A little later he repeated to Dr. Craik: "Doctor, I die hard, but I am not afraid to go." When Dr. Brown came into the room: "I feel myself going," he said. "I thank you for your attention but I pray you to take no more trouble for me. Let me go quietly. I cannot last long."

The exact diagnosis of George Washington's last sickness is still disputed among medical historians. The most convincing study was made by Dr. W. A. Wells of Washington, D.C., in 1927. Up to that time it was believed that Washington had died from diphtheria, corresponding to the diagnosis of "croup," which Dr. Dick had suggested in retrospect. A definite diagnosis cannot be made with certainty as no clinical description of the appearance of the inflammatory process was given. Bacteriological confirmation of a diagnosis was of course unknown. Despite this lack of evidence, Dr. Wells concluded from all the known data that Washington died from a streptococcic laryngitis, an inflammatory swelling of larynx and the vocal cords caused by a strain of virulent streptococci. It is impossible to estimate how much the treatment, with depleting venesections and dehydrating cathartics and emetics, contributed to the fatal outcome.

John Adams

(1735 – 1826)

PANEGYRICAL romances will never be written, nor flattering orations spoken to transmit me to posterity in brilliant colors," wrote John Adams.

He must have felt that he lacked glamor. John Adams succeeded to the Presidency the towering figure who had become a legend in his own time, George Washington; and was followed by one of the most colorful personalities in American history, Thomas Jefferson. Through the veil of history it is hard to discern the true measure of John Adams' own impressive stature beside these giants.

The second American President was a short fat man with a stern face, in contrast to the imposing figures and benign looks of Washington and Jefferson. The serene, paternal countenance of Washington inspired confidence. Jefferson's face expressed humanity and wisdom. Both Presidents represented to the people the ideal of a father—strong, calm, and benign—the image which a nation looks for in its leaders.

There was strength but no serenity in the face of John Adams. Even in repose his jaws seemed to be set in defiance. The smooth brush strokes of the fashionable portrait painters of the time could not completely efface the truculence which tightened his lips.

All his life John Adams carried a chip on his shoulder. He was born with a burning ambition and secret craving for the approval and esteem of his contemporaries, accompanied by an extreme sensitivity and vulnerability which predisposes a person to neurotic reactions. All his life he was oversensitive to the

29

needle pricks and brickbats to which he was exposed in the free-for-all of politics, the career forced upon him by the currents of the time.

With Washington and Jefferson towering above him, John Adams was doubly self-conscious of his own small size. And his pride was stung when he compared his humble origin as the son of a Massachusetts dirt farmer with their social prestige as Virginia landowners. He was always on guard, ready to pounce upon any possible antagonist with sarcasm and invective before the other had time to strike the first blow. His short temper, sharp tongue, and belligerence won him enemies all his life.

Contrary to his own often expressed opinion, John Adams had a rich and successful life by any standard. His temperament made him exaggerate his failures and troubles and minimize his rewards and blessings. He had grown up on a farm in Braintree (later named Quincy), Massachusetts, in modest circumstances. At fifteen John entered Harvard where at the time the college catalogue ranked students according to their social standing. John was ranked fourteenth in a class of twenty-four, in spite of his excellent grades, an experience never forgotten, that deeply wounded his pride and aggravated his sense of inferiority. After his graduation at twenty, John's father wished him to enter the clergy, then the most honored profession in New England. By this time John Adams had come to the conclusion that Christianity was encumbered by "whole carloads of trumpery," and that he was not suited for the pulpit, though he believed all his life in the fundamental principles of Christianity.

Always a voracious reader, Adams at twenty had come across a book by the great Dutch physician, Boerhaave, and for a short while considered becoming a doctor. Upon further reflection he decided that he was better fitted for law. He was admitted to the bar of Massachusetts at the age of twenty-three.

His choice of the legal profession conflicted with Adams' craving for social prominence because lawyers in colonial times were held in low esteem. Socially they were on a par with mountebanks and actors. In 1698, in Connecticut, lawyers were included in discriminatory legislation along with drunkards and keepers of brothels; in Rhode Island in 1730 a law was enacted excluding them from membership in the legislature. Men of John Adams' integrity were responsible for the improvement of the reputation of the legal profession.

In 1774 and 1775 he was elected a delegate to the Continental Congress where he was instrumental in having Washington appointed Commander of the Continental Army. In 1776 Adams served on the committee which drafted the Declaration of Independence, and in Jefferson's words, "was the pillar of its support on the floor of Congress." One year later he was sent to France as Commissioner and assistant to the aging and gout-ridden Benjamin Franklin.

John Adams' greatest service to his country, for which he received the least gratitude, was his prevention of an unnecessary war with France during his term as President. This war was the favorite project of his nemesis, Alexander Hamilton, who virtually controlled the Federalist Party and was to become the field commander of the American Army. Hamilton and his followers had succeeded in stirring up a war hysteria in the American people, which demanded a declaration of war with France. John Adams dared to defy public opinion, as well as his own party, and avoided open warfare through his personal efforts. Fuming with frustration, Hamilton circulated a letter among the Federalist politicians which declared Adams unfit for the Presidency; Adams retaliated by calling Hamilton such descriptive names as "Creole adventurer" and "Creole bastard."

Adams' courageous action brought about the final split in the Federalist Party between him and Hamilton, and cost him re-election to the Presidency. In spite of this cruel blow to his ambition, he was always proud of his accomplishment, which he considered "the most meritorious" of his life. Long years afterward he wrote, "I desire no other inscription over my gravestone than 'Here lies John Adams who took upon himself the responsibility of the peace with France in the year 1800.'"

Outstanding as a statesman, John Adams was found wanting

in the qualities indispensable in a good politician and diplomat. Not only did he lack the tact and self-control, but also the showmanship which a diplomat needs to disguise his thoughts and feelings. Besides this, his inferiority complex made it difficult for him to yield a point or to compromise.

In 1779 he was sent on his second mission to Paris as plenipotentiary to negotiate a peace with England as soon as an opportunity should arise. At this time Benjamin Franklin was the sole American representative accredited to France. Adams disapproved of Franklin's easygoing ways but had no authority to interfere with his affairs. Like a busybody, Adams took it upon himself to begin the exchange of views directly with the Count of Vergennes, Foreign Minister of Louis XVI, completely ignoring Benjamin Franklin's existence.

Apparently he used more vehemence than diplomatic finesse in his discussions with Vergennes. For, at length, Vergennes became annoyed and wrote Adams in plain, undiplomatic language that "all further discussion between us on the subject will be needless." And he asked Franklin to transmit to the Congress the entire correspondence with Adams in order to let them judge for themselves whether Adams possessed the qualifications "necessary for the important and delicate business with which he is entrusted."

The qualifications of John Adams for the delicate business of diplomacy were also challenged at a later date during the peace negotiations with England. The British envoys resented his bluntness and bad temper. One of them remarked to another American representative, "Your Mr. Adams that you represent as a man of such good sense ... is the most ungracious man I ever saw."

Most ungracious, certainly, was his behavior on the occasion of the inauguration of his successor, Thomas Jefferson, after Adams had lost the election to a second term. At dawn on March 4, 1801, the day of Jefferson's inauguration, Adams left the capital in a huff, unable to bring himself to shake the hand of his old friend. John Adams may have been recalling with bitterness his own inauguration when all eyes were turned on the colorful figure of the outgoing President George Washington, and no one paid any attention to the new Chief of State, paunchy little John Adams. And he could not bear the prospect of being again ignored.

No distinct line can be drawn between the frontier zone of normal behavior and the wilderness of psychopathy. The extreme sensitivity and explosive irascibility of Adams straddle the imaginary fence of normalcy. Other mental reactions of his seem to extend beyond it into the shadows of neurosis—his exaggerated opinion of his own importance evidenced by his constant suspicion of being persecuted, and his conviction that his services were not duly appreciated.

The behavior of Adams at different times was so contradictory that it suggests cyclic episodes of a manic-depressive character. There were times when he appeared excessively timorous, others when he would be rashly impulsive. For many months he would make the greatest effort to express himself cautiously in his speech and writings, then suddenly, without apparent reason, he would explode like a bombshell. Franklin wrote to the Secretary of Foreign Affairs in Congress that Adams "is always an honest man, often a wise man, but sometimes, and in some things, absolutely out of his senses." Jefferson in a letter to Madison quotes the same remark, and agrees with it.

When Adams was only twenty-six years old and had become a person of some consequence in the little town of Braintree, he made an entry in his diary expressing his belief that he was hated by everybody in town, which implied his exaggerated opinion of his own importance. He complained, "I am creating enemies in every quarter of the town. The clerks hate Mother Hubbard, Thayer, Lamb . . . this is multiplying and propagating enemies fast. I shall have the ill will of the whole town."

To the same personality pattern belongs Adams' tendency to hold what is called "ideas of reference"—delusions that events of general impact and having no immediate relation to him were directed against him personally. At the age of thirty he wrote in his diary, "Thirty years of my life are passed in preparation for business; I have had poverty to struggle with; envy, jealousy and malice of enemies to encounter, no friends, or but few, to assist me; so that I have groped in dark obscurity, till of late, and had just become known and gained a small degree of reputation, when this execrable project was set on foot for my ruin as well as that of America in general, and of Great Britain." The "execrable" project alluded to was none other than the Stamp Act, which required all legal papers to bear a stamp indicating the tax paid upon it. The Act immediately evoked passive resistance in the colonies and brought all legal business virtually to a standstill. Adams seemed to feel that the Stamp Act was first of all directed at him to ruin him as a lawyer.

Feelings of persecution and of lack of appreciation never entirely left John Adams. In his seventy-sixth year he wrote, "From the year 1761, now more than fifty years, I have constantly lived in an enemy's country." And thinking of his death, he added, "By the treatment I have received and continue to receive, I should expect that a large majority of both parties would cordially rejoice to hear that my head was laid low."

This dirge came from a man who had risen from farm boy to the Presidency of the United States, had retired with honor at the age of sixty-five, to his farm where he lived in comfort in the midst of his devoted and growing family, and among his beloved books. And from the peace of the countryside he would watch his eldest son, John Quincy, follow in the footsteps of the father and bring added fame to the name of Adams.

Believing that his own services for the cause of the United States did not receive their deserved recognition, Adams felt that Washington and Franklin were highly overrated. His primitive reaction was bitter envy of both men. It is a sign of the complexity of Adams' character that on occasion he was able to brighten his expressions of jealousy with sparks of witty sarcasm and unsuspected humor. In this vein he wrote to his friend, Dr. Benjamin Rush, "The history of our Revolution will be one continued lie from one end to the other. The essence of the whole will be that Dr. Franklin's electrical rod smote the earth and out sprang General Washington. That Franklin electrified him with his rod—and thenceforward these two conducted all the policy, negotiations, legislatures, and war." Franklin, he thought, had a great genius, original, sagacious, and inventive; but his vaunted excellence as a legislator, politician, and negotiator was a fable. From day to day he sat in silence at the Continental Congress, "a great part of his time fast asleep in his chair," and in France he was too self-indulgent to attend regularly to the business of the Embassy.

When Dr. Rush asked Adams to what talents Washington owed his "immense elevation," Adams replied—to a handsome face, a tall stature "like the Hebrew sovereign chosen because he was taller by the head than the other Jews"; graceful attitudes and movements; the gift of silence; a large, imposing fortune; and the fact that he was a Virginian, and "Virginian geese are all swans."

John Adams looked upon Washington as his own creation and was angry that he, a mere soldier whom Adams considered his puppet, received all the limelight. Nobody talked about John Adams who, according to John Adams, was really the brains behind the Revolution. In June 1775 he wrote to his wife concerning the farewell given to the General: "Such is the pride and pomp of war. I, poor creature, worn out with scribbling for my bread and for my liberty, low in spirit and weak in health, must leave others to wear the laurels which I have sown, others to eat the bread which I have earned." This jealousy led Adams temporarily to join the anti-Washington faction after the defeats of 1777.

It is surprising to find in Adams' diaries so many complaints of "feeble health" and "fatigue" coming from so wiry and healthy a man who was to live to the age of ninety. Such an entry is found when he was only thirty-four years old, and at the age of thirty-seven he speaks of himself as "an infirm man." In the following year he is again worried about his "infirmities," yet wrote that he rose at five o'clock and walked three miles, which shows that his complaints were of a psychosomatic nature.

In the medical history of John Adams we encounter three prolonged periods during which he felt sick, tired, and barely able to work. At the same time we have no record of specific symptoms of any somatic disease. All these spells followed experiences of unusual stress and frustration, and can be interpreted as depressive reactions to environmental stress in a vulnerable person.

The first episode occurred in 1781 at The Hague while he was negotiating with the Dutch for a loan and for recognition of the United States. It was a laborious and frustrating task, trying the tenuous patience of Adams to the utmost. Under the strain and the restraint, he broke down. For several months he felt so low that he could not take "a pen in hand to write anybody." Finally, in the beginning of the next year he was aroused from his gloom when his labor of two years bore fruit and he won the first official recognition of the United States as an independent nation, together with a loan and a treaty of commerce with the Dutch.

His second breakdown occurred following the signing of the Peace Treaty of Paris in 1783. Adams had hoped that he could return home after four years of separation from his wife and family, when the unexpected news arrived that he had been appointed Minister to the Court of St. James in London, and could not return to America. As he was about to set out on his journey to England, he suffered a complete collapse. This was possibly due to physical and nervous exhaustion from the strain of the difficult negotiations and from personal disappointment. Adams had been shut in for several months in stuffy rooms, working day and night, studying and writing lengthy reports by candlelight, and engaging in fierce discussions during the day. He was advised by an understanding physician to move to the suburb of Auteuil, and there long daily walks in the Bois de Boulogne soon restored his mental balance and physical strength.

Obviously Adams was also suffering from a depressive reaction during his peace negotiations with France in 1799, precipitated by his singlehanded struggle against the intrigues of Hamilton and the pressure of public opinion.

In March 1799 he issued an executive order to send a peace mission abroad; then, without waiting for the implementation of his directive, he disappeared and retired to Quincy. As was to be expected, Hamilton and his stooges in the Cabinet did everything in his absence to sabotage the President's plan. Benjamin Stoddert, the Secretary of the newly founded Navy and the only member of the Cabinet loyal to Adams, sent him message after message urging him to return and personally to enforce his order. Adams could not be aroused from his mental torpor. By his panicky flight from his post of leadership and his temporary inertia of depression, Adams jeopardized the peace with France, for which he had worked so hard.

Adams was passing his time in Quincy reading the literary miscarriages of Frederick II, King of Prussia (a better general than an author), and penning angry notations on the page margins. These notes of Adams' almost leap from the pages, so full are they of furious denunciation and hostility. Books cannot talk back. Adams was exhausted from his struggle with Hamilton and the other warmongers in the Federalist Party. Frederick II in his writings, contemptuous, cynical, and hypocritical, was identified by Adams with Hamilton. Adams could annihilate his enemy on paper with the strokes of his pen, as he would have liked to annihilate his enemy, Hamilton, in the flesh.

It took Adams seven months to recover strength for the final showdown. In October he suddenly reappeared in Philadelphia and peremptorily ordered the sailing of the Peace Mission.

We wonder how a man as undiplomatic, as unbalanced and unpredictable as John Adams could ever have become so eminently successful in public life—that he could have been elected to the Congress, entrusted again and again with the most important missions abroad, and that his opinions carried so much weight in the formulation of the State and Federal Constitutions. And how could such a man finally be elected to the Presidency of the United States?

The answer lies in the fact that Adams' weaknesses and faults were far outweighed by his mental powers and his virtues. Theodore Parker, American preacher and social reformer, thought that "John Adams possessed such virtues that he can afford to have his vices told and subtracted from his real merit."

In the sphere of pure intellect and abstract thinking, Adams was the equal of Franklin and Jefferson. What Adams lacked was their versatility, their scientific genius, and the graceful balance of their personalities. His sharp intellect was combined with a keen memory and tireless energy. Because of his willingness to work hard and conscientiously, even on the most thankless tasks, he excelled in any public office to which he was chosen. In the Continental Congress of 1775 these qualities won him immediate recognition and a fast-growing influence. In the records of the session his name appears as chairman of twenty-five committees and as a member of many others. His working day lasted fifteen hours or more.

Believing as he did in the American Revolution, John Adams was always ready to take risks for the cause. In November of 1777 he felt all worn out from almost four years of arduous labor in public office, and guilty of neglecting his family and business. He asked for a leave of absence from Congress, with the intention of resigning. He had hardly returned to his home when he received from Congress the appointment as Commissioner to France, accompanied by an appeal not to decline. Twenty-four hours later he wrote a letter of acceptance. Travel then was far from safe; ships were frequently captured. In such an event the new Commissioner knew that he would be tried in England for high treason, and possibly hanged. In February of 1778 he embarked for France on a small frigate, accompanied by his ten-year-old son, John Quincy, subjecting himself to the dangers and hardships of a six-weeks' sea voyage.

Corresponding to the unselfishness which Adams showed as a public servant was his detachment of personal feelings in the interest of the common good. Jefferson remarked that Adams "was as disinterested as the Being who made him." The good of the country as he saw it transcended the program of his political party. As the nominal head of the Federalists, Adams bolted the party in making his French Treaty. Ten years later he antagonized them forever by favoring the embargo against England. He wrote, "I am determined to support every administration whenever I think them in the right. I care not whether they call me a Federalist, Jacobin, or Quid." His proud independence cost him not only the acclaim of his own time, but the fame of posterity. Jefferson and Jackson on one side, Hamilton and Marshall on the other, have become the idols of the present-day Democratic and Republican Parties—but no party has claimed John Adams.

Whereas some of the mental traits of John Adams belong in the realm of psychopathology, he was physically one of the healthiest of the American Presidents. The average age of the first fifteen Presidents who died a natural death was close to seventy-one. Adams reached ninety, far beyond the average male life expectancy even today. The explanation is that the earlier Presidents averaged almost sixty-one years at the time of taking office. At this age they had successfully passed the trial of natural selection by the most prevalent infectious diseases; only the healthiest had survived.

John Adams came from sound stock; the medical history of his family was much more favorable than the records of Washington's and Jefferson's families showed. Tuberculosis, the scourge of Washington's family, apparently did not occur in the Adams family. Malaria, which was ravaging the Southern colonies, appeared in Massachusetts only sporadically, and in milder form. There is no record that John Adams ever suffered from it.

In 1775 Adams was stricken with a "fever" on his way to the Continental Congress. The sickness was of short duration and may have represented a mild attack of a gastrointestinal infection. Such mild cases often are the forerunners of a severe epidemic. We know that in the summer of the same year an epidemic called dysentery raged through New England and reached a crescendo along the coast of Massachusetts. Most of the Adams family caught the disease, and one of John's brothers died from it.

An epidemic of smallpox attacked Washington's army in 1776, killing hundreds of soldiers before the General arrested it by ordering compulsory inoculation. The people in nearby Philadelphia, where Adams was then attending the Continental Congress, were in a panic and had themselves inoculated with the matter from the blisters of human pox. Adams had himself inoculated, as well as his entire family back in Massachusetts, without any ill effects.

Another sickness to which John Adams was occasionally exposed without ever contracting it, was yellow fever. Imported from the West Indies, this disease was the summer scourge of Philadelphia when, in 1793, it killed 4,044 persons, and 3,900 in 1803. It even reached New York, where 606 persons died of it in 1803. The last great epidemic in the country occurred in 1878 in New Orleans, when it caused 4,046 deaths. Yellow fever, a virus disease transmitted by a species of mosquito different from that which carries the germs of malaria, derives its name from its most striking manifestation—the deep jaundice caused by a severe inflammation of the liver. The average mortality used to be above 50 per cent among white persons—lower among the less susceptible colored peoples whose contact with the virus for generations gave them a degree of immunity.

It has been suggested by his detractors that John Adams fled Philadelphia in the spring of 1799, staying away for seven months, in fear of yellow fever. The truth is that Adams left the city in March, five months before the usual onset of the epidemic, and that in the midsummer his Cabinet took refuge in Trenton. In physical courage Adams was the equal of his archenemy, Alexander Hamilton, who reappeared in Philadelphia in July of that year during Adams' absence.

In 1785 Mrs. Adams and daughter Abigail went to Europe and were reunited with John in London after a separation of seven years. While living in England, Adams suffered apparently from the only serious illness of his life, accompanied by a protracted fever and followed by a long convalescence. It was probably the "pestilence of London," typhoid fever. Typhoid used to be endemic in cities like London and Paris. The bacteria of the disease, deposited with the flotsam of the sewers, hibernated in the swamps bordering the sluggish rivers from which some of the water supply of the cities was drawn. The plague reached its peak during the late summer and fall when the warm weather favored the multiplication of the bacteria in water and milk.

In November 1800, Adams had barely recovered from his disappointment at not being re-elected to a second term as President, when he received the melancholy news of the death of his talented son Charles. The young man had succumbed to an unknown "fever," leaving a wife and two young children to the care of the grandparents. John Adams had to carry his grief alone. Because of bad health, Mrs. Adams had been unable to join her husband in Philadelphia.

Early in 1812 Adams' only daughter, Abigail, was operated upon for cancer of the breast and died one year later at the age of forty-nine. Adams had the consolation that two of his sons survived, and not less than thirteen grandchildren, to whom three years later four great-grandchildren were added.

In the last years of his life Adams kept remarkably healthy. In 1811 Dr. Benjamin Rush, a mutual friend of Adams and Jefferson, brought about a reconciliation between them. For the fifteen remaining years of their lives (both died in 1826) the two retired Founding Fathers of the nation kept up a lively correspondence with each other between Massachusetts and Virginia. Age had somewhat mellowed the intransigence of Adams, and in spite of differences in their conception of government, the two great intellects were in complete rapport on most other questions of politics, philosophy, religion, and in their mutual admiration for the classics.

At times Adams complained of sciatica and rheumatism, and his eyesight troubled him. He had a "quiveration of the hands," a senile tremor which he painfully controlled when he wrote to Jefferson. Adams retained the use of his limbs for a long time. At seventy-eight he took long rides on horseback, and at the age of eighty-five his short legs still carried him over four or five miles of rocky hills in his walks around Quincy. A time came, at length, when he had to resort to the hand of an amanuensis to write his letters, and Mrs. Adams often acted as his secretary. Following her death in 1818, the grandchildren rendered him the same service and read aloud to him when his eyesight had become poor. This was most unsatisfactory to Adams, for many things had to be left unsaid when the secretary would be a young lady, and many books had to be left unread—French books particularly.

Adams' mind remained fresh and vigorous as ever. A selection of his letters that appeared after his death gave evidence of his wide knowledge, which ranged from Plato to Pythagoras, from Cicero to Lucretius, from Voltaire to Dr. Johnson.

At the beginning of 1826 Adams showed signs of decompensation of the heart, the consequence of hardening of the arteries. He was forced to give up his walks, even in the garden, and spent long afternoons sitting erect, supported by cushions, in an armchair near the window of his study, surrounded by his papers and familiar books. Although he breathed with difficulty, he suffered no particular pain, and his mind remained clear.

Gilbert Chinard described John Adams' last days as follows:

> On the morning of July 4 as the town was preparing for the celebration of the fiftieth anniversary of the Declaration of Independence, Adams' physician, Dr. Holbrook, predicted that his patient would not last beyond sunset. The opening salvos, the strains of the military bands, the huzzas of the crowd did not penetrate the dimming consciousness of the patriot. All day he remained in his big armchair, attended by the doctor and his grandchildren, sometimes struggling to utter words hardly intelligible, but among which some of the attendants could recognize a last thought and a last farewell to his old friend—"Thomas Jefferson still survives." The people of Quincy had not yet heard the news that Jefferson had expired at one o'clock on the same day.

Thomas Jefferson

(1743 — 1826)

THE ideal of Seneca, "a sound mind in a healthy body," appears to have come close to its realization in the person of Thomas Jefferson.

At seventy-six, Jefferson wrote a résumé of his life's habits and his relative freedom from disease.

> I have lived temperately, eating little animal food and that not as an aliment so much as a condiment for the vegetables which constitute my principal diet. I double, however, the doctor's [Dr. Rush] glass and a half of wine and even treble it with a friend; but halve its effects by drinking the weak wines only. The ardent wines I cannot drink, nor do I use ardent spirits in any form. Malt liquors and ciders are my table drink, and my breakfast . . . is of tea and coffee. I have been blessed with organs of digestion which accept and concoct, without ever murmuring, whatever the palate chooses to consign to them. And I have not yet lost a tooth by age. I was a hard student until I entered upon the business of life, the duties of which leave no idle time to those disposed to fulfill them; and now retired at the age of 76 I am again a hard student . . . a stiff wrist, the consequence of an early dislocation, makes writing both slow and painful. I am so regular in my sleep . . . devoting to it five to eight hours, according as my company or the book I am reading interests me; and I never go to bed without an hour or half an hour's previous reading of something moral, whereon to ruminate in the intervals of sleep. But, whether I retire to bed early or late, I rise with the sun. I use spectacles at night but not necessarily in the day, unless in reading small print. My hearing is distinct in particular conversation but confused when several voices cross each

other, which unfits me for the society of the table. I have been . . . so free from catarrhs that I have not had one (in the breast, I mean) on an average of eight or ten years through life. I ascribe this exemption partly to the habit of bathing my feet in cold water every morning for sixty years past. A fever of more than 24 hours I have not had more than two or three times in my life. A periodical headache has afflicted me occasionally, once perhaps in six or eight years, for two or three weeks at a time, which seems now to have left me; and except on a late occasion of indisposition, I enjoy good health; too feeble, indeed, to walk much, but riding without fatigue six or eight miles a day and sometimes thirty or forty.

In this letter Jefferson showed himself as an incurable optimist with the happy faculty of forgetting or minimizing the painful experiences of his life and remembering and magnifying the pleasurable ones. Like most autobiographical records, Jefferson's letter conforms more with the image he had conceived of himself than with impressions left on the perception of others.

We have some definite data about Jefferson's physical appearance. In Washington, D. C., a lock of Jefferson's hair has been preserved, of a reddish blond color. He was well built, slender, about six feet two inches tall. His forehead was high, broad and slanting, his mouth wide, his chin pointed. His prominent cheekbones harmonized with a rather long narrow nose, its tip slightly upturned.

His eyes have variously been described as gray, hazel, or blue. Interpretations of his facial expressions and his social manners differed according to the prejudice of the observer. His enemies described his eyes as evasive, his countenance as vacant, neither open nor frank; his manner cold, stiff, or even unpolished. His friends found the same face kind, good, and attractive to strangers, his behavior always considerate and sympathetic.

Jefferson considered himself an Epicurean in the original meaning of the word. Somewhat similar to the existentialists of today, the great philosopher Epicurus of 300 B.C. preached that man is master of his own fate; the gods are indifferent; the purpose of life is to make the best of it and enjoy it in moderation, avoiding the bitter reactions of remorse and pain. The main ingredients of happiness are contentment, temperance in eating and drinking, tranquillity of mind, and freedom from fear.

All his life Jefferson practiced Epicurean moderation in eating and drinking, as his slender, sinewy body showed, but not frugality in his tastes. He prided himself on his superb wine cellar of selected French, Italian, Spanish and Portuguese wines; and while President he paid as much as $3,000 a year for fine wines and champagnes. His table was famous for the lavishness of its dishes, prepared by French chefs. It was said that the aroma of the French cooking made the mouths of the most unsophisticated Federalists water, so overcoming their political prejudice that they wheedled invitations to dine with "that Jacobin" in the President's House.

Another difference prevailed between Jefferson's conception of himself as a true Christian and the opinion of the established churches of the time. In 1803, in a letter to Dr. Benjamin Rush, he wrote: "I am a Christian, in the only sense in which He wished anyone to be; sincerely attached to His doctrines in preference to all others; ascribing to Him every human excellence, and believing He never claimed any other." Jefferson did not approve of self-denial and asceticism demanded by St. Paul and Calvin. He believed that Christ, without the trappings of formal religion, was the greatest moral teacher of mankind.

The apparent contradictions between Jefferson's preachings and practices were interpreted by his opponents as hypocrisy and duplicity. John Quincy Adams, who bore him a lifelong hatred because he had defeated his adored father for the Presidency, wrote in his letters that Thomas Jefferson was a hypocrite, hiding a boundless ambition, and also a liar and teller of Munchausen tales. It is conceivable that Jefferson, who had a greater sense of humor than he is generally credited with, deliberately pulled the leg of the humorless John Quincy Adams by telling him outrageous tales with a straight face.

Even if he had tried to understand Jefferson, a man of John Quincy's cold sobriety would never have comprehended so complex and imaginative a personality as Jefferson's. He would have never understood Jefferson's human need to see himself and the world around him in the bright colors of a believer in the "infinite perfectibility of man," a faith which Jefferson shared with his great friend Joseph Priestly.

Jefferson's apparent propensity to self-deception, often construed as insincerity, could possibly be traced back to his Welsh ancestors on his father's side, a people imbued with poetic imagination.

Thomas' father, Peter, had studied civil engineering, became justice of the peace, colonel of the militia, and a Virginia burgess. He married into the old, exclusive and inbred colonial family of the Randolphs, who looked down on the Jeffersons. For a living he raised tobacco in the shade of the Blue Ridge Mountains. With less than 3,000 acres of land and not enough slaves, he was not considered a Virginia aristocrat.

Thomas, the elder of two sons, inherited from his father the native democratic agrarianism of the American pioneer farmer. Peter Jefferson, a vigorous man, died at forty-nine after an illness of several months, possibly from a complication of any of the numerous diseases prevalent in the South. He left a widow with eight children between the ages of two and seventeen. Thomas was then only fourteen, while his younger brother, Randolph, was one of the two babies of the family.

Young Thomas Jefferson was apparently more attached to his father than to his mother, who died at the age of fifty-six, exceeding the contemporary life expectancy of a widow with eight children. Thomas showed greater affection toward his elder sister, Jane, who died at twenty-five, unmarried—an "old maid" for the times.

As Jefferson grew up he developed a paternal feeling toward his next younger sister, Elizabeth, and his baby brother, Randolph, who needed his protection the most. Elizabeth seems to have been retarded at the level of infantile helplessness. Randolph possessed a somewhat higher intelligence, at the borderline of low average. Thomas succeeded in getting him admitted to William and Mary College, but he left after a year without having improved his mind. Eventually he became a farmer, married, and begot children.

As for Elizabeth, she was nearly thirty when, in February 1774, a severe earthquake shook Shadwell. It panicked the girl so much that, like a terrified animal, she hid in a ditch, was not found for two days, and died of exposure soon afterward. Jefferson's four other sisters seemed to have possessed no outstanding qualities to arouse the interest of a biographer. Thomas Jefferson stood out as the brilliant offshoot of his family tree, compensating for the mediocrity and deficiency of his siblings.

Like his friend Benjamin Franklin, Jefferson was an outstanding representative of the age of enlightenment. An accomplished musician, he practiced the violin assiduously up to the age of forty-two, when politics began to encroach upon his time. His letters, addresses and documents show his mastery of the English language. Impelled by the insatiable thirst for knowledge, he learned to speak and read five other languages, among them classical Greek and Latin, which he enjoyed all his life. With his linguistic talent, he had a rare gift for mathematics, and so could talk on equal terms with the great French mathematician Marquis de Condorcet, who became his admired and admiring friend.

Jefferson's interest in all kinds of machinery is well known. He was always inventing and improving mechanical devices such as a copy machine, a plow, as well as gadgets like pulleys to wind his bed up to the ceiling, dumbwaiters to bring up wine bottles from the cellar, and extraordinary shelves that sprang out of the walls, filled with delicacies. More useful was his talent for architecture. He drew his own plans for his beautiful residence at Monticello and designed the classical buildings of the University of Virginia.

In his architectural drawings and astronomical observations, Jefferson made practical use of his unusual mathematical knowledge. Paradoxically, the man who could use differential calculus for his computations was never able to balance his budget.

Unlike most idealists, Jefferson combined the prophetic vision of a statesman with the instinct of a politician who could temper his zeal with patience and tact. A born leader, though no orator, he profoundly influenced the American people through the radiance of his personality and the force of his prose.

Jefferson had the ability to size up people at first glance and choose among them his disciples who could preach his gospel of agrarian democracy. He was also deeply interested in medicine, had an intuitive grasp of the irrationality of the therapeutic methods practiced by the medical fraternity of his day. In spite of his friendship with Dr. Benjamin Rush, he condemned the doctor's drastic methods of profusely bleeding his patients and overdosing them with mercury. He believed that the highly poisonous mercury, then given internally in pill form as calomel, or rubbed as ointment into the skin, was killing more people than the maladies for which it was prescribed.

His opinion of the run-of-the-mill physicians was low. He particularly despised the doctors trained in Philadelphia. "I hold in absolute abhorrence," he wrote, "the fanciful and ephemeral theories under which dashing practitioners are so wantonly sporting with human life. Our country is overrun with young lads from the Philadelphia school who, with their mercury and lancet in hand, are vying with the sword of Bonaparte which shall shed the most human blood."

"It is not," he was wont to observe, "to physic that I object so much as to physicians." In the presence of Dr. Everett, afterward private secretary to President Monroe, he remarked that whenever he saw three physicians together, he looked up to discover whether there was not a turkey buzzard hovering overhead.

Jefferson categorically disapproved of the use of cathartics and bloodletting in a wasting disease like typhoid fever, which his two young daughters contracted while in Paris. Jefferson had the good judgment to entrust their care to the unusually progressive English physician, Dr. Gem, who never gave his typhoid patients a single dose of laxative as was then the custom; nor did he bleed them, but tried to keep up their strength with easily digestible foods such as cereals, soups and high caloric liquids like Madeira wine given in small doses every two hours.

Jefferson related how by following the doctor's advice he cured his ten-year-old daughter, Polly, giving her one pint of Madeira wine a day for several weeks. With the same pleasant treatment Jefferson claimed to have saved the lives of several members of his family who were suffering from typhoid, and twenty to thirty of his neighbors and friends besides "without losing a single one"—unbelievably good statistics for the time, possibly improved by a Jeffersonian slip of memory.

Jefferson's ideas of preventive medicine were far advanced for his time. He not only had himself inoculated with human small-pox but also personally inoculated the members of his family, his slaves, and a circle of friends and neighbors. In his first inaugural address, he advocated a practical method of quarantine for yellow fever that during the summer months paralyzed the harbor cities, including Philadelphia, forcing Congress to take refuge in Germantown.

In a pinch Jefferson was not afraid to act as an amateur surgeon. Once, visiting a neighbor, he found a Negro boy severely injured and bleeding profusely from a deep cut in the calf of his leg. Without a moment's hesitation, Jefferson called for a needle and silk thread, skillfully sewed up the wound and bandaged the leg. Nothing is reported about the cleansing of the wound, hands, and suture material. Nor is anything told about the result of the operation. However, during the pre-antiseptic period, a layman's hand, needles and thread were less likely to be soiled by germs than the dirty hands and instruments of a doctor, which were contaminated with the deadly organisms from the pus of lanced boils and infected wounds of previous patients. It can also be assumed that the virgin soil of old Virginia was still comparatively free of septic bacteria bred by cultivation.

Jefferson did not enjoy such good health as he liked to remember, despite what he says in the letter quoted earlier. While there is no question that for his time he was an unusually healthy man, he chose to forget his numerous episodes of severe dysentery, one of which was to be the cause of his death. He also minimized the duration and severity of headaches that plagued him during his life, as well as the repeated attacks of disabling pains that often wracked his lanky body, labeled with the overall term, "rheumatism."

A severe attack of dysentery threatened to interfere with Jefferson's political career at a critical point in 1774. Thirty-one years old, he had become a leader of the patriotic faction of the House of Burgesses of Virginia and the founder member of the Committee of Correspondence which was to meet at an extralegal convention in Williamsburg on August 1, 1774. Jefferson left Monticello two days before with several copies of prepared instructions for the assembly in his traveling bag.

Somewhere along the way he became so violently ill with dysentery that he had to give up the journey. He felt discouraged and disappointed that apparently all his labors for the convention had been in vain and he could not personally deliver his searing indictment of the British government that branded the pages of his draft. After returning to Monticello, Jefferson sent a special messenger from his sickbed with two copies of his arguments for the perusal of the assembly. The documents arrived in time, made a deep impression on the delegates, and won him national reputation as a master draftsman of resolutions, election to the Continental Congress in the following year, and appointment to draw up the Declaration of Independence in 1776.

Literally, the word "dysentery" means a bad condition of the bowels. Its symptoms are the occurrence of frequent, painful passage of loose stools containing blood and mucus. The type of dysentery from which Jefferson suffered was probably of bacillary origin, caused by unicellular immobile microorganisms. Another less common form of dysentery is caused by a motile ameba. In 1896 the Japanese bacteriologist, Dr. Kiyoshi Shiga, discovered the first group of dysentery bacteria; in 1900 the American pathologist, Dr. Simon Flexner, found more widespread and less toxic strains which until recently were endemic in the South.

The main season of bacterial dysentery corresponds to the season of its chief conveyors, the flies, just as the seasons of malaria and yellow fever coincide with the seasons of their specific carrier mosquitoes. The belt of bacterial dysentery overlaps the malarial belt to the north. Whereas malarial mosquitoes live in the swamps and basins of the valleys, flies can live wherever humans live except in cold climates.

Jefferson seemingly suffered only a few mild attacks of malaria during his life because during the summer and early fall months he never remained in Washington but retired to his hilltop at Monticello.

After July 1776, Jefferson returned to Virginia politics in the hope of being able to incorporate his democratic ideals into the Constitution of the new state government. With Madison's support, his statute of religious freedom was eventually adopted, putting an end to the prevailing intolerance that, for instance, imposed the death penalty on those who celebrated the Mass.

Jefferson's decision to return from the Continental Congress to the legislature of Virginia was also inspired by his desire to be close to his beloved wife, Martha, whom he had married in 1772. She had been Martha Wayles Skelton, a handsome and accomplished widow six years younger than he. During the ten years of their marriage she gave birth to six children. The strain of so many pregnancies (she had several miscarriages besides) in so short a time was too great for the frail woman, and she died four months after the birth of a daughter, probably of tuberculosis.

Of the six children, the third child, the only son, died two weeks after birth. Only three of the five daughters survived their mother, and the eldest, Martha, whom Jefferson called "Patsy," alone inherited his vitality. The third daughter, Mary, called

"Polly," grew up into an unusually beautiful woman. She died in her twenty-sixth year, apparently of late complications of childbirth, like her mother. The youngest daughter, Lucy, was a victim of whooping cough, dying at the age of three.

Jefferson was deeply grieved by his wife's death. Although he was only thirty-nine years old, he did not remarry. From his daughter Martha, we have a glimpse of her father's compassion during her mother's last illness. "As a nurse no female had more tenderness or anxiety . . . for four months she lingered, he was never out of calling." As death seemed to be near, Jefferson fainted and had to be carried to an adjoining room. He stayed in his room for three weeks, pacing the floor incessantly day and night, sleeping only in snatches when exhausted. At last he left the room, mounted his horse, and for days roamed aimlessly over hill and dale.

Martha Jefferson was buried in the little cemetery Jefferson had planned at the side of the mountain. At her grave he placed a simple stone tablet engraved with a quotation from Homer's *Iliad* in the original Greek, which, freely translated, would read: "If in the House of Hades the dead forget their dead, yet even there I shall remember my dear companion."

In 1779, at about the gloomiest period of the Revolution in the Southern states, Jefferson succeeded Patrick Henry as governor of Virginia. During his second term, 1780 to 1781, he was blamed for the ineffectual resistance of his militia and accused of personal cowardice, after the state had been overrun by the British. Deeply hurt, Jefferson resigned as governor and swore he would retire from public life. In anger he took his favorite horse, Caractacus, on a break-neck gallop. The mount slipped and Jefferson suffered a severe fall, breaking an arm and collar bone, and was laid up for six weeks.

In 1783 Jefferson returned to politics to escape the loneliness in which the death of his wife had left him, and accepted his re-election to the Continental Congress. One of the burning problems was the creation of a unified federal money system to replace the chaotic and disorganized money market. Jefferson was appointed chairman of the committee, and after a few weeks proposed the decimal system for coinage.

His plan met with apathy and indecision, and his frustration gave him a spell of headaches. It is reported that these headaches plagued him throughout most of the session. Probably they were the same type he periodically suffered all his life—usually labeled by historians as migraine, but rather resembled tension headaches. In the description of Jefferson's headaches there is no mention of localization on one side, nor of nausea and vomiting —characteristics of migraine. One source called them "blinding," suggesting visual disturbances which usually precede attacks of migraine.

The duration of the attacks described by Jefferson was two to three weeks, but apparently they lasted much longer on occasion, whereas migraine headaches usually last from a few to forty-eight hours, rarely longer. Migraine headaches may follow emotional upsets but more often the causes are obscure. Jefferson's headaches seemed to be associated with situations conducive to nervous tension.

Tension headaches consist of a painful spasm of muscles of the scalp, temporal, and frontal regions, but particularly of the neck, and are often associated with constriction of the corresponding blood vessels. They occur mainly in personality types that are unable to discharge their frustration, aggression and hostility in direct physical or vocal outbursts, such as striking, cursing and crying, and therefore convert their emotional tension into some other outlet, such as by contraction of muscles, apparently unrelated to their emotion.

In 1785 Jefferson accepted an appointment by the Congress as Minister to France to assist and eventually to replace his aging friend Benjamin Franklin at the court of Louis XVI. Franklin had asked to be relieved because he was incapacitated by a stone in the bladder and by gout.

Upon his arrival in France, Jefferson found the country in a state of political and scientific ferment. In the field of medicine a revolutionary discovery was disturbing the sleep of the medical savants of Paris. This was the mysterious therapeutic method conceived and practiced by an Austrian physician, Dr. Franz Anton Mesmer. Mesmer was effecting cures without the use of drugs, diets or laxatives. His unorthodox system seemed to heal ailments by invisible forces apparently flowing from the healer to the patient.

Originally, Mesmer employed large magnets to transfuse the healing currents. Eventually he found that he did not need magnets, but that he or his assistants could activate and transfer the mysterious waves either by direct contact or by the use of a variety of conducting objects—even trees touched by the patients.

With this startling method Dr. Mesmer achieved spectacular recoveries in patients suffering from a number of disorders that had not responded to the usual remedies. At present we know that most of these ailments must have been of psychophysiologic nature, not understood and therefore ignored. No objective observer could dispute the fact of Mesmer's therapeutic results. But people, including doctors and scientists, see only what they can comprehend; only the clairvoyance of genius can pierce the horizon of contemporary knowledge.

Mesmer's system was bitterly attacked by his confrères, who were products of the Age of Reason and to whom nothing existed which was not perceptible to the five senses and could not be weighed and measured. Mesmer, himself a well-trained physician, could not fathom the secret force by which his method worked. He believed it to be the living equivalent of the mysterious currents which flow from a magnet. Hence, by analogy, he called it "animal magnetism."

Mesmer did not realize that the success of his practice sprang from the power of self-confidence and authority of the healer. Unknowingly he was using the magic of mental suggestion, which had been ignored over the ages by medical science, although it had been used since the beginning of time by witch doctors and priests. Mesmer, of course, did not grasp the full import of his discovery, which was to become the parent of the future systems of faith healing and psychotherapy.

Thomas Jefferson had one of the most receptive and imaginative minds of his time, yet he also was a creature of the age of rationalism. In a letter from Paris he wrote to a friend, "... I send you a pamphlet on the subject of 'animal magnetism' which has disturbed the nerves of prodigious numbers here. I believe this report will allay the evil." In another letter he called "the animal magnetism of the maniac, Mesmer ... a compound of fraud and folly."

In 1785 Mesmer had become a tremendous fad in Paris, his seances fashionable in high society. He had won the favor of Marie Antoinette and the ardent support of Lafayette and other influential nobles. The more powerful Mesmer's following grew, the fiercer became the opposition from the authorities in medicine and science.

Finally the rumblings of the explosive controversy aroused Louis XVI from his habitual lethargy, and he appointed a medical commission to investigate "animal magnetism" as practiced by Mesmer and his school. Four physicians were chosen by the medical faculty of the University of Paris, among them the famous inventor, Dr. Joseph Ignace Guillotin. These four doctors invited five members of the Academy of Science to assist them in their investigation. All five were famous scientists who had grown old enough to achieve recognition for discoveries made in their youth. The most renowned of them was Benjamin Franklin, whose lightning rod had been rejected by the same Academy of Science thirty years earlier; the same august body that had called Fulton's steamboat a "utopian dream," and had not approved of Dr. Jenner's vaccine against smallpox.

The learned committee investigated Mesmer's unconventional ministrations and witnessed some of his cures. They were unable to fit Mesmer's method into the Procrustean bed of rationalistic science, and could not reconcile his undeniable results with the accepted theories and laws of physics. What science was unable to explain could not be true; accordingly, the phenomena of "animal magnetism" were declared a fraud, and Mesmer was branded a charlatan. Eventually he left Paris and retired to his country home at Lake Constance. His name and ideas sank into temporary oblivion, to be resurrected a hundred years later with acknowledgment and fame.

At the same time that Jefferson joined the chorus denouncing Dr. Mesmer, he was suffering from his tension headaches, intractable by orthodox methods of medicine, but possibly susceptible to Dr. Mesmer's new approach to ailments of psychosomatic nature. After his arrival in France, Jefferson endured one of these painful episodes for six weeks. The Virginia outdoorsman felt unhappy and homesick in Paris. It was raining, misty and cold. He hated nothing more than cold weather, which made him more miserable than anything else in his life; he once said that he would like to hibernate during the winter, and be awakened by the first sunshine of summer.

It is almost certain that Jefferson was not suffering from sinus trouble, another possible cause of headaches, usually produced by allergy or the common cold and aggravated by cold, damp weather.

In the summer of 1786 Jefferson made the acquaintance of Maria Cosway, wife of the famous miniature painter, Richard Cosway, and a painter in her own right. It appears that it was love at first sight between Jefferson and Maria. She was of English and Italian ancestry, twenty-seven years old, possessed of rare charm and beauty and a keen mind.

On a fine September afternoon when Jefferson returned with Maria, he tried to jump over a large barrel in the courtyard of his residence, forgetting that he was forty-three years old and out of condition. He tripped and fell heavily, fracturing his right wrist. The pain was severe. The hand was pushed into a grotesque position. Two surgeons attended him immediately, but, lacking orthopedic knowledge, considered his injury a bad dislocation. We know now that it must have been a Colles' fracture, caused by a fall on the outstretched hand and characterized by a break of the distal end of the radius close to the wrist joint, usually combined with a separation of the tip of the ulna. In a typical case, the hand is displaced in a bayonet shape, up-

ward and sideways. Unless reduced into normal position and
kept splinted until sufficiently well knit, the wrist will remain
painful and motions of the hand will be limited for a long time,
even for life.

All such fractures are accompanied by a painful spasm of the
attached muscles which must be relaxed—as it is done nowadays
with local or general anesthesia—to facilitate proper manual
reduction. In a strong man like Jefferson, brute force could
hardly have overcome the contraction of the forearm muscles
and the bones could not be properly set.

For weeks the injured wrist remained swollen, painful and
useless. Jefferson consulted the best known medical authorities
of Paris. Unable to cure the patient, they sent him far away to
Aix in Provence to try the healing mineral waters for his deformed wrist. He had a rewarding journey. He saw the famous
Roman ruins of Nîmes and found inspiration for his style of
architecture—but no cure for his crippled hand. In the meantime Mrs. Cosway had been spirited away by her husband into
the cold dampness of England, a climate she hated as much as
Jefferson did. They never saw each other again but kept up a
correspondence for twenty-two years. After her husband's death,
Maria Cosway retired to a convent in Lodi, Italy, where she devoted herself to teaching painting and music.

In 1789, Jefferson reluctantly accepted Washington's appointment as his Secretary of State. Returning to Philadelphia, he
found that during his five years' absence abroad the political
climate had completely changed with the general prosperity.
The Federalists in power had become increasingly antirevolu-
tionary, anti-French and pro-English. Besides, Jefferson found
the Department of State degenerated into a kind of wastebasket
in which all the other departments threw their unwanted business. Except for the obligatory foreign affairs, it was also supposed to take care of the Indian problems, weights and measures,
the mint, lighthouses, and patents. Small wonder that Jefferson
again developed his headaches which made his unfamiliar labors
all the more irksome. However, this did not prevent his com-

pleting, in June 1790, a report recommending an extension of the decimal system to weights and measures, which most of the civilized world has since adopted. But the Congress of 1790 was too conservative for such novel ideas and rejected it, bequeathing the handicap of the antique English system of weights and measures to American posterity.

Soon friction developed in Washington's Cabinet between the ideas of Jefferson, the champion of agrarian democracy, and Hamilton, the prophet of the oligarchy of capitalism. Jefferson was particularly unhappy because Washington, whom he greatly admired, took the side of Hamilton in most instances. As a consequence, Jefferson repeatedly expressed his wish to resign, but Washington, who greatly esteemed Jefferson's qualifications as Secretary of State, again and again dissuaded him. Finally, in 1793, Jefferson could no longer bear the tension and refused to remain in the same Cabinet with Hamilton. His resignation was accepted for the following year.

In the late summer of 1794, Jefferson returned to Monticello, his beloved home, now burdened by mortgages and in a state of neglect. Unable to find a competent overseer, he himself had to take a hand in bringing order out of the chaos. It was time to plow the land, caked to rocklike consistency, and to plant the seed. The master, who hadn't done manual labor in years, tried to show the slaves how to plow. The strain gave him a severe backache that laid him up for two and a half months.

The surrounding circumstances and the severity of his disablement make us suspect that he sustained either a severe back strain or injury to a disc, caused by a sudden lifting effort. Unwatched by their master, the slaves loafed, the land remained untilled; in the middle of November, when Jefferson was able to hobble around and painfully mount a horse, the belated plowing and planting began.

Thereafter he repeatedly suffered from similar backaches, defined by his doctors as rheumatism, one of the numerous diagnostic terms which medical tradition inherited from the ancient Greek philosopher-physicians. It stems from the belief that all sickness is produced by an excess of one of the four "humors" which must flow through the body in harmonious balance to keep it in a state of health.

Medical inertia, satisfied with a resounding name, used to throw into the diagnostic file "rheumatism" a great variety of aches and pains, among them strains and injuries to muscles and ligaments; back sprains and slipped vertebral discs; inflammatory conditions of muscles, nerves, bones, and joints, such as fibromyositis, neuritis, rheumatic arthritis and osteoarthritis, and painful muscle spasms of psychophysiologic nature. Excepted only were typical cases of gouty arthritis which were early recognized as a clinical entity and accorded a separate drawer in the filing cabinet of diagnoses.

In March 1797, Jefferson suffered another attack of such pains, after he had returned to Monticello from his inauguration as Vice President. A contributory cause to these and some later pains in muscles and joints possibly was the three-day journey from Washington to Monticello he took twice a year, riding horseback over rough roads and crossing six rivers, three of which he had to ford. When it rained and when the spring floods swelled the rivers, a horseman was soaked to the skin. That spring, Jefferson returned home hoping to be able to repair the leaks in the complicated roof of Monticello, which must have been a roofer's nightmare. Handicapped by his aching body, he had not progressed very far with his work when he was recalled to preside over the Senate, the Congress having been summoned in a special session to discuss the cold war with France, which Jefferson termed a "war without declaration."

In 1801 Jefferson was inaugurated as President. In order to show the people his truly democratic temper, he either walked or rode horseback to the capitol to deliver his inauguration speech. The speech breathed the spirit of moderation and reconciliation, but even in the small senatorial chamber only a few members in the first rows could understand a word of it. Somehow Jefferson was unable to raise his voice in public, and after a few sentences it seemed to sink back into his throat. Either he could not overcome a deep-seated shyness, or he had conditioned himself so well in controlling his emotions so that he could no longer unleash enthusiasm or anger to animate his voice.

After this failure the President never delivered a personal message to Congress, but let a clerk read what he had to say. He rationalized that this impersonal method of presenting an address conformed more with the spirit of democracy, as it left the President inconspicuously in the background instead of turning him into the limelight of public attention. Jefferson's impersonal delivery of presidential messages set the precedent for more than a hundred years, until Woodrow Wilson dared to break it.

In 1806 Jefferson had a prolonged spell of headaches after the shocking news that his old friend, teacher, and second father, the great lawyer George White, had been poisoned by his grandnephew. At the same time there were titanic problems confronting the President, challenging enough to tense the muscles of his neck and head painfully. A neutral power such as the United States had no security in the Western Hemisphere amid the deadly rivalry between England and France.

Public sentiment was aroused by England's insistence on searching American ships and impressing American seamen into the British navy. To alleviate this intolerable situation, Jefferson sent his friend Monroe as his representative to England. Monroe returned with a disappointing treaty. The President's headaches grew worse, becoming almost unbearable at the news that the American frigate *Chesapeake* had been forced by the English to strike her colors and to submit to search and seizure.

In retaliation to this outrage, and as a measure of reprisal short of war, Jefferson rushed an embargo against the warring nations through an unwilling Congress, which revoked it a year later.

At about the same time, the President was suffering from an infected and swollen jaw, unquestionably the result of an infected tooth, proving that his teeth were not perfect as he liked to describe them. Likewise, Jefferson's eyes at middle age showed the normal loss of accommodation, as a letter to his optician proved, in which he ordered bifocal spectacles of the type invented by his friend Benjamin Franklin. As to his hearing, his admission that he could only understand a single voice in a room filled with the chorus of conversation indicated a degree of nerve deafness consistent with advancing age.

Following Washington's example, Jefferson declined a third term. Two days before the inauguration of his hand-picked successor, James Madison, he wrote to his friend Du Pont de Nemours: "Never did a prisoner, released from his chains, feel such relief as I shall on shaking off the shackles of power. Nature intended me for the tranquil pursuits of science, by rendering them my supreme delight. But the enormities of the times in which I have lived, have forced me to take part in resisting them, and to commit myself on the boisterous ocean of political passions. I thank God for the opportunity of retiring from them without censure, and carrying with me the most consoling proofs of public approbation."

The summer of 1811 found Jefferson laid up with a new attack of rheumatism. Dr. Rush sent him a list of remedies. "Wear a piece of calico on the affected parts," he advised. "Quilt bruised rolls of sulphur into pieces of muslin and apply; rub the areas with a dry hand or brush; bathe twice a day with a compound of castile soap, camphor, opium and salt in spirits; and take internally spirit of turpentine and sassafras tea." Despite his rheumatism, Jefferson couldn't be kept from getting up and taking observations of an eclipse of the sun on September 17.

Since 1810 Jefferson had worked with some of his friends on his pet project, the establishment of a state university of Virginia in his neighboring town, Charlottesville. In 1818 the plans were so far advanced that the commissioners, of which Jefferson was one, met to decide the location. There were heated discussions in which he defended his designs and the propriety of the location. In spite of his success in having his plans adopted, his rheumatic pains persisted. He hastened to Warm Springs for relief, but left after a few days, claiming that the company was dull, that the water had "prostrated" his health, produced "imposthume, eruptions with fever, colliquative sweats and extreme debility," as well as boils on his "seat."

After dispatching his carefully drawn plans for the university, Jefferson, in order to avoid personal controversy, decided not to reveal the fact that he was the chief architect.

That year, Jefferson found himself in an embarrassing position because Wilson Cary Nicholas, one of his close friends, had defaulted on two notes amounting to $20,000 which Jefferson had signed. Nicholas was a director of the Richmond branch of the Bank of the United States, and he had helped Jefferson on an earlier occasion. Therefore the cosigner had to mortgage everything he owned. Discouraged by this calamity, he was stricken with the worst attack of rheumatism of all, combined with severe indigestion and complicated by a stoppage of the bowels which seemingly for several days brought him in danger of his life.

Even at the age of seventy-seven Jefferson still indulged in reckless obstacle riding. Another fall from his horse disabled him for twelve days, but caused no permanent damage. Much worse was the blow he received when, two years later, his creditors forced him to sell his valuable library. The loss of his beloved books tore his heart and he felt so dispirited and tired that for a while he abstained from his daily horseback rides and walks. Jefferson attributed his feebleness to the lack of wine, for the unsettled condition of Europe made it impossible to replenish his cellar. Poor as he was, he sent an urgent call to an importer of Spanish wine at Norfolk to deliver the best he had. "Wine from long habit has become indispensable for my health, which is now suffering from its disuse," he wrote.

The dilapidated state of Monticello was responsible for another entry in the long list of Jefferson's accidents. Descending a terrace, he trod on a decayed step, which gave way, and he fell, this time breaking his left wrist. A surgeon set the injured arm and ordered him to remain at home until Christmas. Though the bones eventually knit, he never recovered the use of his left hand. This, added to the deformity of the right hand, made his favorite hobby of writing letters more arduous than ever.

Barely permitted to leave the house again, he went riding, and, unable to control his spirited horse with his two crippled hands, he was thrown, miraculously escaping with no more than severe bruises. Undismayed, he rode again. This time the horse slipped in fording a river and his master, entangled in the reins, was almost drowned. As a consequence he contracted a fever which confined him to bed for three weeks. To cap the climax, a flash flood swept away the mill dam he was building and he had to start it all over again.

The threatening cloud of bankruptcy continued to hang over the last four years of Jefferson's life. Always in a state of insecurity, he could exist only by making new loans and promises, but gradually the pressure broke his strong spirit and health. One idea kept him alive—the wish to see the opening of his University of Virginia. His wish was granted. On March 7, 1825, the University was finally opened and he became Director.

Thereafter, Jefferson's health soon declined. For several years before his death he had suffered from recurring attacks of dysentery which he tried to conceal from his family. Dr. Robley Dunglison, who taught anatomy at the University of Richmond, treated him. For some reason he also made the diagnosis of diabetes. As urinalysis by chemical methods was unknown at the time, the doctor must have arrived at his conclusion by the primitive method of licking his finger for the sweet taste of the urine. Granted that Jefferson was diabetic, this ailment is usually mild in a man of his age.

Other degenerative processes undermined his vitality and strength. In his last year he was unable to walk more than two hundred yards. His memory also began to fail. Jefferson wrote to a friend: "Eighty-two years old, my memory gone, my mind (ditto), for over five months confined to the house by a painful complaint, which, permitting me to neither to walk nor to sit, obliges me to be constantly reclined and to write in that posture, when I write at all." Apparently Jefferson suffered from almost continuous pain which was more annoying than severe. From his account of being unable to sit or to walk and only comfortable in a reclining position, we can assume that he was suffering from a prolapse of the rectum, produced by constant diarrhea or by a cancer.

Historians have often remarked on the curious coincidence that the great friends, Thomas Jefferson who wrote the Declaration of Independence, and John Adams who fought for it, died on the same day, July 4, 1826, the fiftieth anniversary of its adoption.

If we enter the realm of speculation for a possible explanation of the coincidence, we have first to recall that spiritually they were inseparably bound together through sharing the great experience of their lives as the chief architects of the American democracy, having drawn up its blueprint and built its firm foundation.

Out of their selfless collaboration grew a deep friendship, lasting half a century, transcending the fundamental differences of their background, character and political viewpoints. Even twelve years of apparent estrangement could not sever the cords which united them—their memories, their identical cultural interests, their understanding of and admiration for each other.

To their mutual friend, Dr. Benjamin Rush, who brought them together again, the reserved John Adams once confessed, "I have always loved Jefferson." Adams' last words were, "Jefferson still lives." The self-revealing correspondence between the friends continued until three weeks before their death.

In addition to their other similarities, both men shared a profound sense of history and were endowed with unusual strength of will.

All human emotions and impulses interact with the system of endocrine glands, simultaneously controlling them and in turn being controlled by them. It has often been shown that an all-consuming wish can whip up the endocrine system to a superhuman pitch and the intense drive to keep alive can prolong a patient's life beyond the point of apparent physical exhaustion.

At the beginning of July 1826, Adams and Jefferson, separated by hundreds of miles but united in spirit, were simultaneously mortally sick and yearning for release. Their minds remained clear, kept aglow with the desire to relive once more the proudest day of their lives, hallowed by the celebration of its fiftieth anniversary.

Of Jefferson's death we have a number of eye-witness accounts which, like all such accounts, vary in many points, even as to the hour of his death. Among them are the two stories of Dr. Dunglison, and of his faithful grandson, Colonel Jefferson Randolph, which also differ in detail.

During June 1826, Jefferson's condition deteriorated rapidly and he talked often about his approaching death. When on one occasion his grandson wanted to cheer him up, Jefferson shook his head, saying, "I am like an old watch, with a pinion worn out here, and a wheel there, until I can go no longer." Calmly he gave directions concerning his private affairs; "his manner was that of a person going on a necessary journey, evincing neither satisfaction nor regret." His greatest concern was for the future of his University of Virginia and he expressed the wish that James Madison should succeed him as rector, being the best qualified man for this position.

According to his doctor's report, during July 2, Jefferson fell into a stupor with short intervals of consciousness. On July 3 he sank into a coma which continued all day. "About seven o'clock of the evening of that day, he awakened, and, seeing me staying at the bedside, exclaimed, 'Ah! Doctor, are you still there?' He then asked, 'Is it the Fourth?' To which I replied, 'It soon will be.' "

With a sigh Jefferson sank back in his pillow. There was one more night to go. He had to set once more the alarm clock in his subconscious, of which the seconds are the heartbeats, which so often had awakened him to a new day—set it for the last time to ring the bell of its final hour.

Around his bed were assembled the adult members of his

family, his old servants, and his doctor. Randolph wrote, "As 12 o'clock of the night approached, we anxiously desired that his death should be hallowed by the anniversary of Independence. At fifteen minutes before 12 we stood noting the minute hand of the watch, hoping for a few minutes of prolonged life. At 4 A.M. he called the servants in attendance with a strong and clear voice, perfectly conscious of his wants. He did not speak again." At about 10 A.M. he awakened for a few moments and silently indicated the wish to have his back raised on pillows that he might breathe easier. At 11 A.M. he opened his eyelids for the last time and tried to move his lips. Randolph put a wet sponge to his mouth which he sucked and appeared to relish. Thomas Jefferson ceased to breathe fifty minutes after 12 noon on July 4, 1826. Randolph closed the eyes of his beloved grandfather.

James Madison
(1751 — 1836)

WHEN James Madison was President, Washington Irving described him as a "withered little Apple-John." He meant the exquisite kind of apple which attains its finest flavor when it looks wrinkled and shrunken. Since early childhood Madison appeared delicate and fragile and never displayed youthful vigor and exuberance. He had the high, bald forehead and the worried look of a premature infant born into a world for which it is not ready.

Madison was about five feet six inches tall. His weight hardly ever exceeded a hundred pounds. The smallest of all American Presidents, he was one of the mental giants among them. On the other hand, his emotional range was limited. He seems to have been incapable of the fire of passion or of suffering on the rack of guilt, like Jefferson and Lincoln.

The flame of his life burned slowly within his meager frame and could rarely be fanned to a faster pace by the whirlwinds that shook the world around him. He was one of the Presidents who had to bear the crushing responsibility of a war of life and death. And the War of 1812 was possibly the most ill-prepared and inconclusive of all American wars and the most unnecessary. The frail President often looked gloomy and exhausted from his labors and disappointments but never seems to have lost his composure, remaining at all times calm and dignified.

In 1817, sixty-six years old, Madison retired from the Presidency, emotionally unscarred and physically none the worse for having given almost forty-one years of toil to his country. He lived nineteen years longer, most of them in comparative good health and comfort, to the age of eighty-five, the second oldest President up to recent times.

The principal factor influencing a man's life expectancy is heredity. We do not know the ages of Madison's four grandparents, but we know that his mother reached the age of ninety-seven and his father seventy-eight. Contributing to Madison's longevity was the economy of circulatory and caloric energy with which his small thin body could be sustained, also his calm disposition.

Helping him to preserve his emotional equilibrium and physical stamina was his extraordinary wife, who was his perfect foil. He had the unusual good sense, at the age of forty-three, to fall in love with the widow Dolley Payne Todd, about seventeen years his junior, after having been jilted by two other women nine and eleven years previously. Dolley Madison gave him the companionship and affection that most men need in order to be at their best. She had a great and kind heart, unusual thoughtfulness and tact, as well as an extraordinary memory for names. The society women of Washington, D.C., at first looked down their noses at the President's wife, who used snuff and rouge and wore flamboyant oriental headdress and French gowns; but her popularity soon silenced them.

A Quaker's daughter, the widow was the mother of two children. Her first husband and the younger child were victims of the yellow fever epidemic in Philadelphia in 1793. Dolley herself was reportedly stricken by the fever. Her elder child, a son, appears never to have amounted to much, sponging on his mother up to her death at eighty-one in Washington, D.C. It was Aaron Burr who introduced the voluptuous-looking young woman to his austere, apparently sexless classmate from Princeton, and James Madison, with unusual speed, overcame his shyness and proposed. He was accepted after the proper waiting period.

It is not impossible that Dolley married the old bachelor, who was a head shorter than herself, for the sake of security and social prestige. After all, Madison came from a prominent family; he was a gentleman; and had already made a name for himself as the chief author of the American Constitution and the Bill of Rights. Apparently he faced a great political future. Dolley soon learned to admire her husband's mind and to love his sweetness and considerate nature. They had no children, but with the years she bestowed all her maternal affection upon her "Little Jemmie," who returned her love in his unostentatious way.

Madison was born in Montpelier, Orange County, Virginia, the eldest of twelve (?) children. From early infancy his frail and puny appearance deceived his parents and doctors, who believed that he was doomed to fall early prey to the host of diseases surrounding him. With these forebodings, his family, being in comfortable circumstances, gave the firstborn son all possible care and protection. Surviving the critical first decade, he received an excellent education in the classics, French and Spanish.

At eighteen James was considered ready for college. Doctors advised against sending the delicate youth to William and Mary, located at Williamsburg on the swampy peninsula between the James and York Rivers—the fashionable college, where the sons of Virginia landowners acquired their education and the germs of malaria. In order to avoid exposure to the "bilious fever" of the southern lowlands, James was sent north to the healthier climate of the College of New Jersey at Princeton. He became an outstanding student, working so hard and sleeping so little that he could finish the three-year course within two years. After his graduation, he continued his studies, taking Hebrew and Ethics, which was construed as an indication that he contemplated entering the ministry.

However, Madison was full of indecision and returned home. He was twenty-one years old and probably in the stage of delayed adolescence, deeply disturbed and unsure of himself, his emotional equilibrium oscillating with the changing balance of his hormones. He felt unable to tear himself loose from the close family ties and strike out on his own. Added to these conflicts was the primitive sense of physical inadequacy felt by every man deficient in the male attributes of size and strength compared with his competitors.

The stress of all these factors was too much for him and resulted in a depressive reaction characterized by brooding inertia, hypochondria, and wishful expectation of an early death. Contributing to his depression was the shocking news that his roommate and best friend at Princeton, Joseph Ross, had suddenly died. In the summer of 1772, he wrote to another friend, "As to myself, I am too dull and infirm now to look out for any extraordinary things in this world, for I think my sensations for many months have intimated to me not to expect a long or a healthy life . . . therefore have little spirit or elasticity to set about anything that is difficult in acquiring, and useless in possessing after one has exchanged time for eternity."

At the same time Madison suffered from strange seizures during which he suddenly appeared to be frozen into immobility. These attacks were diagnosed by his doctors as epilepsy. Modern historians assumed these episodes to have been of a psychophysiologic nature and manifestations of epileptoid hysteria. In psychoanalytic terms, they probably represented a "conversion reaction" whereby some of the patient's frustrations are relieved by conversion into physical disability.

Madison had the good fortune of having an unusually progressive family physician who did not resort to the customary practice of draining depressed patients of several pints of blood, supposedly containing the mythical black bile of melancholia. The doctor tried to strengthen his patient by physical exercise, like horseback riding and walking. He encouraged him in all kinds of diversions which might take his mind off himself and reawaken his interest in the world around him, and finally sent him away to another climate, to Warm Springs in western Virginia.

Eventually, chance provided Madison with the shock he needed to be jolted out of his depression. It was the cry of a persecuted minority of Baptists in Virginia which stirred his sympathy. The ideal of religious freedom was closest to his heart, and its violation by his very neighbors aroused in him a healthy indignation. In Princeton he had learned to consider the ideals of humanism as embodied in the principles of democracy, not as nebulous theories but as guiding stars toward human progress.

A veil fell from his eyes and suddenly he knew what he must do with his life. He would devote it to working for his ideals and the betterment of his fellow man. In vigorous language he wrote a pamphlet contrasting the religious freedom in Pennsylvania with the intolerance in Virginia. Soon after, he accepted the election to the Committee of Safety in Orange County, his first office in public service.

In 1775, an epidemic of enteric fever swept over the colonies. Madison, twenty-four years old and considered unfit for military service, was one of the few members of his family who did not contract the violent infection which carried away a younger brother and a sister.

The following year he was elected delegate from Orange County to the Virginia constitutional convention, charged with framing a new constitution. He introduced a resolution for religious freedom, which was rejected at the time. He had the hearty support of Thomas Jefferson, already well known for the Declaration of Independence. During their close cooperation in the governors' council in 1778, Jefferson recognized the great potentialities of Madison and the kinship of their minds. Thus began their lifelong friendship.

In 1787, Madison reached the climax of his career, framing the American Constitution in which he reconciled the states' rights ideas of Jefferson with the Federalist tendencies of Hamilton. Convinced of the necessity for a strong central government, he cooperated with the latter in advocating it. During the next year he saw himself forced to fight for the adoption of the Constitution and achieved a great political triumph by overcoming the violent objections of the diehard states' righters of Virginia, led by Patrick Henry, whose booming oratory Madison refuted by the cold facts in his barely audible speeches.

At the time of the crucial debates, Madison was handicapped

and enfeebled by an attack of malaria, a disease his parents had endeavored to spare him but which nevertheless plagued him repeatedly during his later life.

In October 1788, Madison campaigned for election to the first U. S. Congress against James Monroe, who had voted against the ratification of the Constitution. The weather was unusually cold, and during a long ride, his ears and nose were severely frozen, resulting in open sores followed by visible scars—Madison afterward pointed to them with pride as his battle scars. Unquestionably, this was his way of answering the election propaganda of Monroe's supporters, who vaunted their hero's war record and the scars won by shedding his blood for his country, while Madison stayed at home spilling ink. But in spite of "waving the bloody shirt" that all through history proved to be a magic lure in attracting votes, this time the pen was mightier than the sword; the statesman Madison won over the soldier Monroe by a wide margin.

In the fine spring weather of 1791, Thomas Jefferson, Secretary of State, and James Madison, member of Congress, rode northward from Philadelphia on a "botanizing" excursion. In Vermont, they were arrested for riding in a carriage on Sunday. Actually, they wanted to clear their brains from the poisonous political atmosphere of Philadelphia. On this trip their plans matured for the founding of a new party which would uphold the democratic principles of the Revolution against Hamilton's cynical depredations and the reactionary drift of his Federalist Party. No politics were mentioned in their letters; when they wrote letters home about strawberries in bloom and the speckled trout they caught, they were really pondering how to catch the souls of men.

During the Federalists' heyday in 1797, Madison, in disgust, tried to retire from the bedlam of politics and bury himself at his farm in Montpelier. But like Jefferson, he was not granted his wish for very long, but was summoned again by the call of his conscience. In 1798, the Alien and Sedition laws compelled the two friends to break their silence and draw up a resolution declaring these acts unconstitutional and not binding upon the states, a resolution adopted by Kentucky and Virginia.

In March 1801, to his deep regret, Madison was unable to witness the crowning reward of a decade of unstinting labor: the inauguration of his friend Jefferson as the first President from the "new Republican" Party—their creation. He could not leave Montpelier because his father was critically ill, to die soon after. For the same reason he was unable to take up his duties as Secretary of State until May 3.

In October 1805, Dolley Madison wrote of a recurrence of her husband's "old complaint." "I saw you in your chamber, unable to move." The immediate cause of this symbolic expression of frustration at that time is unknown, but quite likely it followed one of the humiliating acts of piracy by the English navy against American ships, acts of violence against which the Secretary of State lacked any stronger means of retaliation than futile paper protests.

President Jefferson's choice of Madison as his successor was not as much motivated by friendship as by his belief that Madison would be able to maintain the uneasy peace with England and France. He hoped that Madison could muddle through long enough, keeping the nation out of war until the holocaust in Europe had burned itself out and the threat of its sparks had passed. On the occasion of his inauguration Madison appeared for once to be overcome by the grave responsibility thrust upon him. He was extraordinarily pale and visibly trembling when he began to speak.

In June 1813, after a year of war disasters, Madison was seized by a severe febrile disease which was diagnosed as malaria. Preceding his sickness, sleepless nights and loss of appetite had wasted him, robbing him of his physical reserves. Monroe, then his Secretary of State, reported that for two weeks "The fever has, perhaps, never left him, even for an hour, and occasionally the symptoms have been unfavorable." The fever continued for more than three weeks, and the physicians did not dare, during his high temperature, to give their patient the bark of quinine.

Like his friend Jefferson, Madison felt greatly relieved when he could retire from the toil of the Presidency into the well-deserved peace of his country home. But also for him there was to be no peace, and the last years of his life were clouded by a continuous struggle for economic survival. Again and again, he had to sell parcels of his land to meet his most pressing debts. His residence fell into disrepair. Like Jefferson, Madison upheld the tradition of Virginia hospitality, and treated his friends and visitors to the best he could provide. According to a friend's description, the host's conversation was rich in sentiment and facts, "enlivened by episodes and epigrammatic remarks . . . His little blue eyes sparkled like stars under his bushy gray eyebrows and amidst the deep wrinkles of his face."

Occasionally, as in 1821 and 1832, he suffered chills and fever, thought to be relapses of malaria, and was treated with quinine. He was quite ill in 1827, and also in 1829 before he served once more as delegate to the state convention. Gradually his little body shrank more and more to skin and bone. In 1834 his eyesight began to fail and he became deaf in one ear.

For several years preceding his death, Madison was plagued by rheumatism, affecting especially his arms and his hands. He was suffering from some kind of deforming arthritis, a chronic inflammation and degeneration of the ligaments, cartilages and bones connected with the joints. This condition gradually grew worse by periodic exacerbations. Scar tissue formed about the diseased joints, causing painful limitation of motion and increasing stiffness. The arthritis crippled the wrists and the fingers of the right hand so severely that with the narrowing arc of mobility Madison's handwriting shrank to minute size. Eventually, he was unable to manage the knife, and the food had to be cut for him.

In time he had to give up all his customary physical activity, his daily drive and even his walk to the porch, and spent all of his time in the bedroom. Here he had his meals on a small table placed near the door of the dining room so that he could chat with his guests. As in most people with superior intelligence, his mind and his memory never deteriorated. His listeners found him bright and alert up to the last.

Unquestionably, he was suffering from the aging process of progressive arteriosclerosis—degeneration and narrowing of the arteries of the brain, kidneys and heart that gradually impaired the function of these organs. The ultimate outcome of this process is the progressive restriction of the vital functions, often accelerated by occlusion of essential blood vessels by blood clots.

As his helplessness increased, Dolley Madison, aided by his favorite niece, devoted more and more of her time to his care. The stoic patient never complained. During the last week of June 1836, it became apparent to his doctors that the end was only a question of days, and they advised Madison to take stimulants which might prolong his life to July Fourth. But, true to his unpretentious sincerity, Madison declined to meddle with his destiny for the sake of vainglory.

On the morning of June 28, 1836, he was moved from his bed to his table as usual. His niece brought him his breakfast, urging him to eat, and left. When she returned after a few minutes, he was dead. He died as he had lived, simply, undramatically.

James Monroe

(1758 — 1831)

OF THE three Presidents of the Virginia dynasty, James Monroe was the least intellectual and most practical administrator. He showed his ability as an executive by choosing and working with strong, able associates, such as the difficult John Quincy Adams, his Secretary of State.

Monroe was often called irresolute, diffident and awkward. In fact, his mind worked slowly, compared with the brilliant minds of his two predecessors. The realization of his shortcoming made him doubly deliberate and often hesitant in his deductions and decisions. His speech was colorless and halting, and his lack of showmanship often made him look awkward. Still, behind the unpolished surface, his mind "was sound in his ultimate judgments and firm in his final conclusions," as summed up by John Quincy Adams, who was not given to flattery.

Even his political opponents had to acknowledge the constructive achievements of his administration, the Monroe Doctrine, the good neighbor policy with Canada, the peaceful acquisition of Florida from Spain, and the Missouri Compromise, which postponed the final settlement of the slavery question for forty-one years.

Physically, he was tall, strong and athletic, a good marksman and rider. His physical and mental qualities made him an excellent soldier who served with distinction in the Continental Army. At eighteen, as a college student at William and Mary, he enlisted and was appointed second lieutenant in the company of Captain William Washington, a kinsman of the Commander in Chief. He participated in the delaying action at Harlem

Heights, the defeat at White Plains, and in the discouraging retreat behind the Delaware River. He also took an important
part in the victory at Trenton, in 1776, which restored the
morale of the American Army and people.

In this battle Monroe was seriously wounded, his life being
saved by a strange coincidence. In the dark of early Christmas
morning he was leading his platoon in the vanguard of his brigade. At the outskirts of Trenton, a man in a nightshirt came
out of a house, awakened by the barking of his dogs, and angrily
swore at the loiterers disturbing his sleep. Monroe kept his composure and politely asked for directions. When the man recognized that the visitors were American soldiers, his anger changed
into surprise and delight. He revealed that he was a doctor (who
apparently did not relish night calls) and eagerly offered to accompany the young lieutenant so "that he could help some poor
devil" who might need his services. He dressed with the typical
speed of a doctor and went along.

Washington's surprise attack was delayed by a howling bliz-
zard and the ice floating in the Delaware River. By the time the
Americans were deployed for action on the opposite shore the
day was dawning and the Hessians were awakening. Monroe's
brigade had been given the important assignment to occupy the
intersection of two main streets in the heart of the city. Suddenly, in the light of the morning, he and his captain saw two
shining brass guns barring their way. Without a moment's hesitation, they made a dash for them. Captain Washington was
struck down by two bullets; Monroe took command and was
also wounded, but the vital guns were captured.

A bullet grazed the left side of Monroe's chest, imbedding
itself in the shoulder and injuring the axillary artery. Blood
gushed through the torn uniform. He probably would have bled
to death if the doctor had not been along and stopped the bleeding by sticking his index finger into the wound. This simple and
direct method of arresting dangerous hemorrhages was common
before the discovery of antisepsis. It saved many wounded sol-

diers from immediate death, but inadvertently introduced into the wound millions of infectious germs.

Monroe was taken to a nearby house where two surgeons also took care of the wounded Captain Washington. They bared Monroe's wound and treated it in the manner practiced during the Revolutionary War. Continuing to compress the bleeding artery, they cleansed the wound with a sea sponge soaked in a washbasin, and removed the loose blood clots and foreign particles, such as bits of cloth. Then they searched with their fingers and metal probes for the bullet. They did not find it, and it remained in Monroe's shoulder for the rest of his life.

How they stopped the hemorrhage is not recorded. Leading surgeons of the time advised, in such cases, to enlarge the wound, if necessary, with a scalpel, catch both ends of the severed blood vessel with a forceps and tie them with ligatures of waxed shoemaker's thread. The ends of the ligatures were left long and hanging out through the wound, to be removed some time later, when they became loose. The wound was pulled together either by some type of sticky tape or by a few sutures of hempen thread with coarse needles dipped in oil. It was covered with lint usually soaked in oil or suet and then bandaged with linen.

The dressing was removed after one to three days, when the first manifestations of the inevitable infection were anticipated or already present. Then, the wound was usually covered with a so-called "digestive"—an odd mixture of substances like egg yolks, rose oil, and turpentine, which was supposed to promote the formation of pus; suppuration was considered necessary for proper healing.

The surgeons of the Continental Army often used a poultice of milk and bread as a dressing, unknowingly utilizing two modern antiseptic principles. The bread soaked in milk became moldy, generating penicillin-like antibiotics. The milk became sour, breeding beneficial lactic acid bacteria which fought the septic germs in the wound.

In most instances, the infectious cocci, previously introduced into the wound, were too virulent to be overcome by externally applied antiseptics or by the natural resistance of the tissues. Swelling, redness, heat and tenderness soon indicated the bacterial invasion of the wound margins; fever and chills told of the absorption of bacterial toxins.

Textbooks of the time recommended irrigation of badly in flamed wounds with diluted alcohol solutions like wine, or with the suspension of turpentine in water. Also advocated was the use of hot poultices of linseed or bran. If necessary, it was advised to enlarge the wound orifices with a scalpel, to facilitate the drainage of pus pockets.

If the bacteria broke through the barriers of defense and invaded the blood stream, general blood poisoning resulted. Especially virulent were the bacteria transmitted by soiled instruments. Hospital wards often swarmed with the deadly germs of hospital gangrene which took the lives of innumerable patients before the discoveries of Lister.

During the Revolutionary War the main reliance in the fight against infections was placed on the treatment of the whole system. "To purify the blood," the patient who had been often weakened by previous loss of blood was still further exsanguinated by repeated bloodletting. He was dehydrated by poisonous emetics, like compounds of antimony, drastic laxatives like calomel, and was given large doses of quinine to reduce his fever. Another popular remedy, believed to be "antiphlogistic," was potassium nitrate, which could have been put to better use in fireworks, matches and gunpowder. The only sensible drug employed in the treatment of wounds and infections was opium given by mouth. At least this relieved the victim's pain.

The patient was in particular danger from septicemia in cases where the missile had fractured a major bone, causing a direct connection between the open wound and the crushed fragments. Therefore it was a common surgical practice up to the latter part of the nineteenth century to amputate extremities with open fractures immediately, without waiting for the inevitable bone infection.

Before the discovery of ether anesthesia in 1846, pain sensation in all surgical procedures was only slightly dulled by a shot of whisky, a draft of laudanum, or more effectively abolished by the merciful anesthesia of deep shock.

The infection of Monroe's wound must have been comparatively slight, as he was discharged after eleven weeks. Deeper was the wound his heart suffered during his convalescence, spent in the house of Judge Winkoop. According to the old story formula, the nineteen-year-old lieutenant fell in love with his nurse, the host's daughter, Christine. Following the same formula and his own deliberate nature, our hero waited for the end of the war to ask for the girl's hand. But the returning lover found that he had been too slow; she had married another man in the meantime.

As soon as Monroe recovered, he rejoined the army. He was appointed captain, and distinguished himself in the battles of Brandywine, Germantown, and Monmouth. At Brandywine, Lafayette, who was only a year older than Monroe and held the rank of major general, was wounded and helped to safety by the young captain. On this day the two men became lifelong friends.

For his exemplary conduct the young Virginian was advanced to the rank of major at the age of twenty. But in the wretched little army there was no opening and no pay for him at this rank. Thus, the valuable officer had to request (and was granted) an honorable discharge. George Washington himself wrote one of his rare letters of recommendation, saying, "He has in every instance, maintained the reputation of a brave, active and sensible officer."

In 1779 Monroe accepted an appointment as an aide to Thomas Jefferson, then Governor of Virginia. Jefferson recognized in his new secretary the virtues of a good soldier, combined with tenacity of purpose, plodding diligence and an utter lack of guile. As Jefferson said of him, he "was so honest that if you turned his soul inside out there would not be a spot on it."

The Governor took it upon himself to instruct his eager secretary, fifteen years younger than he, in the practice of law, using the modern method of analysis and abstraction of actual case reports and court decisions. Monroe became the loyal disciple of his mentor, and looked up to him with the fervent admiration of youth.

Jefferson introduced Monroe to his other protégé, Madison, who was seven years older. From there on the two disciples began to compete for the favor of their master. In spite of their personal rivalry both recognized each other as brothers related by environment, political ideology, and admiration for Jefferson. Soon a fast friendship developed between the two Virginians which temporary political disagreements and misunderstandings could not sever. The delicate little Madison looked up to his big friend, respected his common sense and dogged persistence, and the rugged Monroe felt like a big brother toward Madison, and was proud of his intellect and culture.

In 1782 Monroe was elected delegate to the Virginia legislature, in the next year to the Congress of the Confederation, serving until 1786. During this time he took two trips to the country west of the Appalachian Mountains and into the swampy Mississippi basin to study the question of free navigation on the river. There he contracted a severe type of malaria and was very ill during 1785.

In 1786 he married the eighteen-year-old Elisabeth Kortwright, beautiful daughter of a well-to-do former British army officer. Her friends whispered that she could have done better than to marry the homely Virginian. She had a regal beauty and appeared stiff and formal at the White House receptions, probably hiding her timidity by her aloofness. James Monroe was proud of his wife. He leaned on her as his companion, and shared with her his own insecurity and loneliness. They were deeply devoted to each other and in time had two daughters whom they adored.

Monroe moved to Albemarle in 1788, an hour's ride from Monticello, to dwell at the feet of his master. Previously I mentioned his defeat by Madison in the Congressional election of 1789. However, in 1790 he was appointed to fill a vacancy in the United States Senate.

In 1794, George Washington made Monroe, a known Francophile, Minister to France to quiet French suspicions about a pro-English shift of the American government and to stop French interference with American shipping. Monroe overstepped his authority by openly favoring the French viewpoint; still his personal attitude could not silence French antagonism against him as the official representative of the United States government. Recalled by George Washington, Monroe was officially reprimanded for his open pro-French attitude. Monroe, wounded to the quick, wrote a lame apology for his failure, and retired to Albemarle to sulk at his leisure.

But he was too young and too ambitious to remain idle for long and was gratified to be nominated and elected Governor of Virginia. In 1803 President Jefferson sent him again to France as his special representative to take part in the negotiations with Napoleon that resulted in the Louisiana Purchase. But he was not successful in his mission to Madrid for the purchase of eastern Florida in 1804, nor in his negotiations with the British in 1805 and 1806 for the discontinuance of their piratical practices. Henry Adams noted that during Monroe's endeavors from 1803 to 1807 he had been "insulted by every foreign secretary in France, Spain and England."

The cynical European diplomats laughed at the foolhardy American Ambassador who challenged the might of their navies with the ineffectual weapons of right and righteousness. Only a man with the high sense of duty and the plodding perseverance of Monroe could have kept trying for many months to accomplish at least a part of his mission, undaunted by the rebuffs and disappointments he met all the way.

Ultimately, it was the English weather which accomplished what diplomatic failures could not: the dampening of Monroe's spirit. The London climate oppressed him and impaired the health of his family. His elder daughter Eliza became so ill that he had to take her to the mineral springs at Cheltenham. Mrs. Monroe was ailing too. The humid climate aggravated a rheumatic condition she had contracted in 1804 while witnessing the coronation of Napoleon in the sepulchral chilliness of Notre Dame. The frustrations she shared with her husband also contributed to the derangement of the chemistry of her body. Monroe became ever more anxious to leave the inhospitable and unhealthy atmosphere of London as soon as possible, even at the risk of a winter voyage, so that he could once more feel the warm sun of Virginia.

Monroe returned, in 1807, his diplomatic pouch containing nothing but a scrap of paper full of English promises and evasions. The document seemed so unsatisfactory to Jefferson and Madison that, not daring to submit it to the Senate, they pigeonholed it. Monroe felt deeply humiliated and hurt that his Herculean labors against impossible odds received so little appreciation. Full of bitterness at being made the goat of an unavoidable diplomatic defeat, he returned once more to Albemarle, swearing he was fed up with the ungrateful business of politics.

However, the enemies of Jefferson, among them one of his numerous cousins, the influential John Randolph of Virginia, conspired to take advantage of Monroe's resentment and use him as their tool against his former friends. They wanted to stop Madison's election as President in 1808, figuring that this would only mean a continuation of Jefferson's administration under another name. And they were convinced that James Monroe, just because his name was still associated in the public mind with the magic personality of Thomas Jefferson, was the only candidate who had a chance against Madison. He lost, but like all his previous failures, Monroe's defeat in the presidential election meant only a temporary eclipse of his political star. His fellow Virginians believed him to be too valuable a public servant to let him eat his heart out for long. They drafted him in 1810 to the legislature and in 1811 as Governor of Virginia for his fourth term.

Thomas Jefferson was anxious to utilize Monroe's common sense and rocklike dependability in the federal government. The political atmosphere was turbulent; the war with England appeared unavoidable. Madison, who had more the qualifications of a scholar than a leader, needed a reliable lieutenant to lean on. Monroe was then living a stone's throw from Monticello, but too embittered even to pay a social call on his old mentor.

Jefferson had no false pride and rode down to his younger friend for a chat. In the President's name he offered him any appointment he wanted in the federal government. At first Monroe indignantly declined to serve under Madison in any capacity. As Jefferson kept urging him, he burst out in angry recriminations, pouring out his long-stored-up jealousy of Madison whom the master had preferred to him. Finally, he broke down and with childlike bluntness declared that he would not accept any other post in the Cabinet than that of Secretary of State, formerly held by Madison in Jefferson's Cabinet. Gentle Madison was not a man to bear a grudge; in 1811 he gave Monroe the coveted appointment, relieved to have once more at his side his stalwart friend, reliable as an old war horse.

It was natural for Monroe as Secretary of State wholeheartedly to favor the anti-English course of the government and the declaration of war in 1812. Following the humiliating military defeats of 1813 and 1814, he, a glutton for hopeless tasks, took over the Department of War in addition to his own department, and by his imperturbability and energy contributed to the victories of the last few months. It has been reported that during the darkest days of the war following the burning of Washington by the British, Monroe did not undress for ten days and nights and was in the saddle the greater part of the time.

The period of Monroe's administration, from 1817 to 1825, has been called the "Era of Good Feeling." It represented a breathing spell for the struggling young nation. During his two terms the President was twice seriously ill. He was bedridden with a fever of unknown character in March 1818, and in weakened condition for several weeks thereafter. In August 1823, the President suffered from an unusual affliction of the central nervous system. According to John Quincy Adams he "was suddenly seized . . . with cramps or convulsions of such extreme violence that he was at one time believed dying, and he lay upwards to two hours in a state of insensibility."

It is impossible to know the exact nature of Monroe's seizure. We know that the poison of certain mushrooms may affect the central nervous system, but apparently no one else in the President's menage was ill at the time. Occasionally malaria may also produce nonspecific cerebral manifestations. As apparently no preliminary symptoms preceded the episode and no recurrences followed, the best guess is that it was caused by a subarachnoidal hemorrhage from a bursting blood vessel at the base of the brain. At times an artery in this location has a congenital weak spot that, like an overinflated rubber tube, develops a blister, or aneurysm, and eventually breaks. The outpouring blood damages vital nerve centers, resulting in muscular spasms, paralysis and eventual death. However, if only a smaller vessel is involved, the patient may survive and recover without any tangible aftereffects, as Monroe did.

In 1825 the sixty-six-year-old President retired with his wife to Oak Hill, inherited in 1806 from an uncle, to rest from his labors. Like Jefferson and Madison he found his estate neglected and groaning under mortgages accumulated during his absence. The penny-pinching Congress, which had been stampeded by public enthusiasm to give Marquis de Lafayette $200,000 and a township of land, grudgingly granted its native heroes mere handouts barely sufficient to keep them from starving. To Monroe Congress allowed a compensation of $30,000, which kept him from bankruptcy but was not sufficient to assure him an evening of security and comfort to which a life of public service entitled him.

Added to Monroe's economic worries was his concern about the ill health of his wife, Eliza, who for thirty-eight years had shared his fortunes. During the next five years Monroe left Oak Hill only twice, once in 1828 to visit the young University of Virginia, which made him a trustee, and in 1829 when he returned for the last time to politics, being elected a member and then chairman of the Virginia constitutional convention. He was then not feeling very well and undertook the trip only so that he could sit once more on the same platform with his friend Madison, whom he saw on this occasion for the last time.

Like a true Virginian, Monroe enjoyed riding blooded horses, and after his retirement usually spent several hours a day in the saddle. And, like all horsemen, he had his share of falls and injuries, including a fracture of the right wrist in 1829. This accident kept him for several weeks from writing the scores of letters and memoirs he used to compose, like most of his peers, although his penmanship and style lacked facility and grace.

In the spring of 1830 his wife died of a chronic ailment, possibly tuberculosis of the lungs. His bereavement gravely affected the already declining health of the seventy-two-year-old Monroe. In former times pulmonary tuberculosis often gave the victims of a "broken heart" the *coup de grâce*. Contrary to the widespread opinion that consumption was a sickness of the young, it can actually occur at any age. All of the eight members of the famous Brontë family died of it between the ages of eleven and eighty-four.

After his wife's death Monroe felt too weary to keep up the unceasing struggle of maintaining the expensive mansion at Oak Hill. He tried to dispose of it, and moved to New York into the home of his second daughter, Maria Governor. There he led a secluded life and appeared only once in public. That was to preside over a public meeting in Tammany Hall, November 26, 1830, in celebration of the deposition of Charles X of France.

Thereafter his health deteriorated rapidly. He developed a racking cough with profuse expectoration, which refused to yield to any treatment. His doctors prescribed a rest cure in Saratoga Springs, where the climate and waters were regarded as particularly beneficial for tubercular conditions. In April 1831, he wrote to Madison, "My ill state of health continuing, consisting of a cough, which annoys me by night and day with considerable expectoration, and considering my advanced years, also my lungs are not affected, renders the restoration of my health very uncertain." It is interesting that in spite of the pessimistic appraisal of his condition, the patient chose to believe the doctors' white lie that his lungs were not affected.

Monroe's sickness kept on its downhill course, the infection spreading through the lungs. With the decrease of the breathing area, the respiration became more rapid and labored. A low fever alternated with exhausting night sweats. Spasms of hollow coughing tore the chest, painfully forcing up gushes of blood and mucus. The doctors had to resort to ever larger doses of laudanum to give the sufferer some respite. During the final few weeks the exhausted patient could hardly be moved from his bed.

Monroe's sickness lasted so long and his death was expected for so many days that the actual end on July 4, 1831, came almost as an anticlimax. The American public received the news of his death with little show of emotion. The fast tempo of the events which carried the stormy Andrew Jackson to the top almost cast into limbo the figure of the quiet man of the Era of Good Feeling.

John Quincy Adams
(1767 – 1848)

JOHN and John Quincy Adams both had equally strong characters which left their impress on American history. The particular assortment of genes which every individual inherits from the pool of his ancestry determines the type and the potential pattern of his somatic and psychic development. The evolution of a personality never ceases, but it keeps growing and changing according to its environment.

The Adamses, father and son, grew up in an almost identical milieu, in two houses standing side by side on the same plot; both were rocked in the same cradle; both attended Harvard law school. Usually the parents are the most influential factor that molds a character. The great difference in the social and cultural status of the two generations of the Adams family was reflected in the difference of the parental influences. While John's father was able to imbue his son with the stern moral code of the family, he could not give him social standing and educational guidance, advantages which John could give to John Quincy.

John Adams was not only a devoted father but also a patient teacher to his talented eldest son, who in turn admired and emulated his mentor. In this he was always encouraged by his mother, Abigail, whom he equally admired.

A precocious boy at ten, John Quincy was permitted to accompany his father on his hazardous mission to France in 1777. He crossed and recrossed the ocean with him again in 1779 and spent six of his most impressionable years as his father's companion and private secretary in Europe. All these circumstances contributed in shaping John Quincy's personality in the likeness of his father's and impelled him to follow a similar career, with the result that in certain respects he lived a life that was almost a carbon copy of his father's. Both were ministers to Holland and England, both became President comparatively late in life, and both were defeated for a second term.

Corresponding to the likeness of character was the similarity of their physical constitution and medical history. Both were short, inclined to chubbiness and early baldness. They enjoyed good health most of their lives and died in ripe old age from cardiovascular disease. Their graves lie side by side, in Quincy, Massachusetts.

In spite of these similarities in the general outlines of their lives and characters, closer examination shows many significant differences. One way to explore a person's character is to study his face. Faces may deceive; they never lie. The framework of our faces is inherited with the framework of our character, changing with age, emotional drive and experience; modified by environment. The numerous portraits of John and John Quincy Adams, painted by competent artists, reveal considerable dissimilarities in their features.

The pictures of J.Q.A. as a boy and young man show him handsome, happy and smiling, nothing like his father. His is the face of a youth developing under the guidance of understanding parents, in the shelter of economic security and social prestige. J.Q.A.'s character evolved along the pattern of his father's, so that, as he matured, even his features took on a likeness more and more to those of his prototype. The determination and energy with which he fought for his ideas tensed the muscles of his jaw, tightened his lips, and deepened the lines around his mouth. In his life mask, made at fifty-eight, he resembles the reincarnation of an ancient Roman senator, with the grim features of Cato the Elder, his bald head, on a powerful neck, lowered and combative.

His last portrait was a daguerreotype when he was seventy-nine. The same unyielding pugnacity still showed about the mouth, but his eyes, inflamed by too much reading, express the sad serenity of philosophical resignation, unexpected in a man who, one year later, was to die with his boots on.

What drove him right to the last was his stern Puritan sense of duty which was the mainspring of his life. It made him serve his country in more capacities for a longer time, and to hold more diplomatic posts, than any other American statesman and President. James G. Blaine once ironically declared that the members of the Adams family held office from the cradle to the grave. At fourteen, John Quincy was in St. Petersburg serving as private secretary and interpreter to the American minister to Russia. Two years later he was the United States secretary at the Treaty of Paris which ended the American Revolution. He served successively as minister to Holland, Prussia, Russia and England; as United States Senator, Secretary of State, and Peace Commissioner at the Treaty of Ghent. Finally, he was the only President who, when his term ended, was not too proud to accept nomination for Congress, where he served for the remaining seventeen years of his life.

His Puritan upbringing gave John Quincy his rigid sense of duty and an unswerving quest for perfection through self-discipline and suppression of his natural emotions. In his twenties, he fell in love, but gave up the girl of his dreams because his parents did not approve of her. In 1797 he married the more acceptable Louisa Catherine Johnson, daughter of the American consul in London. She was patient and understanding, but he never forgot his lost love, nor did Louisa compare in wisdom and charm with Abigail, her exceptional mother-in-law. It must have been trying for her, living with a husband who unconsciously resented her, in the shadow of such a mother-in-law, and to feel the inevitable comparisons. Small wonder that she was almost continuously ill during the first few years of their married life.

Her health improved with motherhood. She gave birth to four children, at well-spaced intervals, the youngest of which, a baby girl, succumbed to the rigors of the Russian winter in St.

Petersburg. Of the three sons, only the youngest and most brilliant, Charles Francis, survived his parents. The two others died
in early manhood. A short time following J.Q.A.'s retirement
from the White House, the eldest, George Washington Adams,
died under tragic circumstances. He and his brother John had
been rivals for the hand of their beautiful cousin Mary Hellen.
John won her. George began drinking, and while intoxicated
aboard ship, fell overside and was drowned. This terrible blow
to the parents was soon repeated when, a few years later, John,
too, died.

Such heartbreak increased J.Q.A.'s inherited predisposition
to see the gloomy side of life. Like his father, he lacked the
ability to give himself up to the joy of life, to feel really happy
and contented. Also like his father, he believed that his services
were not appreciated by his contemporaries, and that innumerable enemies wished him ill. At sixty-five he confided to his
diary that "the events that affect my life and adventures are especially shaped to disappoint my purposes. My whole life has
been a succession of disappointments. I can scarcely recollect a
single instance of success to anything that I ever undertook."
Later, he wrote: "The position that I have taken is arduous
enough to crush any man in the vigor of youth; but at seventy-
five, with failing senses and blunted instruments, surrounded
by remorseless enemies and false and scary and treacherous
friends, how can it end but in my ruin? But I must meet the
shock." Though he had been elected President despite his refusal to play practical politics, he never expressed satisfaction
over his personal triumph but bemoaned the fact that he had
won only by a majority of the electors and not by popular vote.

Still, his depressive response to the stress of life was never so
profound and prolonged as his father's. We only know of one
short episode of mental depression which he suffered in March
1814. It was brought on by a combination of circumstances: the
death of the baby daughter during the sad winter in war-ravaged
Russia, the separation from his three sons for whom he could
find no educational facilities in St. Petersburg, and the well-

founded anxieties over the outcome of the war with England.

In his diary he described his symptoms in terms that proved he enjoyed his suffering like a Rousseauan romanticist: "I am very unwell, and have strong symptoms of jaundice; a lassitude which has almost, but not quite suspended my industry, a listlessness which, without extinguishing the love of life, affects the mind with the sentiment that life is nothing worth; an oppression of the heart, which, without being positive pain, is more distressing than the pain itself."

His physician, Dr. Galloway, diagnosed his sickness as jaundice, supposedly produced by too much bile despite the apparent absence of the requisite sign of clinical jaundice, a yellow discoloration of the skin. This diagnosis was in keeping with the ancient theory that all physical and mental disturbances were being caused by a derangement of the normal balance of four basic humors contained in the tissues, one of them black bile. Too much black bile in the system was believed to produce "melancholia," which means, literally translated, "black biliousness," a kind of invisible jaundice, depressing all vital functions.

Dr. Galloway prescribed for the mythical ailment an equally mysterious medicine for his patient, a vial of "sacred elixir." It is quite probable that J.Q.A., always skeptical about the prescriptions of his doctors, did not take it. With or without its help, he recovered in a few weeks and was able to travel to Ghent as head of the American Peace Commission.

The ability of a person to analyze his own emotions and traits of character can, to some extent, serve as a balance wheel for his mental equilibrium. John Quincy Adams had this stabilizing capacity to an unusual degree. In his diary he described on numerous occasions the less attractive features of his character with the cool detachment of a neutral observer. At the age of fifty-two, he wrote: "I am a man of reserved, cold, austere, and forbidding manners: my political adversaries say, a gloomy misanthropist, and my personal enemies, an unsocial savage. With a knowledge of the actual defect in my character, I have not the pliability to reform it."

A dismal outgrowth of his exceptional insight into his own character was his tendency to merciless self-criticism, which at times reached the neurotic stage of self-belittling and self-reproach. As a young man of twenty-five years, he wrote: "I am not satisfied with the manner in which I employ my time. It is calculated to keep me forever fixed in that state of useless and disgraceful insignificance, which has been my lot for some years past." Eighteen years later he wrote: "But I have indulged too much indolence and inactivity of mind, and have not turned my leisure time to good account. I have pursued no object steadily, and the year has left no advantageous trace of itself in the annals of my life." And, two years later: "But passions, indolence, weakness, and infirmity have sometimes swerved from my better knowledge of right and almost constantly paralyzed my efforts of good."

His continuous struggle to control his strong emotions, and his failure to live up to his impossible demands upon himself, magnified his Puritan sense of guilt and his compulsion to punish himself. Up to his old age, he liked to subject his body to ice-cold baths, rubbing it with a horsehair mitten. Daily he took two hours of grueling exercise, consisting of a brisk walk for several miles, horseback riding at a fast pace, swimming long distances, or a combination of these exercises. At fifty-six, he would swim against the tide of the Potomac for as long as an hour and a half.

He never slept more than seven hours, yet bemoaned the fact that he wasted so much time in sleep and leisure. He disciplined himself to arise at daybreak and to read a chapter from the Bible. In the course of every year he went through the Bible from beginning to end. He loved reading Greek and Roman classics, and poets like Shakespeare; but even the reading of his favorite authors he turned into a chore, reading them by the clock and following a rigid schedule.

This compulsion to find emotional release by self-punishment could readily reverse itself and turn against other persons; he could be as hostile to others as he was against himself. He was dreaded by his opponents in Congress, whom he lashed with invective and stinging sarcasm, jarring them with his shrill voice.

He seemed to enjoy fighting in single combat against a multitude of enemies, unsupported by friends. To stand alone and fight the world singlehanded for ideas he believed in gave him a quixotic sense of self-righteousness, power and importance, elating his ego. Self-satisfaction was his compensation, sustaining him from 1836 to 1844 in his seemingly hopeless fight in Congress for the right of petition and against the gag rule tabling all petitions opposed to slavery. He finally won his fight by his irrepressible persistence, stunning his antagonists by his ferocity, and often outshouting the chair when it ruled him out of order.

His fiery debates in Congress, which won him the name "Old Man Eloquent," could evoke storms of rage, rumblings of hatred and the silence of respect, but never the ripple of laughter. The old thunderer lacked utterly a sense of humor and appreciation of wit, qualities his father had revealed on occasion. In spite of the low self-esteem he often professed in his diary, he took himself far too seriously to laugh at his own foibles.

Physically, John Quincy was as robust as his father. He had only one weakness, his right arm, which suffered various mishaps throughout his life, like an Achilles heel which attracts every arrow. When he was two or three years old, he strayed into the street, as any child might do. A terrified nursemaid caught him and gave his right arm a sudden jerk which seemingly dislocated his shoulder. This must have injured the nerve plexus, leading to muscular atrophy that weakened his right arm and hand. According to J.Q.'s own account, all his life he was never able to write as speedily as other people. In spite of this handicap, he put millions of words on paper—in his diary, letters, and official documents. Either he was too pronounced a righthander or too obstinate to train his left hand in writing, as Jefferson did after an injury to his right wrist.

At the age of eight, he badly fractured his forefinger, supposedly of the right hand, which the family physician, Dr. Joseph

Warren, skillfully splinted, saving it from amputation. This was the same Dr. Joseph Warren who, a few days later, fell in the defense of Bunker Hill, where he commanded the infantry as brigadier general. He and his brother, Dr. John Collins Warren, were founders of a family of famous surgeons. The latter served as surgeon general in the Continental Army, was one of the organizers of Harvard Medical School, and the father of a son with the same name who was the first surgeon credited with using ether for surgical anesthesia.

It is probable that the comminuted fracture of Adams' index finger impaired its motion and that this condition, combined with the nerve lesion, prevented him from holding his pen properly. In his early fifties a coarse tremor of his overworked right hand supervened, which further hampered his writing. Eventually he had to use a specially improvised arm rest to steady his hand in order to write. The tremor of his right hand was most likely a localized, nonprogressive form of Parkinson's disease, a shaking paralysis caused by a focal degeneration of some brain centers. "Writer's cramp," the diagnosis usually suggested, is a psychosomatic condition that rarely manifests itself in a coarse tremor of the hand such as affected John Quincy Adams.

In August 1833, when Adams was sixty-six, he complained in his diary about a painful and incapacitating "gathering eruption" on his right hand. As it is mentioned in connection with gardening, it was possibly caused by poison ivy.

Seven years later the final accident to his crippled right arm occurred when he tripped over the newly laid matting in the poorly lighted hall of Congress. He pitched forward and once more dislocated his right shoulder. Several members of the House immediately came to his assistance, and made futile and dangerous attempts to relieve him. Luckily he was taken in time to the home of a friend, where two doctors succeeded in reducing the dislocation.

On the following morning, after a painful night, his right arm in a sling, he nevertheless made his daily entry in his diary, and attended the meeting of the House against the advice of his doctors. For more than four weeks he suffered pain in his right shoulder, and the resulting stiffness further impaired the use of his arm and hand.

The long hours of reading and writing, often in the dim light of dawn and twilight or of a flickering candle, caused a chronic eyestrain. As early as 1815 he had complained of an eye irritation which prevented him from writing a diplomatic report. Repeatedly over the years he mentioned an inflammation of his overworked eyes, at times accompanied by a secretion of tears, giving his face a pathetic look. Of the gaslight newly installed in the streets of London in 1815, John Quincy wrote that it was almost "too dazzling," and called the dull open flames, not yet covered with the brightening mantles, "remarkably brilliant." He commented that "they are also attended with an inconvenience of offensive smell, which I thought perceptible even in the streets, and are thought to be unhealthy."

Always concerned about his health, he devoted quite a few paragraphs of his diary to his colds, sore throat and indigestion. In spite of his Puritan stoicism, he seemed to feel sorry for himself on such occasions. However, he never spared himself in his congressional work even during his advancing years. The longest and most grueling sessions did not daunt the old lion. Grimly he remained at his post for twenty-five hours during the filibuster over the admission of Arkansas and Michigan in 1836. On another occasion, during a session lasting two days and one night, he went without food for twenty-eight hours and remained in his seat and actively engaged in debate throughout the night. Eventually his fellow members in Congress came grudgingly to admire the cantankerous old man for his sincerity and consistency.

Meanwhile, the inevitable hardening of his arteries was gradually progressing, making them more narrow and brittle. We cannot estimate how far his strenuous activities in Congress accelerated the degeneration of his blood vessels, and the extent to which his fierce political battles overstrained the worn channels of circulation of a man of his age. Certainly he would have had a better chance to equal his father's longevity had he likewise retired from the frustrating grind of politics. But he preferred to keep on and die fighting.

On November 20, 1846, on his way to Washington, J.Q.A. visited his son Charles Francis in Boston. He rose in the dark of the November morning, between four and five o'clock, bathed and rubbed himself vigorously with his horsehair mitten, and came down to breakfast. Later, out with a friend on a morning stroll, he suffered a stroke and fell down. A blood vessel of the brain became occluded by a clot or else had ruptured, and the resulting lack of oxygen had paralyzed the vital brain centers. He was taken back to his son's house where he remained in coma for several days. He recovered slowly, and in about three months was again on his feet. Against the advice of his family, he returned to Washington once more to take up his post in Congress.

When he entered the chamber in 1847, the whole membership spontaneously arose and applauded. All business was suspended. Because Adams had not been present at the beginning of the session—and was not expected to return—his seat had been assigned to a new member, Andrew Johnson, of Tennessee. As the sick old man slowly walked down the aisle, Johnson rose and graciously conducted him to Adams' former seat. J.Q.A. sank into his chair, tears in his eyes, and said softly: "Had I a more powerful voice I might respond to the congratulations of my friends and thank the members of this House for the honor which has been done me, but enfeebled as I am by disease, I beg you will excuse me." He spoke in the House only once after that. The stroke had put an end to his political infighting, although he regularly attended the sessions of Congress.

On February 21, 1848, the House was considering a resolution for the award of medals to the generals of the Mexican War, a war that J.Q.A. had never approved. He sat quietly writing at his desk. As the speaker arose to put the question, he was interrupted by cries of "Stop! Look to Mr. Adams!" The old patriot had risen, perhaps to address the chair, when he toppled over, insensible, into the arms of a nearby member. A second massive stroke had cut off the blood supply to the centers of consciousness. He was placed upon a couch and carried into the adjacent room of the Speaker. The House forthwith adjourned. In the Senate also an adjournment was unanimously agreed to.

Adams lingered through February 22 and 23, unconscious most of the time. He spoke once, calling for his wife, who with the members of his family remained with him until the end. Both Houses adjourned from day to day, out of respect. Late in the afternoon of the twenty-third, he was understood to say, "Thank the officers of the House." Just before nightfall, he murmured, "This is the last of earth. I am content." For J.Q.A., as for the hero of Goethe's *Faust*, living meant to be discontented and to strive for perfection. For him, contentment was tantamount to death.

Andrew Jackson

(1767 — 1845)

MAY 30, 1806, marked the halfway point and the dramatic crisis in the life of Andrew Jackson. On that day Jackson killed a man in a duel and in turn received a chest wound from which he never fully recovered and which eventually caused his death. As in the Greek drama, the tragic guilt of the hero was inexorably followed by his punishment and his redemption. After the fatal duel Jackson was doomed to semiinvalidism for thirty-nine more years, kept alive by an iron constitution and driven by a superhuman will.

During this period Jackson transcended his physical handicap and became a great general; he rose from country politician to selfless American patriot.

The fatal duel was the climax of a long and bitter feud between Jackson and the young Nashville snob, Charles Dickinson, who had made slurring remarks in public about Andrew's wife, Rachel. Dickinson was well known as a crack pistol shot, whereas Jackson was no great marksman.

The dueling parties met on the bank of the Red River in a clearing in the poplar woods. General Overton was Jackson's second; Dickinson's, a Doctor Cattlet. A pair of identical pistols owned by Jackson were the weapons to be used. The guns, with seven-inch barrels, were loaded with deadly one-ounce 70-caliber lead bullets.

A distance of twenty-four feet was paced off. The principals took their stance. Dickinson wore a short coat of blue with gray trousers. Jackson wore a bulky dark blue overcoat and trousers to match. He liked to wear his coats well-padded and loose, to hide his extremely narrow shoulders which gave his long, lean body a quixotic appearance.

General Overton called, "Gentlemen! Are you ready?"

"Ready," said Dickinson.

"Yes, sir," said Jackson.

"Fire!" cried Overton.

Dickinson fired instantly. He had boasted that he would shoot Jackson through the heart. The ball tore a large hole in Jackson's coat. He felt a searing pain in his chest and clutched his side with his left hand. For an instant he felt he was dying, wondering what kept him standing. Then he steadied himself and, as in a dream, slowly raised his pistol and took careful aim, mechanically carrying out his plan to hold his fire for one careful shot, whatever the risk.

Opposite him Jackson saw his horror-stricken enemy standing defenseless with folded arms and averted eyes. He pulled the trigger. There was a metallic click as the hammer of the pistol stopped at half cock. He pulled it back and aimed again. This time it fired.

Dickinson swayed and slumped to the ground. The bullet had hit him squarely in the abdomen, tearing through his intestines. His friends tried to comfort him saying that his bullet had lodged in Jackson's chest and would inevitably kill him. They did not know how close this pious lie was to the truth. Dickinson died that night after a day of agony.

Jackson made light of his own wound, though blood was oozing from his chest and filling his left boot. He did not want Dickinson's cohorts to know he was badly hurt. Refusing help, he mounted his horse. We can only marvel how a man in his condition was able to ride horseback to Nashville, a distance of forty miles.

Back home Jackson's doctors told him how serious the wound was. Dickinson's bullet had missed his heart. The loose overcoat had deceived the sharpshooter's calculation of the vital mark, but the bullet had shattered the chest wall, breaking a couple of ribs and embedding itself deep in the left lung, and probably carrying in its track pieces of cloth and fragments of bone.

The heavy lead bullet was to remain in Jackson's chest as a life-long memento of the duel—a wound that never healed. No surgeon of that time dared to remove the ball from its dangerous position near the heart. Even today, it is only some fifty years since surgeons first invaded the living chest cavity, one of the last areas inviolate to surgery. The abdominal cavity, once held in equal dread, had become the "surgeon's playground" in the 1880's.

Jackson remained in bed for a month after the duel until his wound had closed superficially and he had recovered from loss of blood. Then, against the advice of his doctors, his restless spirit drove him to get up; but from this time on Jackson was never the same.

He had possessed a comparatively sturdy constitution until the duel, otherwise he might not have survived to the age of thirty-nine the prevalent diseases along with the poverty, deprivation, and hardship of his youth.

After this fateful affair of honor Jackson suffered from ever-recurring attacks of chills and fever, pain in the chest, followed by coughing and hemorrhages from the lungs. Some of the attacks of fever might have been caused by malaria, from which everyone in the South suffered but which could usually be controlled by quinine. The symptoms point to another diagnosis —that the bullet, together with the particles of cloth and bone, caused an abscess of the lung. As long as this abscess was sealed off, it would produce fever and pain in the chest. The abscess would spread gradually, the fever rise, and chills and fever would alternate with profuse sweating. Finally, the pressure of the abscess and the digestive power of the pus would cause a perforation into a bronchial tube. Through this opening the pus would drain and be coughed up with blood. The severe strain of the coughing and the sudden emptying of the abscess cavity would leave the patient feeling faint and exhausted, but soon afterward the fever would drop and he would feel relieved.

A period of relative well-being for Jackson would follow, lasting as long as the connection between the abscess and the bronchial tube remained patent and draining. Then the only discomfort would be caused by intermittent coughing spells which brought up bloodstained mucus. After a while, granulation tissue would gradually fill up the fistulous tract and occlude the channel which had served as a valve for the septic process. Then the pus in the abscess cavity would accumulate again, the temperature of the patient would rise and the same succession of symptoms recur.

Occasionally the pus would erode a larger blood vessel in the vicinity, bringing on a copious hemorrhage and an acute crisis. This vicious cycle of septic fever and malaise when the abscess was sealed off, alternating with remissions of relative well-being while the abscess was draining, repeated itself over the years with ceaseless regularity. Gradually it sapped Jackson's vitality and undermined his iron constitution.

Contemporary doctors interpreted his combination of symptoms, fever and sweats, and coughing of blood and pus as typical for pulmonary tuberculosis. They believed that in Jackson's case the tuberculosis possibly had been activated by the severe chest wound. This diagnosis has been accepted by most later historians but is improbable in the light of modern medicine. Tuberculosis of the lungs, with Jackson's severe symptoms, would, without proper treatment, have taken a more rapid downward course. It would not have allowed Jackson to live so long following the duel.

After the tragic duel with Dickinson, Jackson was involved in several other such acts of ceremonial mayhem and took part in numerous fights of a more informal nature. He was a born fighter. He had to be to survive, for he grew up in a world of struggle. His father, also named Andrew, was a tenant farmer from northern Ireland who, in 1765, had emigrated to America with his wife and two sons, settling in the wilderness of North Carolina. The elder Jackson died two years later, a few weeks before the birth of Andrew in Waxhaw, South Carolina.

In 1780, when Andrew was thirteen, he served as a mounted messenger to an American encampment. He was captured with his older brother, Robert, by a body of British dragoons. The officer in command ordered the boys to clean his boots. They refused, whereupon the enraged officer drew his sword and struck them. His slashing blow cut Andrew's upraised wrist to the bone and crashed on his forehead, leaving a scar which he carried for life. It left an even deeper scar on Andrew's mind, an indelible hatred of everything British which was to become one of the leading motivations of his life.

His brother Robert was even more seriously wounded in this encounter. As prisoners, both boys contracted smallpox. They were released in the custody of their plucky mother who had come for them. Robert soon died of his wounds and the smallpox. Andrew recovered after several weeks of critical illness, probably complicated by malaria. Soon afterward, Andrew's mother died from deadly typhus fever contracted while she was nursing other American boys captured by the British. Andrew's oldest brother Hugh had died the year before.

At fourteen, Andrew was left to shift for himself. He was a tall, skinny, freckle-faced youngster with red hair and steel-blue eyes; unfortunately he drooled when he talked, especially when excited. Because of this failing he was the butt of many cruel jokes, against which he could retaliate only with his fists.

At sixteen, Andrew inherited three to four hundred pounds sterling from his wealthy Irish grandfather. This sum he spent on high living, gambling, and horses. The brief taste of the better things of life was enough to arouse in the boy a determination to acquire them again. After a short period at school he decided to study law, relying on the standard law books for his theoretical training. He served as clerk for two attorneys, and obtained enough practical experience to be admitted to the bar within two years. Soon afterward, at twenty-one, he was appointed prosecutor at the court of Nashville, presided over by twenty-six-year-old Judge John McNary.

In Nashville began the great romance of Andrew Jackson's

life. He was living at the boarding house of Mrs. John Donelson and there met and fell in love with her attractive daughter Rachel. Their courtship, difficult from the start, had about it the flavor of a medieval romance. Like an Arthurian knight, Jackson was the fearless soldier and devoted lover throughout their years of marriage.

When the two first met, Rachel was the estranged wife of Lewis Robards of Kentucky. After a brief and futile attempt at reconciliation, Lewis informed his wife that he had started divorce proceedings. Rachel and Andrew Jackson were married in 1791, unaware that Robards meanwhile had dropped the proceedings. Two years later they were shocked to learn that Robards was now asking for a divorce on the grounds of his wife's adulterous second marriage. Though they had married in good faith, Andrew and his wife were to be plagued until the end of their lives by the circumstances surrounding Rachel's separation and remarriage. The divorce eventually was granted, and in 1794 the Jacksons went through a second ceremony. Jackson's enemies, in addition to their other charges against him in political campaigns, always dropped innuendoes that he had married an adulteress. Throughout the years Jackson defended his wife's name with every weapon at his command—whips, fists, and pistols, as he did when, in defense of her honor, he received his chest wound.

The wretched poverty of his youth as an orphan created a yearning in Jackson for a life of a gentleman farmer in the Virginia style. Now, as a successful lawyer, he was able to acquire The Hermitage, near Nashville, which he enlarged and improved until it became the plantation of his dreams, among the finest in Tennessee. But though Jackson had achieved his idyl, his fighting spirit did not allow him to enjoy the peace of the countryside for long. The scent of battle and the clamor of party politics lured him again and again from his retirement and into the thick of the fray until chronic invalidism eventually confined him to The Hermitage.

When Tennessee became a state in 1796, Jackson, as its first representative in Congress, became an irreconcilable opponent of President Washington. Later he was to serve as United States Senator, as Justice of the Tennessee Supreme Court, and, in 1802, as major general of the militia. In 1812 he was appointed major general of the U.S. Volunteers and, two years later, became major general of the Regular Army.

Jackson, even after narrowly escaping death in the duel with Dickinson, with the reminder still giving him pain, never learned to control his violent nature nor to balance valor with discretion. He challenged and fought his peers at the drop of an invective. In 1813 he got mixed up in another gun battle, the outcome of a tavern brawl in Nashville. For some reason, Jackson was trying to horsewhip his former friend and later champion, Thomas Hart Benton. He was shot from behind by Benton's brother Jesse.

The bullet shattered his left upper arm at the shoulder joint, causing an open compound fracture. Andrew was carried across the street to the Nashville Inn, where doctors tried in vain to arrest the hemorrhage. The blood stopped only after two mattresses had been soaked through and the patient's blood pressure had dropped to shock level. All the doctors except one advised Jackson to have his shattered arm amputated in order to save his life. The one who was against amputation probably thought it was too late anyway, but Jackson refused to have his arm cut off. And, as throughout all his life, he fooled the doctors, keeping arm and life both.

An inevitable infection of the bone set in, which became chronic and plagued Jackson for the next nineteen years, in addition to his pulmonary abscess. The shoulder wound would close at times and the break open again. It did not heal completely until 1832, when the lead ball was finally cut out.

A short time after the Benton shooting, the news reached Nashville that the Creek Indians in the nearby Mississippi Territory had risen up, sacked Fort Mims, and massacred two hundred and fifty settlers. A committee on public safety hastened to The Hermitage where the wounded General was recuperating. He received them at his bedside and assured them that he would be ready to go in a few days.

"The health of your general is restored. He will command in person," he said, propped against a pillow, his shattered arm in a sling. In the words of Marquis James, "Jackson was too sick to leave his bed but strong enough to make war."

It sounds unbelievable that a man in Jackson's condition, just five weeks after a serious injury, should have been able to take active command of a whirlwind campaign and lead his infantry on a forced march of thirty-two miles in nine hours. This Jackson did. If it is true that an army marches on its stomach, Jackson's army had little to march on. The supply system was deplorable. That "meagre monster, Famine," which Jackson dreaded more than the hostile Indians, was stalking his column. There were only a few cattle for two thousand men. Jackson ordered these butchered, taking for himself and his staff only the leavings, on which they lived without bread or salt. A few acorns supplemented this starvation diet.

Jackson spent most of his days in the saddle. His festering arm was in a sling; he suffered also from intestinal cramps and diarrhea. Eyes hollow and stomach empty, he ignored discomfort, pain and fatigue, planning and directing all the details of the campaign. With his men, he spent his nights on the frozen ground. At critical moments of a battle he would rush to the scene to rally the wavering ranks. Like the real soldier he was, he gave vent to his personal misery not by complaining but by swearing like a top sergeant. His men could not help admiring their general, who scorned polished brass buttons and was as tough as hickory. It was they who gave him his famous nickname, Old Hickory.

Jackson's dysentery, aggravated by lack of care and improper diet, also became chronic. His digestive system from this period on remained delicate, disposed to new flare-ups of diarrhea and cramps. This tendency was not alleviated by one of the medical panaceas of the time, the mercurial calomel which Jackson took in large doses for his intestinal upsets. An overdose of mercury alone can cause spasms. Unknowingly, Jackson added these cramps to the bacillary paroxysms of the bowels. All this time the wound in his left upper arm was draining pus. While Jackson was on the way to New Orleans, in the fall of 1814, a large fragment of bone sloughed off. Jackson, with a gruesome sense of humor, sent it to Rachel as a token of his love.

Wrecked by his two chronic infections and his dysentery, Jackson was not the picture of a victorious general when he entered New Orleans, in December of 1814, to defend it against Wellington's veterans. An eyewitness described his ghostlike appearance—". . . a tall, gaunt man, very erect . . . with a countenance furrowed by care and anxiety. His dress was simple and nearly threadbare. A small leather cap protected his head, and a short blue Spanish cloak his body, while his . . . high dragoon boots [were] long innocent of polish or blacking. . . . His complexion was sallow and unhealthy; his hair iron grey, and his body thin and emaciated like that of one who had just recovered from a lingering sickness . . . [a] fierce glance . . . [lighted] his bright and hawklike eye."

If the appearance and physical condition of the General were not conducive to confidence he amazed people by his accomplishments. The compulsion of hatred which, several years before, had given the badly wounded fighter the strength to kill Dickinson, now made him forget his weakness and summon the last ounce of his energy to get revenge on the archenemy of his life, the British.

A few days after his arrival, the English navy, by an unexpected coup, took possession of Lake Borgne, only a few miles from New Orleans. General panic gripped the city. The sudden threat aroused Jackson to feverish activity. According to Marquis James, "Jackson galloped to his headquarters in Royal Street, and for thirty-six hours the place shook with his tumultuous energy. Too ill to stand he laid on a sofa, and, whipping his strength up by force of will, and an occasional sip of brandy, exhausted a corps of robust aides with the dictation of orders, the enlistment, concentration and dispatch of troops, and the multitudinous details which before another sun had set were to transform frightened New Orleans into an armed camp."

The results are well known. In the famous battle of New Orleans on January 8, 1815, Jackson inspired his motley array of backwoodsmen, Negro troops and former pirates to defeat the most renowned English regiments of the line. Jackson wrote, immediately after the battle, that the body of the English commander, General Packenham, was already on its way to the fleet "in a casket of rum, and to be taken to London," an interesting sidelight on the primitive embalming methods practiced at the time by the British navy.

The multitude and severity of Jackson's ailments profoundly affected his moods, his behavior and, ultimately, his character. It was an almost unbearable trial for him, who was by nature impatient and aggressive, to suffer in sullen helplessness the ever-occurring attacks of sickness and pain. His violent resentment and anger, normal reactions to the assaults of disease, smoldered, ready to burst through the shell of self-control when ignited by the least provocation.

Thomas Jefferson mentioned with a shudder Jackson's "terrible rages." In 1817, when Jackson was still an active general, he challenged General Winfield Scott to a duel, calling him "a hectoring bully" and one of the "intermeddling pimps and spies of the War Department." Scott, not without reason, had accused Jackson of an act of mutiny, and in reply to this outburst said that though he acknowledged Jackson as his master in the use of epithet, he had to decline the challenge on religious grounds, and added that he preferred to risk his life to a better purpose "in the next war."

In 1818 Jackson received the command against the Seminole Indians. His conduct in pursuing them into the Spanish territory of Florida, and in executing two British subjects as spies, led to international complications and bitter criticism in Congress. To get out of the way this headstrong General, who was too difficult to control and too popular to censure, President

Monroe appointed him military governor of the newly purchased territory of Florida.

During the few months of his governorship of Florida Jackson suffered from new attacks of severe dysentery; he used this
condition as an excuse to resign from his office, which was not to
his liking. He returned to The Hermitage in the fall of 1821,
suffering from a "distressing cough and inflammation of the
lungs." In the following year he had a prolonged spell of constipation with severe cramps. Dr. Philip Marshall Dale of Los
Angeles, thinks that these colics were produced by lead poisoning, caused by the two large slugs of lead he carried, from which
enough poison could eventually be absorbed to kill a normal
person.

As if this were not enough, he introduced more of the same
metallic poison into his system by habitually using lead acetate
(sugar of lead), a time-honored remedy which has only lately
been ingloriously discarded. Jackson used it freely as a cure-all,
externally and internally. He bathed his eyes with the cooling
solution, poured it into his wounds, and often drank it for his
intestinal cramps, adding further insult to his long-suffering
intestines. In the same year Jackson contracted a bad cold in a
church at Nashville, which brought a relapse of his chest condition and of his old bowel complaint. He wrote of "having in
the last twelve hours upwards of twenty passages," and ended,
"In short, sir, I must take a rest or my stay on earth cannot be
long."

Any other man but Jackson, with so many crippling ailments,
would have retired from public life. Although deep in his heart
he wished to spend his remaining years in his beautiful Hermitage with his adored Rachel, his character and his fate dictated otherwise. Counting on the enormous popularity of Jackson as a national hero, the general assembly of Tennessee drafted
him as a nominee for President in 1822. He accepted this call to
duty with the reservation that his health would not permit his
active participation in the campaign.

All during the campaign Jackson was in poor health. He

repeatedly complained of copious sputum—"great quantities of slime," as he called it. The pus which had been draining over the years from the lung abscess had gradually infected the adjoining branches of the bronchial tree, and in time was leading to a chronic condition known as bronchiectasis, a dilatation of the bronchial tubes combined with profuse secretion of infectious mucus. In spite of his inability to do any personal electioneering in the presidential campaign of 1824, he received the majority of votes.

Through the political machinations of Clay, John Quincy Adams, who had the second largest vote, was elected President. Jackson felt cheated; his fighting spirit was aroused. Ignoring his precarious health, he carried on a most vigorous political campaign for the next four years, which was crowned by his overwhelming victory in the election of 1828.

In 1825, a severe fall caused profuse hemorrhage from the abscess cavity of the left lung. The chronic systemic infection contributed also to a softening of the gums and tooth decay, a complication which was not helped by his habitual use of calomel, itself damaging to the gums. Thus the tortures of toothache were now added to the chest pains and shoulder wound and the recurring abdominal pain.

If the presidential campaign was strenuous for him, it was even harder on his sensitive wife. The archconservative enemies of Jackson, the champion of the people, hated and feared him. They used any means to prevent his election, even stooping so low as to revive the old story about the Jackson's early marital mix-up. Rachel was deeply hurt by the cruel insinuations against her, printed in scandal sheets that were widely circulated. She was a naïve and kind-hearted woman, who had spent most of her life in the country. Short and dumpy, she had no idea how to wear fashionable clothes, and she liked to smoke a corncob pipe. She dreaded moving into the limelight of the capital as the first lady of the land.

"I assure you, I had rather be a doorkeeper in the house of God than to live in that palace at Washington," she told a friend in November, 1828. Her wish was soon granted. In December 1828, Rachel had a severe heart attack, probably coronary thrombosis. The hastily summoned doctors bled her repeatedly and thereby apparently benefited her condition temporarily. Bloodletting, indiscriminately and unscientifically employed as it had been through the ages for practically any kind of ailment, can be useful and even life-saving for a failing heart, relieving the back pressure into the pulmonary circulation. After three days the patient felt better and by the sixth she was fairly comfortable. On the evening of that day she was permitted to get up. As she was sitting by the fire, smoking her corncob pipe, she repeated her previous remark, "I had rather be a doorkeeper in the house of God than to live in that palace." Twenty minutes later she cried out, "I am fainting!"—and collapsed.

The desperate husband could not comprehend the irreversible fact of her death. He could not understand that his unconquerable will, which had triumphed over all his mortal enemies and defied the greatest afflictions of his own body, had not power against the finality of death of the one he most loved. Frantically, he had her bled at the wrist, and, when no blood appeared, at the temple. Two drops, no more, stained her cap. He had her body placed on a table, covered with blankets, and kept watch the whole night, waiting in vain for a sign of breath, feeling a pulse which never returned.

Heartbroken and lonely, a physical wreck, the sixty-two-year-old President arrived in Washington in March 1829 for his inauguration. Weak as he was, on his inauguration day, he rose to the occasion, as usual, and walked bareheaded from the capitol to the White House.

During the first year of his administration, the President was more than ever a picture of misery, suffering from the afflictions of Job, without Job's patience. The chronic infectious processes passed through some of their more acute phases, leading to new complications. His breathing became short and wheezing and alarmed those in the same room with him. His legs and feet started to swell, and the doctors feared a fatal attack of "dropsy."

He had excruciating headaches; his vision became blurred; the diarrheas recurred with a vengeance. The opinion has been expressed that the combination of these symptoms pointed to an inflammation of the kidneys, a nephritis, caused by the bacterial toxins circulating in his system.

The tortures of his body did not improve Jackson's moods, and he became, if possible, more edgy, short-tempered, and quarrelsome than ever. He would not tolerate any contradiction; he fired most of the members of his first Cabinet for their refusal to accept socially the wife of his friend, Secretary of State John Henry Eaton, because of Mrs. Eaton's questionable reputation. He replaced the dismissed Cabinet members with more pliable personalities. Not that he ever paid much attention to his official Cabinet—preferring to consult with his circle of old friends, cronies, and yes men, his so-called "Kitchen Cabinet."

A visiting surgeon from Philadelphia had the courage to cut out Jesse Benton's bullet from Jackson's left shoulder. The bullet had by this time traveled below the skin where it could be easily felt. The operation, in 1831, was done with dispatch, without anesthetic, and with the patient standing up. It is reported that Jackson's health promptly improved after the excision of the bullet which had probably kept up the suppuration of the bone.

In 1838, Jackson consulted the most famous surgeon of the time (remarkably named Dr. Philip Sying Physic), for his persistent chest pain. But even the renowned Dr. Physic could advise nothing for the chest condition but "cupping," the application of heated suction cups to the skin overlying the painful area.

From Philadelphia the President went on a tour through conservative New England. The trip was a surprising personal triumph. In Cambridge the august faculty of Harvard University condescended to confer the honorary degree of Doctor of Laws on the lowly born President who had never seen the inside of a college. (Only John Quincy Adams violently objected to this disgrace to his alma mater. He hated Jackson, who had defeated him in the election for a second term, and called him a "barbarian" who could hardly read and write.)

The President's round trip from Washington took twenty-seven days, and while it was a great political success, medically it was a nightmare. During his stay in Boston, Jackson contracted a heavy cold which brought on one of his more severe pulmonary hemorrhages. Yet his powers of recuperation were so extraordinary that he finished the trip as planned and returned in fair condition to Washington.

During his second term, the President's health was possibly even worse than during the first term. He still held a firm grasp of the reins of government, and once having made a decision, nothing could move him to alter it. Sickness and age only increased Jackson's suspicion and hatred of those he considered his enemies. His fierce clashes with Clay, Calhoun and Webster are well known. He considered Nicholas Biddle, director of the Bank of the United States, as his archenemy, convinced that Biddle had used the resources of the bank to finance the campaign of his opponent at the presidential election.

Jackson had the peasant's suspicion of banks. He did not understand that the function of the Federal Bank was to regulate the supply of money in circulation. With the blind hatred of ignorance, he fought the bank relentlessly, and in his last presidential year succeeded in having its charter revoked. By this and other ill-advised economic measures, Jackson sowed the wind for the great depression of 1837; his unfortunate successor, Van Buren, reaped the whirlwind.

Jackson's unyielding stubbornness, which led to such disastrous domestic results, served him better in international politics. The stern language of his notes convinced the various European nations that they had better pay the long overdue claims for damages inflicted during the Napoleonic Wars. We may not agree with some of Jackson's principles, and regret his prejudices and arbitrary methods, but we should never forget that as a whole his aims and actions as President and statesman were not dictated by selfishness but by the sincere belief they were for the best interests of the United States and the common man.

In his last year as President, Jackson suffered from an unusually severe attack of coughing, leading to another profuse pulmonary hemorrhage. It is reported that his doctors treated Jackson by bleeding him of two additional quarts of blood. The indestructible patient survived even this murderous therapy.

To the surprise of all, the President, who had been considered physically unable to outlast his first term, survived his second term in March 1837, though in such poor shape the doctors thought he could not stand the three-week trip back to The Hermitage. Against their advice the patient insisted on departing immediately, and at President Van Buren's request, the surgeon general and a relay of other army doctors accompanied him all the way.

Jackson arrived safely and lived eight more years in the quiet surroundings of The Hermitage, but even there he had no peace. He could not bear to sit quietly by and watch from a distance the political upheaval which, after four years, dethroned the Democratic Party and brought the Whigs into power. From his armchair, Jackson hurled his thunderbolts at anyone who dared to disagree with him, and quarreled violently with his most intimate friends. He was the intransigent champion of the cause of slavery which he believed to be in danger.

His sick body tormented him without let-up. Since 1829, Jackson had passed through several episodes of dropsy, with swelling of the feet and legs. This condition had occurred and subsided a number of times, but during his last years it was constant. The swelling gradually increased and spread upward in the body. Dr. Gardner, a medical biographer, presented the plausible theory that Jackson's terminal dropsy was caused by a specific degenerative condition of the body called amyloidosis. This had developed as a consequence of the various suppurative processes. Amyloidosis, a rare condition at present, can be brought on by severe chronic infections. It is characterized by the formation of a peculiar protein-like substance in various organs, especially the kidneys, liver and spleen, and leads to a water-logged state of the tissues called edema.

Any pathological process which diminishes the viscosity of the blood below a certain point will induce edema. The normal circulation within the blood vessels depends on a certain thickness of the blood maintained by the proper amount of protein. If the protein content is reduced below a critical level by much loss of blood, by severe secondary anemia, or by nephritis or amyloidosis, the watery blood plasma seeps through the vessel walls and accumulates in the adjacent tissues. The degree of the doughlike swelling of dropsy corresponds to the severity of the primary process responsible for it.

In Jackson's case, we are unable to determine the causes of the dropsy episodes he suffered. He repeatedly lost great quantities of blood by pulmonary hemorrhages; his chronic infectious process in chest, shoulder and bowels led to a severe secondary anemia and also to inflammatory and degenerative changes in his kidneys. The repeated bleedings increased his anemia.

Contributing to Jackson's misery were the financial worries which beset his last years, and the heartache which his adopted son, Andrew Jackson Donelson, brought him. Like other strong, lonely and childless men, such as both Michelangelo and Beethoven before him, Jackson tried to fill the void of his paternal frustration by adopting a nephew as his son. His fatherly devotion, like theirs, was repaid by ingratitude and disappointment. Andrew Junior proved to be an improvident wastrel, who mismanaged The Hermitage plantation during his father's long absence in Washington, and brought him to the verge of bankruptcy.

There were further afflictions which struck Jackson during his last few years. In 1837 he became blind in his right eye. A year later, he developed a condition suggestive of erysipelas, high fever and delirium, followed by a huge swelling of head and ear that broke out in blisters. His shortness of breath made it more and more difficult for him to move around. Yet each day he walked the few steps to Rachel's grave.

Sick as he was, in January 1840 the General accepted an invitation to New Orleans to commemorate the twenty-fifth anniversary of his great victory over the British. On the way he hemorrhaged so badly that on his arrival he was too weak to make a speech, but he managed to make a short personal appearance, supported on each side by a friend, and to force a smile and wave to the enthusiastic crowd. The tonic of public adulation invigorated the old warrior so much that he was able to continue his trip for more celebrations at Jackson and Vicksburg and somehow to get back to The Hermitage. This was his last long trip.

Finally, the chain reaction of disease affected the one organ which had for so long withstood the ravages—his sturdy heart. There can be no doubt that Jackson's chronic pulmonary disease strained and weakened the right chamber of the heart, which had to pump the blood through the pulmonary vessels increasingly constricted by scar tissue. The right ventricle reacted to the increased burden with hypertrophy of its muscles, followed in time by overstretching of the muscle fibers and impairment of function. The blood started to stagnate in the veins and the plasma extravasated into the tissues. Thus a dropsy of cardiac origin became superimposed on a pre-existing edema from a deficiency of blood proteins.

In 1843 the physical deterioration was accelerated by a more acute phase of gastroenteritis. Inexorably the dropsy climbed higher and higher. The shortness of breath forced Jackson to give up his brief daily walk to Rachel's grave. By 1844, he could not walk at all, but had to be lifted from a sitting position in bed to the same position in a chair. His mind, however, remained clear. In May 1845, he wrote to his foster son, "I am swollen from my toes to the crown of my head and in bandages to my hips."

At this late time a fashionable French painter arrived to make a portrait of Jackson. The artist found a tall man propped up in a chair, fighting for breath, his face a mask of swollen flesh crossed by the lines of pain; one eye was covered by a white scar, the other a glowering slit between puffed eyelids. Jackson was a gruesome sight. The Frenchman fled, preferring to copy a painting of Jackson made several years previously by another artist and to embroider it with his own imagination.

The end was near. On June 2, 1845, the abdomen became so distended that Dr. Esselman of Nashville had to tap it. He obtained "much water" without giving the patient much relief. Opiates were freely administered but did not quiet the restless spirit. He could not eat. He could not sleep. Up to the last, Jackson's greatest concern was the fate of the Union. Two days before his death, he dictated a letter to President Polk, commending his strong stand on the Oregon question and expressing confidence in a settlement, peaceful or by war, but to the advantage of the United States.

The end came on June 8, 1845. The old warrior's great spirit, which for so many years had animated a broken body, was finally faltering and longing for rest. He who had so often defied death no longer resisted but welcomed him as a friend.

Martin Van Buren

(1782 — 1862)

MARTIN VAN BUREN was the first of the eight Presidents who held office between Andrew Jackson and Abraham Lincoln. His chief claim to fame rested on his political acumen, which earned him nicknames such as "The Red Fox," "The Little Magician," and "The American Talleyrand." As a political craftsman he was conspicuous among the Presidents who preceded and followed him: the uncompromising John Quincy Adams, the autocratic Jackson, the faded General William Henry Harrison, and the unpredictable John Tyler.

However, it seems far-fetched to compare the good-natured, God-fearing American Van Buren with the cynical Frenchman Talleyrand, who, in Napoleon's words, "had betrayed everybody and would sell his own father." After all, the country boy from Kinderhook, N. Y., had few opportunities to try his hand beyond the bailiwick of American machine politics, whereas the French diplomat was a Mephistophelian figure whose stage was the world. What they did have in common was a physical handicap they had to overcome to prove themselves—Van Buren his diminutive size, Talleyrand his clubfoot.

Martin Van Buren was of pure Dutch ancestry, born of a family which for six generations had intermarried and not ventured beyond the Hudson valley. His father owned a little tavern which he ran economically with the help of his numerous offspring. There was hardly enough money and time to spare to send little Mat to the country school where he acquired the bare rudiments of the three Rs. His handwriting was so awkward that it was almost illegible, and improved so little as to arouse the suspicion that the boy was born left-handed, forced by the schoolmaster's cane to conform with the right-handed majority. Andrew Jackson, who could not boast of his own penmanship, used to make fun of his friend's undecipherable hieroglyphics, the meaning of which he had to guess.

Except for his handwriting Martin was an exemplary pupil with an eager and nimble mind. After Martin had finished his elementary curriculum at fourteen, a lawyer friend took the bright boy into his office as a clerk. There, between cleaning and dusting the premises and painfully taking down notes, he snatched up enough crumbs of legal procedure to surprise his neighbors two years later by winning a case in court. He completed his training in New York under a prominent attorney and was admitted to the bar at twenty-one.

He enjoyed perfect health and a happy disposition. An ingratiating smile and a freckled face crowned by red-blond hair reassured the people he met of his friendliness and good will, made him a ready success in his practice, and subsequently in politics, in which he took part on the county level. His wit was keen and his quips made even the grim Jackson roar with laughter. Endowed with these gifts he became a senator at thirty, and at thirty-three attorney general of the state of New York. In the meantime he had married a classmate, one of his numerous cousins, Hanna Hoes, and moved to Hudson, in Columbia County. They had four sons.

Without the benefit of prenatal care, Hanna Van Buren developed tuberculosis of the lungs during her fourth pregnancy. A few months after her delivery, she coughed up a mouthful of blood, closed her eyes and died. Driving his wife's coffin through the snows to the Kinderhook churchyard, Van Buren's face looked pinched and bitter as if it had never known how to smile. The thirty-seven-year-old widower never remarried. He drowned his loneliness and sorrow in the whirl of politics and society. His four young boys he farmed out to friends, relatives and boarding schools. They grew up without the roots of emotional stability to complement their intellectual gifts.

In 1820 Van Buren was elected U. S. Senator and, in 1828, Governor of New York. In the following year he was appointed Secretary of State by the grateful President Andrew Jackson, whose victory in New York State had been due to Van Buren's work. From 1831 to 1832 he served as Minister to England, in 1833 became Vice-President, and in 1837 President. He tried to follow closely in the footsteps of his great predecessor, who bequeathed to him with the Presidency the abysmal economic slump of 1837. In this emergency, Van Buren showed that he was more than a clever politician but a man of conviction and courage when his political creed of noninterference by the government in private enterprise—then the basic democratic dogma —was challenged. His consistency in resisting the people's pressure for direct government aid lost him his popularity and re-election.

The President took his defeat as a matter of course, without losing any sleep about it. At the expiration of his term he cheerfully retired to his estate at Kinderhook, but not from public life. He was only fifty-nine years old and full of vitality, and he liked to keep his hands in politics, to pull the strings behind the scenes. On two occasions when the circumstances looked auspicious, he could not resist the lure of the limelight and returned to the stage to take part once more as a candidate for the Presidency. All the while he had amused himself by placing unsportsmanlike bets on elections he himself manipulated.

His digestion and disposition remained excellent. Like his old Dutch ancestors, he liked rich food, fine wines and good company. His waistline grew in proportion to the number of courses his French chef prepared for him, and his exquisite Madeira and port wines—even taken in moderation—were no help for the gout he developed in his sixties. With advancing years his brow became ever more towering until it joined his bald pate. His hair receded to his temples, merging with his bushy sideburns. It turned white, with a yellow tinge as the last reminder of its former reddish hue.

In 1854, at the age of seventy-one, he took a trip to Europe, and on the advice of his doctors went to Aix-les-Bains in southern France, famous since antiquity as a spa for rheumatic disorders and joint diseases. Seventy years before, Thomas Jefferson had vainly tried to soothe the pain in his right wrist with its healing waters. Apparently the springs were more salutary for Van Buren's gouty joints—or perhaps it was the restricted diet the resort doctors prescribed.

He felt better after a few weeks and went to Italy, staying in Sorrento for several months. He seems to have been content to spend the evening of his life on the same golden shore where the retired Roman senators used to sun their gout-ridden limbs, when the sobering news arrived that his third son, Martin, had died in Paris. Sadly, the former President left his paradise to take his son's coffin back to the family plot in the Hudson Valley, and to close the circle of his own life at the point where it had begun. There was enough resilience and vigor left in him to enjoy life for several more years. At seventy-six he wrote from his Lindenwald estate at Kinderhook, "My health is better than it has been ever before and I enjoy life admirably." Barely a year later, in 1860, Van Buren contracted a severe bronchitis accompanied by asthma, apparently not of allergic origin, and possibly induced by a virus of the influenza type.

He voted for the Democratic fusion ticket in New York, but after Lincoln's election became his staunch supporter.

The bloody defeats of the first war year disheartened Van Buren and made him wish to close his tired eyes on the gruesome spectacle of national self-destruction. Meanwhile he suffered from several prolonged episodes of spasmodic coughing and shortness of breath. Most of January 1862 he spent in bed, propped up on pillows, tormented by coughing spells and labored breathing. His physicians made the ambiguous diagnosis, "malignant catarrh." Unquestionably, his bronchial tubes were chronically inflamed and dilated, his lungs affected by a secondary bacterial invasion.

As soon as the patient could be moved he was taken to New York City and placed under the care of Dr. Alphonso Clark, one of the most prominent physicians of the time. Late in May he returned to Kinderhook, where he spent the last two months of his life. The pulmonary process was incurable and irreversible. Van Buren's terminal symptoms were similar to those which had ended the life of his tough predecessor, Andrew Jackson, being the consequences of a decompensated heart which finally gave out. On July 15, Van Buren's condition became critical. His circulation began to fail, his skin became bluish and clammy. Soon the higher centers of the brain, deprived of the necessary oxygen, stopped functioning and started to disintegrate. When his sons arrived at his bedside, the patient could hardly recognize them.

Coma set in on July 21 and continued for three more days. Van Buren was seventy-nine when he died.

William Henry Harrison

(1773 — 1841)

WILLIAM HENRY HARRISON presented a complete contrast to the "man of the people" he succeeded as President. He was a descendant of an old family of Virginia landowners with a revolutionary tradition. While most members of Virginian aristocracy had been British Royalists, one of Harrison's ancestors had been a colonel on Oliver Cromwell's side, who had voted for the execution of King Charles I. True to the family tradition, Harrison's father had signed the Declaration of Independence.

In some of his pictures as President, William Henry Harrison himself has the appearance of a cavalier of the old school—tall, slender, with long, narrow features. His thin lips are tightly compressed, the small eyes seem to look straight through the spectator. Such a stern facial expression was not consistent with Harrison's enjoyment of his role as President. Van Buren, a good loser and an impartial judge even of his opponents, was reported to have said, "The President . . . does not seem to realize the vast importance of his elevation. He thinks and talks with much ease and vivacity. . . . He is tickled with the Presidency as is a young woman with a new bonnet!"

Harrison's austere pose was probably the reflex of an old general before a multitude looking to him for guidance and assurance. However, the emaciated cheeks that give the President almost an ascetic look were probably the consequence of a chronic digestive disorder, from which he had suffered since youth. He seems to have been sensitive to a variety of foods and had learned to confine himself principally to milk, cheese and

127

meat, which relieved his discomfort. Such a medical history points to the probability that he was suffering from hyperacidity, one of the causes of duodenal ulcer, which he neutralized by proteins and fat.

He did not drink, which was unusual for a Southern gentleman and soldier. His father had been a gourmet, who died from complications of the "gentlemen's disease"—gout. The abstinence of his famous son, much praised by moralists and historians, may have been the result of necessity rather than of virtue, his sensitive stomach being unable to tolerate alcohol. Because he could not ingest enough bulk in the form of vegetables, Harrison suffered from chronic constipation, forcing him to resort to strong laxatives. The inevitable result was an irritable colon.

At seventeen, Harrison was apprenticed to a physician in Richmond, whom he assisted for a few months. He then enrolled as a student in the medical department of the University of Pennsylvania, in Philadelphia. The entire medical course in his day consisted of two series of lectures of sixteen weeks each. William attended practically the full course and acquired as much knowledge as the average physician of his time. He was a special protégé of his father's good friend and co-signer of the Declaration of Independence, Professor Benjamin Rush. But the famous doctor could not instill much enthusiasm for medicine into his young pupil. William saw his renowned teacher, who had been trained in the bloodthirsty school of Dr. Cullen in Edinburgh, dispatch his patients by the hundreds, bleeding and purging them to death.

Young William soon discovered that he had no stomach for these methods of manslaughter by medicine, but preferred the more direct approach of a soldier. When his father died, he enlisted in the Regular Army, where he soon became an aide-de-camp of the old Indian fighter, Anthony Wayne. In 1795 he married, and in 1798 he resigned from the army to accept the position of Secretary of the Northwestern Territory. In 1800 he was appointed the first governor of Indiana.

In this capacity he introduced smallpox inoculations and forbade the sale of intoxicating liquors to the Indians. One day, sitting in his living room, holding his infant son John Scott in his lap, an enraged Indian took a pot shot at him through the closed shutters, but missed. Two future Presidents were spared, for John became the father of Benjamin Harrison.

After Governor Harrison by his santitary measures, had built up the health and morale of his Indians, he was forced to break their rising spirit of independence by surprising and crushing them at Tippecanoe in 1811. The poor showing of the other American generals in the war of 1812 led to Harrison's appointment as brigadier general in the Regular Army, and in 1813 he won the important victory of the Thames over the allied English and Indians. He resigned in 1814 and took up his residence near Cincinnati, where he tried to make a living by farming and failed in several commercial enterprises.

According to Holmes Alexander, who based some of his statements on John Q. Adams' sardonic remarks, old Tippecanoe's career after the battle of the Thames was a twenty-three-year-long quest for a sinecure. It is possible that duodenal ulcers, the result of hyperacidity and frustration, kept him from working at a steady pace. In order to support his wife and children he was looking for a soft spot in politics and frantically tried again and again to get a lucrative public office. He attempted not less than ten times to win an election and failed seven times. Seven times he applied for appointive offices and was four times disappointed.

His search for a sinecure was temporarily interrupted by a severe attack of "ague and fever" during February and March 1832. This was either a recurrence of malaria or severe influenza. A big flood of a tributary of the Ohio River forced Harrison prematurely out of his sickbed and to expose himself to the elements. In consequence he suffered a serious relapse.

Two years later he wrote a friend that he was in good health for a sixty-one-year-old man, but then he had a new attack of malaria. All this time Harrison's economic affairs were unsettled, his farm yielding barely enough to keep his family from starving. Finally, charitable friends procured for the aging General a minor clerkship at Hamilton County, which allowed him to live in genteel poverty. He seems to have been content to end his days in this fashion, when the Whig convention of Ohio surprised him by nominating him for President.

The propertied classes, represented by the Whigs, were alarmed about the spreading of the vote among the footloose urban population during the sway of the Democrats and they blamed the party in power—not without reason—for the existing economic panic. They felt that these dangerous Democrats had to be defeated at any price and believed they had found a sure-fire winner for the Presidency in the politically unsoiled, aged military hero whom they disinterred and ballyhooed in a melodramatic campaign.

The Whig leaders did not realize that they could have saved their money and efforts and defeated Van Buren with anyone who looked the part of President. Like all Presidents serving during a depression, Van Buren was blamed by the voters for not having found a cure for the economic crisis which had struck the country.

Except for his chronic digestive weakness, Harrison at sixty-eight was in comparatively good physical condition. March 4, 1841, was one of the coldest inauguration days in history, yet the old General disdained to protect himself on this occasion with such unheroic trappings as a top hat, overcoat or gloves. Bareheaded, he faced a raw north wind as he stood before a gradually dwindling crowd and addressed them with the longest inauguration speech on record—an hour and forty minutes—composed by Daniel Webster, his Secretary of State. The result was a severe cold that ran the usual course.

The next two weeks in the poorly heated, drafty White House were not favorable to the President's recovery. The Whig politicians were as eager for the spoils as the Democrats had been, who had originated the spoils system. With his secretarial staff not yet properly organized, the sniffling and coughing President personally had to interview the thousands of hungry office seekers.

On Saturday, March 27, Harrison's cold took a turn for the worse. Since his medical apprenticeship he was accustomed to doctor himself for minor ailments. Now he felt too sick to depend on home remedies, and entrusted himself to the mercy of the profession he had spurned as a young man. The doctors did their worst. They made the diagnosis of pneumonia of the right lower lobe, complicated by congestion of the liver. With suction cups and stinging ointments they blistered the skin over his right side. To the patient suffering from chronic irritation of the colon they gave drastic cathartics like calomel and castor oil, followed by more calomel and rhubarb and the emetic ipecac.

When the doctors realized that the violent purging and vomiting had seriously debilitated the sixty-eight-year-old patient, they switched to antidotes—opium, camphor, and brandy. The exhausted President grew weaker, and the desperate physicians, not knowing what else to do, resorted to the equally primitive remedies of the Seneca Indian medicine men—mixtures containing crude petroleum and Virginia snakeweed.

The sturdiest liver could hardly have withstood these toxic medicines. No wonder the President developed jaundice, a visible symptom of hepatitis. Finally, a continuous watery diarrhea showed that the rebellious gastrointestinal tract refused to absorb any more poisons.

The President died on April 4, 1841, exactly one month following his inauguration. The immediate cause of death was exhaustion and depletion by loss of water and electrolytes through diarrhea, probably the effect of drugs on an irritable gastrointestinal system. The primary causes of death were a virus pneumonitis and hepatitis, aggravated by medication.

John Tyler

(1790 — 1862)

THE Whigs had added John Tyler of Virginia as Vice-President to the Tippecanoe ticket, counting on his name to attract the South which, like the nation at large, had been severely stricken by Andrew Jackson's disastrous financial policies. He had been an outstanding Democratic Senator who in 1833 had resigned from the Democratic Party, and in 1836 from the Senate, in protest against the administration.

In their eagerness to win, the party leaders must have ignored the possibility that their sixty-eight-year-old candidate for President might not live out his term and be replaced by his running mate who, after all, had a Democratic background. They miscalculated, as later the Republicans did when they nominated Andrew Johnson as Vice-President with Lincoln. John Tyler proved to be an individualist and a man of his convictions, who could not be controlled by the party that adopted him. The result was an executive without a party and a government torn and paralyzed by internecine struggle.

John Tyler was born in 1790 at Charles City, Virginia. His father, John Tyler, was a friend of Thomas Jefferson and Governor of Virginia from 1808 to 1811. Young John graduated from William and Mary, in 1807, and in 1809 was admitted to the bar. In 1830 he married Letitia Christian, daughter of a prominent Virginia family. He served in Congress from 1816 to 1821. In February 1820 he was stricken by a strange sickness. From Washington he wrote to his family doctor back home as follows:

133

I sustained a violent singular shock four days ago. I had gone to the house on Thursday morning having before experienced a disagreeable sensation in my head which increased so much as to force me to leave the hall. It then visited in succession the hands, feet, tongue and lips creating on each the effect which is produced by what is commonly called a "sleeping hand," which all of us are subject to. But it was so severe as to render my limbs, tongue, etc. almost useless to me. I was bled and took purgative medicines which have rendered me convalescent. The doctor here ascribed it to a diseased stomach, and very probably correctly did so. I am now walking about and am to appearance well, but often experience a glow in my face and over the whole system which is often followed up by debility with pains in my neck and arms.

In this instance the diagnosis of the doctor in Washington may have been correct, that Tyler's condition was caused by food poisoning. Certain toxins generated by spoiled fish and mussels have a specific affinity to the nervous system. Tingling and prickling sensations, numbness of the extremities, the lips and the tongue, have been repeatedly described as symptomatic of such food poisoning. Another possibility is a cerebral vascular accident from a thrombosis. Apparently Tyler was slow in recuperating and felt weak for a long time thereafter.

Blaming his physical condition for his decision, John Tyler resigned from Congress and politics for two years, at the age of thirty-one. Probably there were other reasons why he resigned. One was his dissatisfaction with the current Democratic politics; another was the necessity to put his personal affairs in order, that had been neglected during his four years' service in Washington.

Physically, Tyler was never very robust. He suffered from frequent attacks of painful diarrhea of bacterial or amebic origin, and was highly suspectible to colds. All his life he was thin, and his beaklike nose was a caricaturist's dream.

In 1823 Tyler re-entered politics as a member of the Virginia legislature and, like his father before him, became governor in 1825. He later served as Senator (1827-1836) and was the despair of the party regulars for refusing to take orders and following his own counsel. In 1833 he left the Democratic Party and joined the Whigs, resigning from the Senate in 1836. After more political meandering he became, in 1841, Vice-President and then, upon Harrison's death, President.

True to his personality he played a lone hand as President, going so far as to oppose his own Cabinet, which he had inherited from his more pliable predecessor. His Cabinet officers resigned in a body when he reversed himself by vetoing a compromise banking bill he had previously approved. Only his Secretary of State, Daniel Webster, temporarily remained at his post, compelled by a sense of duty. Webster was then in the midst of negotiations with England over the northeast boundary. Like his ancient prototype Demosthenes, Webster has been accused of taking retainer fees from his political clients and supporters; however, the patriotism of both men transcended monetary considerations.

When Tyler moved into the White House, his wife, mother of his seven children, was partially paralyzed as the result of a stroke. After eighteen months of invalidism another brain infarction ended her life. In June 1844, the fifty-four-year-old President shocked many of the bigoted by marrying Julia Gardener, twenty-four years old, whose father was a Catholic. In her portraits she is the typical angelic beauty of her time. She bore seven children to add to Tyler's large family.

In the last year of his term the President narrowly escaped death during an inspection tour of the battleship *Princeton,* when a naval gun backfired and killed several of his entourage, including his new Secretaries of State and of the Navy. Thus, the first Vice-President to succeed a deceased President almost set a second precedent concerning the order of succession, a question that has definitely been decided by Congress as late as 1947. John Tyler owed his life to good manners. He had paused on the lower deck to answer a toast of the visiting ladies instead of remaining at the head of the inspection group.

After leaving the White House, Tyler retired to Sherwood

Forest, his estate in Virginia. There he suffered recurring attacks of dysentery almost every summer, and during the winter
he seemed to catch every cold his numerous children brought
home from school or church.

When he was not ill Tyler enjoyed the usual recreations of a
Southern gentleman—riding, hunting and fishing. Toward his
slaves he displayed the traditional paternalistic attitude. His
standard treatment for their chills and fevers was a stiff dose of
quinine spiked with a jigger of whisky. After all, slaves were
expensive commodities which had to be kept in good humor and
working order. Like his peers, Tyler believed in the inequality
of the races, but was human and patriotic enough to make every
effort to avoid bloodshed over the issue. He remained a political
power in Virginia, and was a hard-working member of a peace
delegation to Washington in 1860 and chairman of the convention of the border states in February 1861, trying to find a last-
minute compromise.

After the outbreak of the Civil War in April 1861, he was
elected representative to the Confederate Congress in Richmond. On January 10, 1862, Mrs. Tyler hurried to join her
husband at the Exchange Hotel a week earlier than planned,
because of a dream in which she saw her husband's life in danger. To her relief she found him apparently in good health,
though disconsolate about the war.

Next morning he felt dizzy and nauseated and vomited bile.
Having experienced similar dizzy spells, Tyler made light of it.
In spite of his wife's remonstrances, he went downstairs to the
dining room for a cup of tea. After drinking the tea, he suddenly
lost consciousness and slumped heavily to the floor. He was
placed on a sofa in the next room. He opened his eyes after a
few moments. Half-dazed, he insisted on climbing unaided up
to his room, in order not to alarm his wife. He felt ill enough
to submit to examination by four doctors. The dignified gentlemen put their heads together and, because the patient had vomited bile, came up with a diagnosis of "biliousness," the broad
term which since ancient times has covered a variety of symp-

toms. To this the doctors added a second diagnosis, bronchitis, when the patient started to cough.

In retrospect, it is obvious that Tyler had had a vascular accident affecting the frontal part of the brain. His previous dizzy spells probably had been similar "little strokes." The doctors did not regard the case as serious and permitted the patient to be up and around conversing with his friends. After a few days, the patient started to complain about headaches and the cough became worse. At last he was put to bed. A cough medicine containing morphine eased the cough and gave him some rest. Tyler seemed to hold his own until the night of January 17, 1862, when he was aroused from sleep by a feeling of suffocation. He felt he was dying and told his doctor, "I am going . . . perhaps it is for the best."

He died before he could take his seat in the Confederate Congress; his age, seventy-one. The cause of death: probably an extension of a vascular thrombosis paralyzing the respiratory center.

James Knox Polk

(1795 — 1849)

JAMES KNOX POLK was the most important of the Presidents between Andrew Jackson and Lincoln. At the time of his election the forces of expansion within the nation had built up to an explosive stage, waiting to be primed and directed by a leader. A great store of fresh ideas, new data, and potential energy had accumulated in the spheres of American science and medicine, ready to be set in motion by daring discoverers.

Almost at the same time the forces of expansion burst the old political frontiers and opened up the vast spaces of the West. The invention of the telegraph opened the field of communication; and the discovery of ether anesthesia removed the barrier of pain that had hampered the progress of surgery, which, characteristically, was first among the branches of medicine to assert itself in the pioneer spirit. In 1809, Dr. Ephraim McDowell of Kentucky was the first surgeon to successfully remove an ovarian tumor. It was Dr. McDowell whose skill also saved young Polk, three years later, from chronic invalidism and probable early death.

Jim was the eldest of ten children of Judge Samuel Polk of Mecklenburg County, North Carolina. He was a small, frail-looking child. Apparently his physical development was retarded by a chronic disorder of his urinary tract caused by a stone, or calculus of the bladder.

Small stones, or calculi, in the bladder may originate in the kidneys, be pushed down by urinary pressure, and eventually excreted through the urethra. If a stone has become too big to pass, it remains wedged in the neck of the bladder causing such symptoms as increased urgency and frequency of urination, bloody urine when the sharp edges of the stone injure the tender bladder lining, and intermittent stoppage of the urinary flow, when, valvelike, it blocks the outlet. Pain is most intense during and immediately following voiding, and by jarring from the outside. Pus is always present in the urine, a sign of an inevitable secondary infection.

These symptoms, particularly pain and chronic infection, sapped the young Polk's strength for many years. He was too weak and listless to participate in games with the other children. His father tried to build him by taking the eleven-year-old boy on a survey trip into the wilderness. But the sickly youth could not keep pace with the others, remaining in camp, caring for the horses and tending the fire. His understanding father tried to hide his disappointment over his oldest son; everyone else treated him with the thinly disguised contempt or condescending sympathy of a normal healthy male toward a weaker companion.

What Jim missed most was the approval of his own age group, which every youth needs to grow the wings of self-confidence. All his life his joyless boyhood left its mark on him. He never learned to play or to joke, and felt compelled to prove he was not a weakling. His character was also influenced by his pious mother, who had given him the name of one of her ancestors, John Knox, and imbued him with the stern moral attitude of the Calvinist reformer.

In 1806, Sam Polk moved with his family to the Duck River Valley in Tennessee. He consulted the best doctors thereabouts, who diagnosed Jim's trouble as stone of the bladder and advised surgery. Dr. Ephraim McDowell was known to have successfully "cut for the stone" in more than a score of patients, an astonishing achievement at a time when anesthesia and antisepsis were unknown. Sam Polk wanted the best for his son, so in the fall of 1812 he and Jim mounted their horses for the 230-mile trip to Danville, Kentucky.

This long journey on horseback over rough trails was agony

for the seventeen-year-old boy, every jounce of the horse pushing the sharp facets of the stone against the sensitive bladder wall. What a relief it must have been for him when they finally drew rein before the unpretentious white house that served as the doctor's residence, office and hospital. Young Polk was so spent and emaciated by that time that the doctor ordered several weeks' rest before he dared to operate.

On the morning of the operation Jim was given a slug of brandy and some laudanum, then strapped to a plain wooden table, his legs bent at the knees, feet securely tied to the hands on each side. Two strong men held his thighs apart. The surgeon inserted a grooved metal probe through the urethra into the bladder, to serve as a guide, quickly made a short incision between the scrotum and the rectum, and through this inserted his left forefinger into the wound. Feeling the director in the urethra, he rapidly made a cut in it long enough to admit the tip of his finger. Carefully he pushed his finger up through the yielding bladder neck into the bladder, and followed it immediately with a special forceps as the guiding probe was withdrawn. Then he quickly opened the forceps, caught and extracted the stone.

The operative procedure took only a few minutes—minutes of hellish torture for the half-conscious patient. Young James Polk could not suppress a wailing moan. No sutures or ties were used. Bleeding was only moderate and could be controlled by pressure on the wound for a few minutes with a wad of lint. A napkin was applied to the perineum and frequently changed as it became soaked with urine. Opium powders were administered to relieve postoperative pain. Within a week the urine started again to flow normally through the urethra, and in four to five weeks the wound was completely closed. In December 1812, young Polk was back home, proudly exhibiting his stone, the size of a hazel nut, to his friends and neighbors.

To Dr. McDowell Jim wrote a thank-you letter, poor in spelling and grammar, but sincere in gratitude. A second letter,

which Polk wrote fourteen years later as member of Congress
from Tennessee, expressed his feelings better:

> My dear Doctor, I have been enabled to obtain an edu-
> cation, study the profession of Law, and embark success-
> fully in the practice; have married a wife and permanently
> settled in Tennessee, where I now occupy the station on
> which the good wishes of fellow citizens have placed me.
> When I reflect, the contrast is impressive indeed, between
> the boy, the meager boy with pallid cheeks, oppressed and
> worn down with disease, when he first presented himself to
> your kind notice in Danville, nearly 14 years ago, and the
> man today, in the full enjoyment of perfect health.

In 1815, Polk entered the sophomore class of the University
of North Carolina and was awarded first honors in mathematics
and the classics. From 1823 to 1825, he served in the state legislature of Tennessee and made the acquaintance of the man of the
hour—Andrew Jackson. In 1824 he married Sarah Childress, who
was well educated, well read and cultured and possibly his intellectual superior. Their union was childless, possibly due to
Polk's early genitourinary damage.

Sarah overcame the frustration of childlessness by devoting
herself to all kinds of good causes. She lived by the tenets of
strict Methodism. As first lady, she banned liquor and dancing
in the White House. It was the more remarkable that in spite
of these Puritan tendencies she was one of the most popular
mistresses of the White House, admired by many who despised
her husband.

Beside his vivacious, raven-haired and dark-eyed wife, Polk
looked inconspicuous and ordinary. He was a short, slightly
built man who tried to look taller and more impressive by his
military bearing and energetic gestures. His plain face was
framed by long black hair beginning to turn gray, brushed back
from a broad forehead. His nose was prominent, in proper balance with his angular chin. His tight-set thin lips and his stern
steel-gray eyes gave his homely face an expression of unusual
determination.

This was the man who had patiently climbed to the pinnacle of his party. He typified the aspirations and dreams of the American people, saw clearly the dominant issues of his day; and was never assailed by doubts as to his course. Because he had the courage to openly advocate annexation of Texas and Oregon, Polk won the Democratic presidential nomination as the first dark-horse candidate in American history, easily overtaking the front runner, Van Buren, and beating in the election the old professional, Henry Clay, who was pussyfooting the question of annexation. At forty-nine, he was one of the youngest Presidents and was, until Wilson in 1916, the only candidate to be elected with the vote of his own state against him.

Up to the time of his presidency Polk had been in reasonably good health following his earlier operation. However, during his four years in the White House, in the midst of the steaming marshes of the Potomac River, Polk made many entries in his diary about malarial chills and fevers combined with severe fatigue. There are also many notations about gastrointestinal upsets and painful diarrhea.

The swampy flats of the Potomac River were fertile breeding grounds for swarms of malarial mosquitoes and flies carrying the germs of dysentery and typhoid. High tide brought great quantities of garbage and offal to the flats, which putrefied in the hot sun. Here innumerable crows feasted on thousands of drowned cats. During the Mexican War it was said that the crows and buzzards populating the marshland had flown all the way from the battlefields where they had been gorging on the bodies of the slain.

As a leader, Polk was not carried by the enjoyment of power nor by the thrill of accomplishment; he was driven by a compulsive sense of duty: a joyless instrument of his own determination. Few Presidents have gone into office with a more definite program and been more successful in completing every point of it in so brief a period ... the reduction of the tariff, the independent Treasury, the settlement of the Oregon boundary question, and the acquisition of California.

Except for official receptions and invitations, Polk, who never knew how to play, rarely took time out from his work. The only diversion he knew, horseback riding, which had been so painful in his youth, he did as methodically and seriously as any other of his tasks. To his contemporaries he seemed to be singularly lacking in a sense of humor. This impression was not altogether justified, as an entry in his diary revealed. Once, when a sleight-of-hand performer showed his tricks at the White House, Polk wrote that his mind was much too preoccupied with turning over the Oregon question and other state affairs "to find any diversion in the juggling."

A diary, like a self-portrait, is the mirror of a personality, reflecting the light and colors in which the subject sees himself. Polk's entries cover a narrow range of themes and interests. Again and again he complained about the pressure of his duties, his unending labors, his solicitude and anxiety: "With me, it is emphatically true that the presidency is not a bed of roses." He never mentioned books, or anything about art, music and nature. Yet he accumulated a choice library, and showed his interest in it by personally arranging his bookshelves as one of his first tasks after retiring to his home in Nashville.

The most severe strain on President Polk was the Mexican War. It was the necessary consequence of his undeviating plans of expansion which he tried to execute consistently, often with Machiavellian adroitness. Failing to reach his goal by peaceful means, he felt that war was unavoidable.

Posterity has lost sight of the achievements and difficulties of the Mexican War, which served as a training course for the future generals of the North and the South fifteen years later. The conflict was a touchstone for the President, proving his genuine qualities as a leader and organizer. His incessant labors under the external stress of the war and the inner burden of guilt for having started it were too much for a man with a comparatively weak constitution and Calvinist conscience.

He was saved from a complete breakdown by the limitations of his emotional range, which also prevented him from being a sympathetic and inspiring figure, both in his own time and in history, although he gave all he could of his limited store of physical and spiritual resources.

Numerous reports relate how shockingly fast he aged during his term. He had accepted his nomination as President with the reservation that he would serve only four years. This was long enough to undermine his system so that he lasted only three months longer.

When Polk left the Capitol on March 6, 1849, he had a bad cold and was dead tired, and he would have preferred to return home to Nashville by the shortest route. But he had already accepted an invitation to take a swing through the Southern states. This trip was financed by public subscription and a tight schedule had been arranged. Even between stopovers, no rest periods had been allowed for and committees had been appointed to escort him from city to city. Arriving in Montgomery on March 16, he had a severe relapse of his cold, and sneezed and coughed through the public reception.

At that time a pandemic of Asiatic cholera that had started in 1846 somewhere in east India had reached the harbor cities of the United States and was carried up along the Mississippi and its tributaries. In the spring of 1849 the cases occurring in the South were of comparatively low virulence. It was well known that Asiatic cholera was a highly communicable disease, but its bacterial origin and specific microbes were not discovered till thirty-four years later by Robert Koch. The usual measures of quarantine were ineffectual against it because it was transmitted chiefly by water contaminated by sewage and by milk that was diluted with such water. Like other enteric diseases, cholera can also be spread by flies, ants, cockroaches and rodents, which transfer the microbes from the human excrement to accessible foods.

In immune or convalescent human beings, the microbes of cholera, as of other intestinal parasites, can live for a few weeks. Their reservoir is the biliary system, which can serve as point of departure on a new trip for the world-traveling microbes.

It has been found that hydrochloric acid in the normal stomach can kill the cholera germ, *Vibrio comma,* or at least attenuate them to such a degree that they cannot penetrate the healthy mucosa of the intestinal tract. Invasion of the mucus lining seems to be favored by preceding irritations such as a spoiled stomach, diarrhea, cathartics and exposure. It also has been observed that emotional upsets like fright, grief and anxiety may cause susceptibility to the disease. Emotions that constrict the blood vessels of the skin and impede vital functions can also dry up the stomach mucosa, and paralyze the intestines, making them vulnerable to bacterial infiltration.

On March 21, Polk reached New Orleans, one of the main ports of Asiatic cholera invasion. There had been comparatively few cases at that time. The water of the Mississippi was still too cool for the bacteria, which favor the heat of late summer. The former President had been advised not to stop at the city so as to avoid exposure to the threatening epidemic. However, he did not wish to disappoint the public, and submitted to sumptious breakfasts, noisy processions, dinners and banquets, at which the hosts feasted on fancy French dishes and choice wines while the abstemious guest of honor embarrassedly asked the waiter for a piece of cornbread and boiled ham, and sipped lukewarm water. After two days of being on exhibition, Polk finally was able to board a steamer for Nashville.

By this time he was fatigued and tense, and slept poorly. The cholera supposedly left behind was his silent traveling companion on the ship. On the very first day aboard, a passenger died of it and his body was hastily disposed of. Two days later Polk complained of "a derangement of stomach and bowels," which, however, did not prevent him from seeing a number of visitors who came on board. His condition grew worse, forcing him to remain in his stateroom. Finally, on reaching Paducah on the Ohio, a doctor warned him to change to another boat and not to expose himself further to the dangerous disease in his susceptible condition. After a short stopover, Polk took passage

on another ship, but in doing so was unable to avoid the celebrations of his grateful fellow citizens.

When he arrived home in Nashville, the chronic diarrhea,
which had troubled him intermittently for several years, flared
up anew. After taking opiates, he rallied and felt somewhat
better for a month or so. Then, at the end of May, the cholera
epidemic struck with full fury. Overnight it swept into Nashville and spread like wildfire through the city. Those who were
able fled in panic. The city fathers tried to purify the air by
exploding gunpowder. Ministers held special services to pray
for divine mercy. Doctors advised purifying the bowels with
laxatives as a preventive against the disease, unknowingly weakening their resistance to it.

On June 1, the Polks decided not to tempt the fates by remaining in the pestilential city. They were packed and ready to
leave town on Sunday, June 3, but wanted to avoid traveling on
the Lord's day. It would have been too late anyway. Early Sunday morning, Polk again suffered an attack of diarrhea which
did not respond to the customary home remedy containing
opium. Vomiting followed. He collapsed on a couch and urged
his wife to go to church without him. As she was about to de-
part, she heard him begging her in a husky tone not to leave
him. Startled she turned to see his face ashen-gray, the pinched
face of the cholera victim. Presently cramps doubled him up,
and he fell from the couch to the floor in a faint.

He was carried to his bed. Doctors were summoned, and
miraculously the patient rallied. On the next day he seemed on
the way to recovery. He could again retain fluids; no cramps
recurred; the diarrheas decreased in violence, though they did
not disappear altogether; and the subnormal temperature of the
acute phase changed into the remittent fever of the "typhoid
stage" of cholera.

Most patients recover from this form of the disease, but it had
been too much for Polk's exhausted body, driven beyond its
endurance over the years. The tribulations of office, the lack of
rest following the chronic dysentery, and now the superimposed

attack of cholera, had depleted the adrenal glands until they were below the point of recovery. His mind remained clear to the end. His last thoughts concerned his wife, who had been his partner for twenty-five years. As she leaned over his bed, a last smile lighted his face, and in a halting voice he told her what provisions he had made for her. Then he died peacefully, only fifty-four years old.

Sarah Polk survived the President by forty-two years. She died in 1891 at the age of eighty-eight, and rests beside her husband in the garden of their Nashville home.

Zachary Taylor

(1784 — 1850)

ZACHARY TAYLOR was the third of nine children of Richard Taylor, a colonel in the Revolutionary War. He grew up in Orange County, Virginia, then a wilderness; learned early to hunt, fish and swim, but had little formal education. At twenty-four he got a commission as officer in the Regular Army, in which he served for the next forty years. His first station was Fort Pickering, at the site of the modern city of Memphis, surrounded by the sluggish bayous and stagnant swamps of the Mississippi where, during the summer, malaria mosquitoes competed with the less common but deadlier species carrying yellow fever, and with flies transmitting dysentery and typhoid.

Fort Pickering was an outpost of the military camp of New Orleans, which was located in a similar bacterial environment. Concerning the sanitary conditions under which the soldiers lived at this camp during 1809, American state papers contain the following description:

> Long before these raw troops were battling the British, they were fighting mosquitoes, disease and death. Their camp was poorly located in spite of instructions from the War Department to move to higher ground. Many were soon suffering from excessive fatigue, resulting from the work of clearing and draining the camp ground and sleepless nights caused by the busy mosquitoes. Without wholesome food or proper medicins and with no shelter for the sick but tents, which neither protected them sufficiently from the heat of the sun, nor kept them dry from the dews and rains, the troops were easy victims of disease.
> Chronic diarrhea, dysentery, scurvy, bilious and intermit-

tent fevers, and other diseases decimated the ranks. During the ten months following May 1, 1809, there were 686 deaths, 108 desertions and 58 discharges among the 2,000 troops concentrated at New Orleans.

The enormously high mortality among the troops points to an epidemic of yellow fever, carried from the Caribbean by dying seamen and spread by mosquitoes. It is reported that young Taylor contracted this usually fatal disease.

He had barely recovered from his ordeal and returned to his company, when the first warmth of spring generated a new crop of flies, the harbingers of dysentery. Taylor got such a severe attack of it that he had to be sent home to Virginia to recuperate. Appointed captain in 1810, he was assigned the following year to the command of Fort Knox, menaced by hostile Indians. There, in the late summer, he was stricken severely with malaria. During the night of September 4, the Indians attacked the post in force. Taylor was still weak from the fever, and many of his men were either partly or wholly incapacitated by it. The Indians succeeded in setting fire to the blockhouse where the provisions were stored. The handful of defenders, debilitated by disease, had barely the strength to fight both the flames and the enemy, and the fire threatened to spread over the stockade. The captain and his company seemed to have a desperate choice between death by fire or massacre.

On this as on other occasions, Zachary Taylor proved cool and undaunted. He was the sort who did not fear things he had not personally experienced. He conquered the Indians, the fire, and malaria, and lived to be famous as "Old Rough and Ready." This nickname expressed the admiration the enlisted men felt for their gruff General, who was a real soldier despite his unmilitary bearing and odd appearance.

He had a big head, thick unkempt hair, coarse features and a short neck. His eyelids were half-closed, the heavy brows pulled down over nearsighted eyes in an instinctive attempt to sharpen the focus of vision, but giving the impression of a fierce scowl. At close range and in reading, Taylor had to shut one eye to avoid double vision. His body was big and barrel-shaped, supported by legs that were so short that he had to be helped into the saddle by an orderly.

Possibly the awareness of his unsoldierly appearance was a compelling challenge that made young Zachary want to be an officer, like his father. His lack of education and poor eyes would have stood in the way of his appointment to West Point, founded in 1802. He prevailed upon his relative, James Madison, to use his influence with President Jefferson, who granted Zachary a commission as first lieutenant in the small American army.

Taylor was apparently always careless about his appearance and dress. The higher he rose in rank and independence, the less he felt inclined to conform to army regulations. In this way he expressed his contempt for the spic-and-span West Point boys who set the army fashions. At the same time, it enhanced his ego to exaggerate his comical appearance by making himself look grotesque. His instinct for showmanship achieved its objective when, as a general of the Regular Army, he wore an old battered straw hat and a long linen duster. To his soldiers, who hated to polish shoes and brass buttons, the unkempt General became their funny-looking "old man" about whom they could joke, though they looked to him for leadership.

In the Mexican War, as in most wars before 1900, the losses of Taylor's army from disease far outnumbered the battle casualties. After defeating the Mexicans in two battles, Taylor established his base at Camargo at the mouth of the San Juan River. "Camargo," wrote one of his generals, "is the sickliest place I think in the world and it is only a matter of surprise and wonder that I am still alive. I suppose we must have buried a thousand poor volunteers at that river port." One of the regiments which left Tennessee a thousand strong was reduced by sickness and death to less than five hundred men. At the end of July 1846, the army took Monterrey, where the climate was far better, but even there the soldiers fared badly. Infectious diarrheas and several types of malaria incapacitated nearly a third of the troops. Their tough General had only one brief spell of fever, in Corpus Christi, but remained in good health afterward.

With victory, Taylor was a popular hero and a promising presidential candidate for the Whig leaders, who started to sound him out about his availability. It is claimed that Polk, a Democrat, tried to sidetrack Taylor politically by giving Winfield Scott, the senior officer of the army, instead of Taylor, command of a second decisive campaign against Mexico City.

There were other, more pertinent reasons for not making General Taylor the commander of the new campaign. According to President Polk, "General Taylor, I fear, is not the man for the command of the army. He is brave, but he does not seem to have resources or grasp of mind enough to conduct such a campaign." Indeed, Taylor was a hardy frontier soldier, but he knew nothing of military science. He was scornful of the West Pointers and their book strategy. Like the old Russian General Suvorov sixty years before him, he believed in the bayonet in preference to fire power and artillery preparation.

That he nevertheless won battles against an enemy who vastly outnumbered him was due to the excellence of the denounced West Pointers under him, who checked the untrained Mexicans by their good use of artillery and superior infantry tactics. The courage of the American soldiers could be depended upon inspired by absolute loyalty to their general, who exposed himself freely and often unnecessarily. Credit the notoriously poor aim of the peons rather than Taylor's good luck that he was never wounded during the Mexican War. His only battle souvenirs were several patched up bullet holes in his loose-fitting uniform coat. His skin was never more than scratched.

Taylor's last and most famous victory at Buena Vista, that assured his election as President, was actually the result of an unnecessary and strategically unpardonable action into which old Rough and Ready let himself be goaded, in disobedience of strict orders from Washington to remain on the defensive at Monterrey. On his own initiative, he advanced on a wild goose chase into the trackless desert with his reduced army, to meet the ruthless Mexican general, Santa Ana, whose raw enlistments, though four times stronger, lacked equipment, provisions and ammunition. Inspired by their imperturbable General, the American troops held fast, and after two days the Mexicans were forced to retreat, beaten by lack of water, food and ammunition. Newspaper reporters made a glorious victory out of the senseless slaughter. If Taylor had lost the battle, as he almost did, a court-martial would have awaited him instead of the Presidency.

Reluctantly he remained with his army in Monterrey until November 1847, when he resigned, believing himself snubbed by the administration in jealousy of his growing popularity. This conviction increased his willingness to become a Presidential candidate. For a while he seemed to be playing coy, although he may have actually hesitated because of his wife's strong objections.

Elected President against a split Democratic ticket, Taylor, without political experience, at first was lost amid the clamor of patronage, and bewildered by the raging conflict between the free and slave states that was aggravated now by the annexation of Texas and the pending admission of California. He proved his inherent patriotism and personal integrity when, as President, leader of the Whig Party, Southerner and slaveholder, he heeded the advice of the high-minded Senator from New York, William H. Seward, a leading opponent of slavery. He resisted the pressure of his son-in-law, Jefferson Davis, by advocating the admission of California as a free state.

Taylor warned the Texans, who were claiming half of New Mexico, that he would personally lead the army to prevent such an expansion. In spite of his lack of political finesse and his Southern birth, Zachary Taylor exhibited during his administration of only sixteen months more resolute leadership and a greater national consciousness than all three of his Northern-born successors: Fillmore, Pierce, and Buchanan.

The President did his best to prevent the passage of the infamous compromise bills, concocted by Clay and supported by Webster—particularly the amended fugitive slave law, an inhuman document that aroused the passions of the North and South to a new pitch.

It was during the heat of the argument for and against Clay's omnibus bills, in July 1850, that the President suddenly was stricken with a fatal gastroenteritis. His symptoms resembled those to which Polk had succumbed thirteen months previously. In the absence of any epidemic of Asiatic cholera at the time, Taylor's ailment was diagnosed as the homegrown form of "cholera nostras" or "cholera morbus."

A clinical diagnosis is difficult without bacteriologic and pathologic confirmation, because there are only a restricted number of ways that the body reacts to injurious agents. The gastrointestinal tract may show symptoms of cholera, though the damage may be the result of toxins of various organisms, arsenic poisoning, spoiled food, or other substances that can disrupt the delicate chemical and bacterial balance of the digestive tract.

On the sultry afternoon of July 4, 1850, President Taylor was standing bareheaded in the sun, participating in the ceremonies at the erection of the Washington Monument. They were long-winded and noisy; the sixty-five-year-old guest of honor had to stand for several hours in the burning sun. To quench his thirst he drank several glasses of water. When he returned to the White House, he ate quantities of cherries, washing them down with quarts of iced milk and water.

At dinner he could not resist several more handfuls of cherries, against the warning of the family physician sitting beside him. About an hour after dinner, Taylor became violently ill with cramps and diarrhea. During the night the diarrhea became watery and cholera-like. The usual remedies, containing opium, proved ineffective. With increasing dehydration the patient developed cramps in the calves of the legs. The symptoms persisted for the next two days, and three more physicians, one a specialist from Baltimore, were called in consultation. Brandy and more opium were prescribed. After a slight improvement, a typhoid-like fever set in, initiating the second stage of the disease. On the evening of July 8, the diarrhea subsided, to be replaced by a gradual distension of the abdomen, violent vomiting and difficulty in breathing. The President felt somewhat easier the following afternoon, but died during the night.

Millard Fillmore

(1800 — 1874)

THE history books praise Millard Fillmore for overcoming
all obstacles on his arduous climb from bootblack to President,
but once he had unexpectedly reached the top, he found himself in the center of a storm which overwhelmed him. His contemporaries were impressed by his good looks, imposing presence
and gracious manners; yet his letters and speeches indicate a
colorless figure. For the medical historian, Fillmore is colorless,
with no interesting diseases to compensate for the apparent dullness of his personality.

Fillmore's early life in some ways parallels the youth of Andrew Jackson. Both were poor, apprenticed to trades. But though
Jackson broke his bondage by running away from his master,
peaceful Millard bought his freedom for $30. As young men,
both were taught writing by the women they afterward married.
Fillmore, at twenty-six, married his schoolteacher, Abigail
Powers. He was then a struggling young lawyer, but in later
years became prosperous in this profession.

In 1828 he met Thurlow Weed of New York, who introduced
him into politics and managed his career for the next twenty
years. He was in succession assemblyman, congressman, chairman of the Ways and Means Committee, comptroller of the
State of New York, and Vice-President. As chairman of the Ways
and Means Committee, he carried an appropriation of $30,000
for the first experimental telegraph between Baltimore and
Washington, built by Samuel Morse. As Vice-President he broke
with Thurlow Weed and William H. Seward over the antislav-

ery question, and under the influence of Daniel Webster took the spineless position of compromise at any price.

As a consequence, the first thing Fillmore did after becoming President was to sign the Fugitive Slave Bill, and with this endorsement signed his political death warrant by alienating his home state, New York. Asked why he had signed the bill, so odious to his constituents, he placed the responsibility on Daniel Webster, whom he had appointed Secretary of State.

The institution of slavery has been compared with the plague of the frogs in Egypt. It seems more appropriate to compare it with a parasitic growth, like a cancer, which feeds on its victim whose life it menaces. In 1820, the palliative of the Missouri Compromise had arrested its visible growth for a time. The annexation of Texas and California gave it new nourishment, aggravating its virulence.

Thereafter until 1861, it could no longer be arrested with the quack medicines and soporifics of the practical politicians. All they could do was temporize and try to postpone the threatening dissolution of the states until the times called for a great physician, who would dare to cut out the evil by the roots and save the Union.

In 1850, Abigail Fillmore stirred Washington social circles when she installed the first bathtub, made of sheet metal, and a kitchen range in the White House, which had been left in a very unsanitary condition by the Taylors. She established the first White House library. It is related there was not even a Bible in the house when she arrived.

In contrast to the hard-drinking and gourmandizing social set in Washington, the President was a health addict who did not smoke or drink, but preferred milk and simple foods. He must have consumed great quantities of them, as indicated by his paunch, the ancient badge of prosperity until life insurance statistics made it unfashionable. Overweight may have shortened his life span a few years; nevertheless, he was healthy up to his last sickness. Not so Mrs. Abigail Fillmore, who was ill most of the time during her residence in the White House. Her gifted daughter Mary Abigail on many occasions acted as hostess.

The climate and bacterial environment of the White House, in the midst of the disease-breeding marshes, did not agree with Mrs. Fillmore. Reading the fragmentary medical records of the mistresses of the White House, one gets the impression that they suffered more frequent and severe attacks of malaria and enteric fevers than the Presidents. While there is no statistical proof for this notion, it might be explained by the fact that the Chief Executive required a tougher constitution than his wife, and greater potential of immunity to survive the arduous journey to the top. Over the years, he had to pass through many strange bacterial strata during his electioneering, while his resistance was weakened by heat, cold and fatigue. He had to shake thousands of germ-covered hands and breathe the foul air of hundreds of halls teeming with microbes from disease carriers among the audiences.

On the other hand, the majority of the Presidents' wives had spent comparatively sheltered lives, confined mostly to their homes. The chief dangers threatening their health were the home-grown tuberculosis bacilli and the contaminated hands of midwives when their children were born. Moving into the virulent bacterial milieu of the White House they were ambushed by swarms of strange mosquitoes and flies that infected them with unfamiliar strains of microorganisms to which they had not acquired immunity. Thus they became an easy prey of the endemic fevers of Washington.

For President Fillmore, the signing of the Fugitive Slave Act brought with it a train of bad luck, like a curse. Through it he lost caste with the Northern Whigs, who frustrated him as President and defeated his renomination at the convention of 1852. Mrs. Fillmore caught a cold during the inauguration services of his successor, Franklin Pierce, in the treacherous March weather of Washington, and died of pneumonia three weeks later. A year afterward, his only daughter, Mary, died of cholera, leaving him alone with a schizoid son. In 1856, he ran once more for President as candidate of the American, or Know-Nothing Party and suffered a humiliating defeat, carrying only one state.

He found redemption by marrying a wealthy widow, with whom he lived happily the rest of his life in Buffalo's largest mansion.

On the morning of February 13, 1874, just after Fillmore had finished shaving, his left hand suddenly dropped powerless to his side. The paralysis soon spread to the left side of his face and to the muscles of the larynx and pharynx, making breathing and swallowing difficult. The symptoms indicated a paralysis of some of the centers located in the part of the brain called the medulla. It closely resembled the bulbar form of poliomyelitis, which, however, could be ruled out because of the further course of the disease. This leaves the diagnosis of a stroke.

There was a temporary improvement, then the patient had another stroke two weeks later that paralyzed the entire left side of his body. For twenty-four hours he was unconscious and thereafter was unable to leave his bed. The partial paralysis of the swallowing muscles caused difficulty in feeding him, and probably some food particles were aspirated by his lungs. Such an accident usually results in aspiration pneumonia, which may have been a contributary cause of death. He died on March 8, 1874, at the age of seventy-four.

Franklin Pierce

(1804 — 1869)

FRANKLIN PIERCE was one of those tragic figures who—
born with all obvious advantages, which should add up to a
successful and happy life, an influential family, wealth, good
looks, intelligence and personal magnetism—are beset by weakness of character and unfavorable circumstances. He was born
in Hillsborough, New Hampshire, in 1804, in the same year as
his life-long friend Nathaniel Hawthorne.

His father was General Benjamin Pierce, a veteran of the
Revolutionary War, and famous for his hospitality. His big house
was always filled with guests, like a tavern; he had to take out a
liquor license on occasion. Thus, Franklin grew up in an atmosphere of conviviality and alcohol and got to like the taste
of both at an early age; however, he never learned to carry his
liquor well. In later life he claimed that he had inherited his
craving for, and intolerance of, alcohol from his mother—a confession which, true or not, reveals a rejection of his mother.

In 1824 he graduated from Bowdoin College, in Maine, and
was admitted to the bar in 1827. In the same year, his father
became Governor of New Hampshire; he served two terms.
Franklin was elected member of the state assembly in 1829, and
in spite of his youth, became Speaker in 1831 and 1832.

Pierce's physical health seems to have been good until the
summer of 1833, when he was stricken with a serious "bilious"
attack, the nature of which is not described. It could have been
a malaria, a gastrointestinal infection, or a combination of both.
It does not appear to have been cholera, of which an epidemic
was then raging in the United States. It is reported that his life

was despaired of by the doctors; however, he got well in spite of them. In 1833 he was elected to Congress, and after two terms became U.S. Senator in 1837. He enthusiastically supported Andrew Jackson and subsequently came under the influence of the Southern Democrats.

In 1834 he married Jane Appleton, daughter of Reverend Jesse Appleton. She was a mousy woman, shy, inhibited and strait-laced, and seemingly suffered from chronic tuberculosis. She presented a complete contrast to her buoyant, genial husband whom she admired. On his part, he felt a protective love toward his helpless-looking little wife; and knowing that she needed him kept him from surrendering completely to his craving for alcohol.

During his first years in Washington, as a young Congressman, he kept company with a hard-drinking crowd. Just because of his poor tolerance of alcohol he had to show his manliness by competing with his companions in drinking capacity. Again and again he awakened with a hangover of physical misery and mental agony, his wife looking at him with sad reproachful eyes.

Once, when he had a bad cold, he went on one of his alcoholic sprees and got into a fight in a theater. He woke up in bed with a stabbing pain in his side and a high fever. A doctor was called, made the diagnosis of pleurisy, and took a pint of blood from his veins. Next day, he drew twelve more ounces of blood, by making multiple scratches on the skin of the affected side and applying suction cups over them. The patient soon recovered, though for several weeks he remained mentally depressed, filled with self-reproach.

At thirty-three, Pierce was the youngest member of the Senate. His vivacity and brilliant conversation made him a refreshing exception from the majority of his dignified colleagues and a much sought-after dinner guest. However, the Washington climate—social and weather—did not agree with Mrs. Pierce, who usually begged off participating in social affairs with a real or pretended indisposition. Introverted and repressed, she grieved over the death of her first two children from sickness.

In 1842, she left Washington for good, to give birth to another child in Concord, refusing to expose the new baby to the unhealthy weather of the capital.

To the father, the birth of a new son gave fresh purpose. He decided to mend his ways and to retire from the glitter and the temptations of Washington into his peaceful little country town. He seriously meant to devote the rest of his life to his family and his private law practice, and declined the governorship of the state, which his father had held, and the office of U.S. Attorney General in Polk's Cabinet. But he kept his hand in the local Democratic campaigns, and in 1846 was persuaded to accept the position of district attorney of New Hampshire, which permitted him to remain close to his family.

All during this time Pierce seemingly kept his drinking under control, until his peaceful life was interrupted by the Mexican War. Like other volunteers, he could not resist the adventure of war as an escape from the humdrum life. Like other unstable people with hidden conflicts, he could shed his responsibilities in the regimented life of the army, and find solace in the thrill of danger. Appointed colonel and brigadier general, he distinguished himself for bravery and extraordinary coolness under fire, traits often displayed by neurotics with self-destructive drives.

In the battle of Contreras on August 19, he was severely injured when his horse, at the blast of a gun, reared and threw him on a jagged lava bed. The examining surgeon diagnosed his injury as a fracture of the pelvis and dislocation of the left knee. He reduced the dislocation of the knee and bandaged the pelvis. In spite of severe pains and his limp left leg, Pierce insisted on being helped on another horse and resuming his command. That he was able to remain in the saddle until far into the night argues against the pelvic fracture. However, Pierce's injuries were so severe that next day he collapsed in pain and fainted when he tried to lead his horse on foot across a ravine.

During September he was in a hospital, recovering from his injuries, but at this assembly point of all prevalent infections he contracted a tropical fever, probably a virulent form of malaria. This was followed by an infectious diarrhea, unavoidable in any hospital at the time. He returned to the army in time to participate in the crowning military event, the storming of Mexico City. The day before, the Commander in Chief, Winfield Scott, called a council of war. Robert E. Lee was for an indirect approach; Scott and Beauregard favored a frontal attack on Chapultepec, key to the city.

Pierce was won over for the latter plan. However, the next afternoon, he collapsed from a recurrent spell of diarrhea and was unable to lead his brigade. His friend Colonel Ramson, who took his place, was killed at the head of his troops.

After the war Pierce returned to his law practice and became one of the most prominent and successful lawyers in New Hampshire, content to remain in Concord and stay out of the limelight of national politics. As the election of 1852 approached, both parties were looking around for presidential prospects unsoiled by outspoken convictions, records clear of embarrassing statements on controversial subjects—particularly the vexatious question of slavery. Pierce was named. He had been out of national politics for ten years, with the additional advantage of having been a general with an excellent war record. However, when some of his political friends approached him about his availability, he answered that the office of President "would be utterly repugnant to my tastes and wishes."

When the Democrats were unable in thirty-four ballots to agree on a candidate, Pierce's friends pressed him to be a good sport and, for the sake of the party and the nation, accept the nomination. Like President Warren G. Harding later, Pierce could not say "No," and he won the nomination on the forty-ninth ballot.

Against him the Whigs put up the pompous old war hero Winfield Scott, Pierce's former Commander in Chief, hoping to repeat with their general their prior victories with Generals Harrison and Taylor. Pierce made no speeches, presented no issues, yet won by the most decisive majority since the second election of Monroe.

Franklin Pierce's pattern of life did not permit him to taste the joy of victory for long. On January 6, 1853, two months before his inauguration, his only surviving son, Benjamin, eleven years old, an exceptional boy, was killed in a railroad accident before his parents' eyes when the car they were riding in was suddenly hurled from the roadbed. Themselves practically unharmed, the parents saw their son crushed under the wreckage.

Franklin Pierce entered the White House in a state of deep dejection. He sought escape from his overwhelming grief and the added burden of office in alcohol. Jane Pierce was never seen to smile again. Soon after Pierce's inauguration, on a trip through New England, one of the members of his party wrote of the President: "I deeply, deeply deplore his habits, he drinks deep.... A great mistake was made in putting him in at all."

During his residence in the White House Pierce suffered from a persistent cough, caused by a chronic bronchitis, perhaps of allergic origin—one of the allergens being alcohol. Possibly it was a smoldering form of tuberculosis from his wife. Doctors blamed it on dampness and insufficient heat in the executive mansion during the winter months, and so President Pierce installed the first furnace in the White House.

The new heating system warmed the air but not the spirit pervading the White House. Most of the time the President's wife sought seclusion in her room, sick in mind and body, scribbling pitiful little notes to her dead boy. The wives and daughters of Pierce's Cabinet members substituted as hostesses at White House social functions. After one such affair Charles Mason wrote in his diary: "Everything in that mansion seems cold and cheerless. I have seen hundreds of log cabins which contained more happiness."

In his first message to Congress on December 5, 1853, Pierce spoke of the "sense of repose and security" that had come as a result of the compromise of 1850, and vowed to oppose any move to upset it. Yet, less than two months later, he was closeted with his Secretary of War, Jefferson Davis, and Senator Stephen A. Douglas, giving his approval to a measure that was not only to disturb this repose, but also precipitate the Civil War. It was the Kansas-Nebraska Bill, which gave the states and territories the right to decide for themselves all questions pertaining to slavery within their borders.

The summer of 1855 was unusually hot. An epidemic of Asiatic cholera struck the seaport cities, to add terror to the discomfort of the weather. The President suffered an episode of chills and fever, and Mrs. Pierce became so ill that vacation plans were postponed. During this time, bloody battles were taking place in Kansas over the issue of slavery. It was a dress rehearsal for the Civil War. The President was powerless to turn back the forces of destruction he had conjured up. Finally, he sent federal troops to Kansas to suppress the warfare between the factions.

Pierce's friends entreated him to seek renomination as President. He was deeply hurt when James Buchanan won the nomination over him. However, another attack of malaria in the fall of 1856, his wife's continued illness, and the climate of the capital made him look forward to leaving the White House.

Like many American Presidents, Pierce, released from responsibilities, took an extended trip through Europe. Returned home, he was alarmed by the threatening clouds of secession and wrote a ringing appeal to his Southern friends to refrain from war. Up to the last he did not realize the strength of the anti-Northern feeling in the South. He squarely took his place upon the outbreak of the war on the side of the North, but expressed his bitter opposition to Lincoln's dictatorial war measures. In taking an unpopular attitude in the midst of a Republican community, he showed more moral courage and consistency than he had ever shown as a practical politician.

Mrs. Pierce's health declined steadily. Her death in 1863, and that of his friend Hawthorne the following year, broke what was left of Franklin's spirit. All his life he had struggled against his addiction to alcohol; now he no longer resisted it, and became an uninhibited alcoholic.

The overconsumption of alcohol resulted in a chronic inflammation of the stomach, interfering with proper digestion. It may be assumed that, like most alcoholics, Pierce did not take sufficient food containing protein and vitamins. The result: liver damage, aggravated by his chronic bronchitis, which by this time had taken the aspect of a creeping tuberculosis. During 1864 and 1865 he had several acute exacerbations of his cough, with fever and night sweats. The climax came in the fall of 1865 when a recurrence brought him near death.

Up to that time, Franklin Pierce had merely paid lip service to religion. Now he looked for ultimate refuge in the inflexible tower of faith and became baptized in the Episcopal Church. He stopped drinking altogether and lived a quiet, secluded existence. At last he gained the peace of mind he had been yearning for.

However, the change had come too late to stop the progress of the pathologic processes. In his last remaining years, Pierce suffered from ever increasing malaise, nausea, and pain in the stomach. During the last summer he developed dropsy, a distention of the abdomen by watery exudate. His symptoms were typical for a cirrhosis—shrinking of the liver—a condition in which the liver cells, bile ducts and blood vessels are gradually strangulated by an increase of fibrous tissue, and the liver, which is the most important chemical plant of the body, fails in its function.

Alcoholism is a factor in 70 per cent of the patients suffering from liver cirrhosis. In the other 30 per cent a variety of other factors, among them malaria, can cause or contribute to the disease. Pierce died four years after he had given up alcohol, and many more years after his last malaria attack. However, cirrhosis of the liver takes a long time to reach a point incompatible with life. Once the disease had developed clinical symptoms, it could not be stopped.

At present, it can be arrested up to a certain point, by proper diet and vitamins, eventually by surgery. In Pierce's time the condition of cirrhosis of the liver was well known to medical science, but apparently not to his physicians. Even if they had known of it, they would not have been able to help him. Franklin Pierce died in a stupor, characteristic of liver failure, on October 8, 1869, friendless and forgotten in his sixty-fifth year.

James Buchanan

(1791 — 1868)

JAMES BUCHANAN was one of the two bachelors who became President. Grover Cleveland was the other, though he married during his first term. Buchanan remained single all his life. A successful lawyer at twenty-nine, he became engaged, but unexpectedly the girl broke the engagement after hearing some gossip about her fiancé's alleged philandering, became ill and died—by her own hand, it was whispered—before he could convince her of his innocence.

Cruel gossip dragged the melodrama to greater lengths. During Buchanan's presidential campaign, a New York newspaper accused him of having attempted suicide by hanging, to escape the vengeance of his fiancés brother. The tale was widely believed because it seemed to account for Buchanan's peculiar habit of tilting his head to one side, the abortive hanging supposedly having resulted in a permanently twisted neck.

Actually the condition seems to have been caused by a combination of two anomalies of the eyes. One was a divergence of his pupils, the left being placed slightly higher than the right one, the consequence of a congenital imbalance of the eye muscles. The other anomaly was that one eye was nearsighted, the other farsighted, an inequality deduced from Buchanan's curious habit of closing either one eye or the other, according to the distance of the object he was looking at.

The permanent twist of his neck was the result of his effort to correct the distortion of his stereoscopic vision, not from a mysterious neck injury. In spite of his visual defect, Buchanan loved to read, and until his last year did not need glasses, his nearsighted eye compensating for the increasing farsightedness of the other.

The portraits of Buchanan as President show the color of his eyes as light blue, in keeping with his fair complexion. His face was long, angular and smooth-shaven, his hair silky white. He was a broad-shouldered, well-built man, over six feet tall, somewhat heavy with age. The deficiency of his eyesight was compensated by an unusual acuteness of hearing. He confessed to a niece that in his prime his hearing was so keen that he would often hear whispering in the adjoining room and be embarrassed at learning things he was not supposed to know. Equally remarkable were his power of observation and quickness of perception. Little went on around him that he did not know and understand.

In intellectual capacity and political acumen, he surpassed most of the Presidents after him. Along with his extraordinary capabilities, he was acutely sensitive to others' feelings, tactful always, and he had the gift of making—and keeping—friends. Buchanan had been successful in all endeavors and offices before facing the challenge of the Presidency during a period of changes that had baffled all his predecessors since Andrew Jackson.

As a young lawyer of twenty-four he had been a kind of prodigy, earning more than $11,000 in the third year of law practice. He volunteered in the War of 1812, was representative in the Pennsylvania legislature from 1814 to 1816, in Congress from 1820 to 1831. From 1831 to 1833 he was Minister to Russia, Senator from 1834 to 1845, Secretary of State from 1845 to 1849, and Minister to England from 1852 to 1856. The Democrats nominated him candidate for President over Pierce.

Elected President in 1856, Buchanan chose his niece, Harriet Lane, to be hostess in the White House. She was a tall, auburn-haired beauty of twenty-five, who had served as his popular hostess during his Ministry in London. She had been orphaned at an early age and her uncle had taken her under his wing and guided her education. A close relationship had developed between uncle and niece, he finding the gratification of his paternal instinct, she the security and affection a child expects from a parent. As the President's hostess, she charmed guests with her social graces, her attractiveness and intelligence, and brought gaiety back into the White House. The President had the executive mansion redecorated, replacing some of the worm-eaten French furniture from Monroe's time with new American-made pieces.

Always in good health, Buchanan remained well even in the malarial and dysenteric atmosphere of Washington, because he had the good sense to leave the city during the sultry summer months for a higher and healthier location. He expressed the notion that, because of its unhealthy site the White House soon would be given up as a residence, to be used only as an office building.

The national crisis boiled to the surface, during the last year of his administration confronting the sixty-nine-year-old President with a situation he was unable to cope with. He made a pitiful attempt to halt the catastrophe of secession by declaring it illegal. Torn by indecision, he could hardly wait for the day when he could turn the helm of government over to the strong hands of The Rail Splitter from Illinois.

Buchanan's health declined fast after his retirement. He was stricken with recurrent and severe attacks of gout, a metabolic disorder, characterized by retention and deposition of uric acid at the joints, which caused agonizing inflammatory swellings. Besides, the President seems to have suffered from a chronic inflammation of the connective tissue supporting the muscle fibers. His gastrointestinal tract, which all through life had been remarkably resistant to the prevalent infections, also began to trouble him; during the summer of 1863 he suffered from indigestion and diarrhea. From 1863 to 1867 he was repeatedly disabled by painful swellings of the muscles and joints, a condition labeled gout or rheumatism by various doctors. He sprained his ankle in the fall of 1864, thus aggravating an arthritic condition.

Buchanan was a deeply religious man. He carried the burden of disease and age with true Christian forbearance. Toward the end of 1867, shortness of breath with any effort, along with increasing fatigue and exhaustion, indicated a weakening of the heart. During April 1868, progressive heart failure manifested itself by pulmonary congestion and a distressing cough. At the end of May, Buchanan developed terminal pneumonia and died on June 1, 1868, at the age of seventy-seven.

Abraham Lincoln

(1809 — 1865)

O N THE morning of March 14, 1865, President Lincoln was too tired to get out of bed. The giant who had carried a super-human burden for four war years, was overcome by the accumu-lation of fatigue and worry. He needed rest.

Lincoln's face looked gaunt and sallow within its massive frame of dark hair and beard. His eyes were sunk deep within their sockets, reflecting the pain of grief and misery they had seen for so long; the high cheekbones protruded from the emaci-ated face. Years of anxiety had dried up his appetite and given him short and fitful sleep.

The family physician, Dr. Robert K. Stone, was called. He examined the President and announced that the case was one of "exhaustion, complete exhaustion." An important Cabinet meeting scheduled for that day had to be held in the President's bedroom, three hours later. Word went out that his illness was influenza, and it was so reported to the press. The next morn-ing Lincoln dragged himself out of bed and went to his office. No appointments were made for that day. Surgeon General Barnes was afraid that Lincoln was on the verge of a nervous breakdown.

The newspapers expressed concern over the President's health. The *National Republican* stated that he was exhausted as a re-sult of prosecuting the war to a successful conclusion and from the badgering of swarms of office seekers that infested the execu-tive mansion. The newspaper urged that these people be ban-ished from Washington at once, or else the nation would run the risk of a presidential breakdown. The *New York Tribune* was even more emphatic, warning that the President's energies would have to be spared if he was to live through his second term, and unless something was done promptly the Union would mourn a dead President.

Horace Greeley, who had seen the President in early April, said, "When we last saw Mr. Lincoln, he looked so weary and haggard that he seemed unlikely to live out his term."

The series of photographs of Lincoln taken over the four war years shows how much he aged under the burden of responsibility.

Lincoln was convinced that his interpretation of the Constitution of the United States was the right one, and that the first duty of the President was to preserve the Union—if necessary, by war. Yet he could not get over his feeling of guilt for not having found another way out, as had preceding Presidents. In the later stages of the war the pressure on him to end the death struggle by compromise became almost irresistible, especially following the slaughter of The Wilderness and Cold Harbor in May and June of 1864, and he could hardly stand up to his conviction that the war must be pursued to the bitter end in order to ensure victory for the Union and a new birth of freedom.

Self-reproach was a part of Lincoln's emotional pattern. A related characteristic was his feeling of insecurity, which he never completely overcame, that was traceable perhaps to childhood experiences. Up to the age of eight he lacked the safe haven of a real home, his father changing the family quarters three times in moving from Kentucky to Illinois.

At nine, the sensitive boy lost his mother, and but for his sister was without an anchor in the loneliness of orphanhood. His father was too busy providing a bare subsistence to pay much attention to his two children. Like many a neglected child, Abraham might have grown up with distrust and resentment in his heart, had it not been for the timely arrival of a kind stepmother. She gave Lincoln affection and understanding, planting in him the seeds from which stemmed his great capacity for sympathy and love.

Lincoln's depressive impulses erupted on several occasions under the pressure of unusual stress. The medical term for a melancholy state of mind at that time was "hypochondria," wryly called "the hypos" by Lincoln.

According to Herndon, his long-time law partner, Lincoln suffered from an episode of deep depression at the age of twenty-six, in Salem. This occurred after Ann Rutledge, whom he had loved, died of typhoid fever. Lincoln was then in a weakened physical condition, suffering from an attack of malaria. According to Herndon, the bereaved lover talked wildly and incoherently. His friends feared that he might commit suicide and they kept close watch over him. Brooding over his loss, Lincoln reproached God for having allowed such a cruel thing to happen. Herndon claims that, as a consequence, Lincoln leaned toward atheism, as a way of angry defiance toward a trusted parent who had disappointed him.

Lincoln's friend, Dr. John Allen, a deeply religious man, tried to console him by imbuing him with the Calvinistic idea of predestination. He had a lasting influence on Lincoln, implanting in him the philosophy of fatalism concerning life and death.

In later life Lincoln found it impossible to carry the overwhelming weight of his responsibility and the impact of his personal tragedies, without the belief in a personal God, although he never joined any religious denomination.

The most profound and prolonged depressive reaction of Lincoln's life occurred in 1841, starting with the sudden breaking-off, after two years of courtship, of his engagement with Mary Todd. The prospect of marriage frightened him; he could not make up his mind to take on the added responsibility and subject himself to the dependency of marriage. All confidence in himself and his future left him, and for weeks he could neither sleep nor eat. His misery was such that he was unable to attend the sessions of the Illinois legislature, of which he was a member from 1834 to 1842.

He wrote to Dr. Daniel F. Drake, distinguished Dean of the Medical Department of the College of Cincinnati, asking his

advice. Dr. Drake replied that it would be impossible to prescribe without a personal interview, including a physical examination. Lincoln then turned for help to a local friend, Dr.
Antoon G. Henry, of Springfield, who advised him to try to
build himself up physically with rest and proper food, and to
divert his mind with a change of surroundings. He also prescribed large medicinal doses of brandy as a tranquillizer.

Apparently Dr. Henry could not make a living among the
eighteen doctors practicing in the little country town of Springfield. Therefore, on January 20, 1841, Lincoln wrote to his congressman and close friend in Washington, John T. Stuart, appealing to him to obtain the Springfield postmastership for Dr.
Henry. "I have within the last few days been making a most dis-
creditable exhibition of myself in the way of hypochondriism,"
he explained, "and thereby got an impression that Dr. Henry
is necessary to my existence. Unless he gets that place, he leaves
Springfield. You therefore see how much I am interested in the
matter."

Three days later he wrote another letter to Stuart: "I am now
the most miserable man living. If what I feel were equally distributed to the whole human family, there would not be one
cheerful face on the earth. Whether I shall ever be better, I
cannot tell; I awfully forbode I shall not. To remain as I am is
impossible; I must die or be better it appears to me."

Lincoln followed Dr. Henry's sensible advice. He accepted
an invitation from an old friend, Joshua F. Speed, to stay at his
plantation in Kentucky, and he recovered after a few weeks.

Eventually friends brought Lincoln and Mary Todd together
again, and in the following year he summoned the courage to
marry her. Like Lincoln, Mary Todd was born in Kentucky;
however, she came from a well-to-do family belonging to the
self-appointed Southern aristocracy, a family blighted by too
much intermarriage. Among six sisters and brothers reaching
maturity, Mary was one of four with psychotic tendencies. She
gave Lincoln the companionship he needed, but often made his
life miserable with her hysterical outbursts, quarrelsomeness,

insane jealousy, spending sprees, and migraine headaches. In spite of her emotional instability she was a devoted wife and mother.

The very weakness of his wife enabled Lincoln to gain strength and to develop his great human potentialities. Mary Todd's temperamental outbursts taught him a greater degree of self-control. Realizing that she could not be held responsible for her immature behavior, Lincoln learned to practice infinite patience, understanding, and tact. Even when Mary made his life almost unbearable, Lincoln remained a devoted husband and father. These qualities of self-control, patience, and understanding also served Lincoln well in dealing with the emotions of the people.

All depressive reactions converge in the wish to escape at any cost from the tortures of anxiety and guilt which haunt the victims. In his later years Lincoln kept his depressive impulses under control, but his unconscious wish to escape found occasional expression in dreams—dreams that occurred under conditions of increased stress. Lincoln believed in the prophetic quality of dreams which only "children of Nature" like himself could experience and interpret. He claimed that he had a recurrent dream which preceded important battles like Bull Run, Antietam, and Gettysburg. He would find himself in some singular undescribable vessel which was moving with great rapidity toward an infinite shore. It is interesting that this dream of escape toward an infinite shore occurred at times of extreme apprehension, on the eve of important battles, when Lincoln had reason to dread a crushing and perhaps decisive defeat.

Ward Hill Lamon, a faithful friend and biographer of Lincoln, tells of another curious dream which Lincoln related in the presence of Senator Harlan and his daughter and one or two other people. It occurred several weeks before his death, possibly after he had returned from a performance of Gounod's *Faust,* and about the time when Lincoln was so weary that he had to hold a Cabinet meeting in his bedroom. He dreamed that he was awakened by the sound of subdued sobs from many weeping people. He wandered down the stairs and walked from room to room, all of which were lighted but empty. Puzzled by the mournful sounds he heard from the distance, he kept on until he reached the East Room. Entering, he was met with the shocking appearance of a catafalque on which lay a corpse wrapped in funeral vestments. Stationed around it were soldiers on guard, and there was a throng of people gazing mournfully at the corpse, the face of which was covered. "Who is dead in the White House?" he demanded of one of the soldiers. "The President," was the answer; "he was killed by an assassin." This strange dream represented either an unconscious expression of the death wish in a depressed person, as psychoanalysts interpret it, or an extrasensory premonition of a man endowed with second sight—as Lincoln believed himself to be.

Lincoln was certain that he would not live through a second term. This presentiment originated from a vision he had in November 1860 at Springfield, after his first election. Exhausted from days and nights of excitement, he sank on a lounge opposite a looking glass. Too tired to fall asleep, he suddenly perceived a double image of his face in the mirror. One of the faces depicted "the glow of life and breath, the other showed ghostly pale and white." Lincoln confided this weird experience to his wife. They agreed that the meaning of the illusion was that he would pass safely through a first term as President and would be re-elected to a second term, but that death would overtake him before the end of a second term. With morbid curiosity, Lincoln vainly tried to conjure once more the double image in the mirror.

The possible physiologic explanation is that Lincoln suffered from a muscular imbalance of his eyes, which was almost completely compensated under normal conditions. In some photographs it can be seen that Lincoln's left pupil is higher and closer to the upper eyelid than the right. Such an imbalance of the eyes can be aggravated by extreme fatigue. When the eyes diverge far enough in a vertical direction, double vision will result. Of the two images, one may appear sharp and clear, the other vague and distorted.

Lincoln's firstborn son Robert had a similar muscular imbalance, but in the horizontal direction, causing crossed eyes. As a child he was tormented by other children on this account. When he was twelve years old his mother took him to a famous New York surgeon who performed, without anesthesia, a painful operation that corrected the condition.

Lincoln's eyesight seems to have been good up to the age when persons with normal vision become farsighted. He was forty-seven when he felt the need of glasses. This was at the time when, as a busy lawyer, he had to read a great deal of small print, and was occupied with research and study for the formulation of the platform of the newly founded Republican Party. While on a shopping tour to Bloomington, he went into a jewelry store and, with the assistance of the proprietor, selected a pair of eyeglasses through which he could see small print in the largest and sharpest outlines. These glasses, which cost thirty-seven and a half cents, are still preserved. They are six and a half diopters strong; a person with average vision at the age of forty-seven requires only two and a half diopters. This explains why Lincoln often complained of headaches after reading for hours through these magnifying glasses that were about three times stronger than necessary.

Lincoln knew that he was color-blind, unable to enjoy the colorful blooms in the White House garden. No doubt he hardly ever noticed the many new flowery dresses that Mrs. Lincoln loved to buy—perhaps not even the glittering gown she wore at the second inaugural ball and which cost $2,000.

We wonder what Lincoln's life expectancy would have been if he had not become President. One of his grandmothers is supposed to have lived to be a hundred; and his father lived to the age of seventy-five—unusual at that time for a poor pioneer farmer whose life was toil and privation. Lincoln's mother, Nancy Hanks, died at thirty-five of "milksick," an illness common among the settlers of the Middle West, and caused by a poison transmitted by the milk from cows that had fed on such poisonous plants as snakeroot and goldenrod.

Lincoln had a baby brother, Thomas, who died in infancy. A sister, Sarah, two years older, died at the age of twenty-one in childbirth.

Living in the backwoods of Kentucky, young Abe once fell into the rushing Knob Creek and was saved from drowning by a neighbor's boy. When Abe was seven, the family moved to Indiana. There, he grew into a tall, angular, rawboned youth. As the boy outgrew his homemade clothes, he also outgrew the mental horizon of his group, although he received scarcely any formal education.

Young Abe helped his father in clearing and farming the virgin soil, and to supplement the meager family budget, he did odd jobs for neighbors, earning at most thirty-seven cents a day. One of his jobs was to watch and urge a tired old mare turn a gristmill. Impatient with the lack of enthusiasm of the old nag, the youth used the whip, when unexpectedly she let fly with her unshod heels and caught Abe in the head. He was knocked unconscious, suffering a concussion of the brain, and did not come to for almost a day.

At nineteen the tall, rangy youngster constructed a flatboat with the aid of a friend, loaded it with farm products and took it down the Ohio and the Mississippi to New Orleans. One night, on the Louisiana sugar coast, the sleeping boatmen were attacked by a band of marauding Negroes or Indians. Young Lincoln fought them off, receiving a cut on the right side of his forehead which apparently healed without leaving a scar.

Little is known about the diseases Abraham Lincoln suffered during boyhood and youth. In the spring of 1830 the Lincoln family moved to central Illinois where they built a log cabin on the north bank of the Sangamon River. Like all the sluggish tributaries of the Mississippi basin, the river was a breeding place for malaria mosquitoes. In the fall of 1830 almost all of the family came down with the ague and fever.

Most of such cases responded promptly to quinine, which was given in the form of a nauseating concoction of the Peruvian bark in whisky. Reactivations of latent infections and reinfections with malaria were a common occurrence. We know that Lincoln had such an attack at the time Ann Rutledge died in 1835. Later on he probably had other brief attacks which could be checked with doses of quinine.

Lincoln married Mary Todd in 1842. Four boys were born to them in ten years (no girl, to the regret of both parents): Robert Todd in 1843, Edward Baker in 1846, William Wallace in 1850, and Thomas, called Tad, in 1853. Two of the boys were afflicted with congenital malformations—Robert with the previously mentioned converging strabism, and Tad with a cleft palate. In 1850, little Eddie, not quite four years old, died from complications of diphtheria. In 1859, Tad was critically ill from "lung fever," possibly an acute flare-up of tuberculosis of which he died in adolescence. The following year, in the middle of Lincoln's presidential campaign, Willie and also possibly Tad caught scarlet fever. Willie had an unusually severe attack which left him in delicate health. As it often does, the scarlet fever probably damaged his kidneys permanently. At this same time Lincoln complained of a severe sore throat he himself diagnosed as a mild case of scarlet fever.

In March 1861 the Lincoln family moved from their home in Springfield, not exactly a paradise of health, into the White House, not without reason called by John Hay, one of the President's secretaries, "The White Pesthouse." The executive mansion was inadvertently a kind of import and exchange center for an assortment of diseases brought from all parts of the country. Despite his numerous executive responsibilities, Lincoln spent much of his time meeting personally the hundreds of petitioners and office seekers who flocked to the White House from everywhere.

These daily sessions, though they wore him out physically, refreshed his mind and spirit. Through them he felt the pulse beat of the people; he called the sessions his "public-opinion baths." Added to the citizens' visits after the Civil War began, came military personnel from the far-flung fronts of the South and West, to report to the President or to be decorated by him. Unknowingly, many of these callers brought a variety of disease germs. In the wintertime they spread the common cold and other respiratory infections with their sneezing and coughing.

More dangerous visitors were the not uncommon "carriers" of typhoid and diphtheria; themselves immune, they were capable of giving the diseases to others. The hardy streptococci of scarlet fever and the tenacious virus of smallpox were usually transmitted by victims of mild forms of these diseases; they could also be transferred by intermediate objects such as clothing and toys.

Oblivious of these dangers, generally unknown at the time, Lincoln, the indulgent father, permitted his two youngest sons, Willie and Tad, to roam all over the halls and stairs of the White House, enjoying the admiration of the throngs of visitors and coming in close contact with them and their germs.

The White House was encircled by other possible sources of infection. Hospitals crowded with soldiers suffering from dysentery and typhoid were no farther than a fly can travel. These insects easily transported germs through the unscreened windows of the executive mansion. On humid nights, swarms of mosquitoes from the nearby canal of the Potomac River, attracted by the flickering gaslights, repaid their unprotected host with the plasmodia of malaria for his drop of blood.

Livery stables were common along the wide, unpaved streets, and ducks and chickens nimbly dodged the hoofs of the horses, the principal means of transportation. Pennsylvania Avenue, called "The Avenue," had only one paved sidewalk; on the other side were open market stalls and a drainage ditch.

In those days it was believed unsanitary to have toilets under the same roof as the kitchen. So, at the White House, outhouses were located on the south grounds, together with stables and work buildings facing the Tiber Canal, which served as a place for public garbage disposal and exhaled a sickening odor in warm weather.

The hygienic conditions of the White House were not improved by the presence of a menagerie of pets kept by Willie and Tad, attracting more flies. The miniature zoo consisted of goats, rabbits, ponies, kittens (the favorite pets of Lincoln), and a little dog named Jib who often sat in the President's lap at mealtime enjoying the morsels slipped to him. The goats were allowed to roam freely through the White House and gardens, where they especially enjoyed eating the flowers—to the gardener's despair. Added to the private menagerie in 1863 was Jack, the turkey, who upon the tearful entreaties of Tad, was officially reprieved by the President from being executed for Christmas dinner.

In these unsanitary surroundings the Lincoln family, and especially the more susceptible children, were always sick. Sickness started inauspiciously when, after an incubation period of ten days following the inauguration, Willie and Tad broke out with the measles. Soon after, the whole family suffered from an attack of food poisoning after eating shad caught in the Potomac. In July, Robert came down with the mumps. During the damp and chilly winters of Washington, everybody in the drafty, poorly heated rooms of the White House was sniffling from colds; and the shivering President kept his favorite gray shawl forever wrapped around his shoulders.

The mild, uncomplicated attacks of malaria were taken for granted and scarcely mentioned. Quinine was used indiscriminately for all kinds of fevers; it retained its penetrating bitterness regardless of how much whisky and syrup disguised it, and the children detested it. Tad would not swallow the bitter medicine unless his adored father gave it to him personally. An instance is reported when the President was summoned from an important meeting to cajole Tad into taking his medicine.

In spite of his courage in other respects, Lincoln was afraid of dentists, all the more since a dentist had broken off a piece of his jawbone during a tooth extraction—without anesthetic. One day, in 1862, the President had a severe toothache and surprised Dr. G. S. Wolf, who had offices near the White House, with his patronage. At that time anesthesia, particularly chloroform for tooth extraction, was not yet being used in Washington, although it was being administered in Chicago, and was known to Lincoln. As Dr. Wolf selected his forceps and prepared to apply them, the President waved his hand. "Just a minute, please," he said, and took from his vest pocket a small bottle of chloroform, inhaled deeply a few times, then drowsily gave the signal to proceed.

The large feet of Abraham Lincoln were much afflicted with corns. He would often slip off his shoes and sit in his stocking feet until the fastidious Mrs. Lincoln noticed it and sent for his slippers. The President often employed the services of a chiropodist named Dr. Isachar Zacharie, to whom he also entrusted some confidential missions. In gratitude, Lincoln signed a Presidential testimonial for the chiropodist, which read: "Dr. Zacharie has operated on my feet with good success, and considerable addition to my comfort."

The President's family was hardest stricken by the illness that attacked the two younger boys during February 1862. The diagnosis was "bilious fever," usually meaning malaria, but more likely it was typhoid fever, which in Willie's case possibly reactivated a dormant malarial infection. Tad got well, but Willie, the parents' secret favorite—who resembled Lincoln most—succumbed. Apparently left with kidney damage from his scarlet fever two years previously, Willie was easy prey to the toxins of typhoid combined with reactivated malaria.

The mother never recovered from the shock of the death of her favorite child. For many months she would not leave the house, and grieved to the end of her days. The father was overcome by his sorrow. The scene is described by a friend:

"Mr. Lincoln came in . . . he came to the bed, lifted the cover from the face of the child, gazed at him long and earnestly murmuring, 'My poor boy, he was too good for this earth. God has called him home. I know that he is much better off in Heaven, but then we loved him so. It is hard, hard to have him die!' Great sobs choked his voice. He buried his head in his hands and his tall frame was convulsed with emotion."

The same disease wave that carried off the favorite son of the President early in 1862 endangered his chief lieutenant and commander of the Army of the Potomac, General George McClelland. For six weeks the General was incapacitated with typhoid fever, delaying his cautious preparations for the well-conceived but ill-fated peninsula campaign against Richmond. This campaign, thus ill-augured, ended in discouragement and defeat of the great Army of the Potomac, which suffered far greater losses from disease in the fever-ridden marshlands of the James River than from battle casualties.

There is a little-known incident surrounding the famous Gettysburg Address. When Lincoln left the White House on November 18, 1863, young Tad was sick in bed with scarlet fever, according to the doctor's diagnosis; actually it was an early case of smallpox. The father had contracted the disease from the boy and was in the incubation period of smallpox, while delivering his address. During the return trip to Washington on the train, November nineteenth, the first clinical manifestations of the sickness appeared. The President felt unusually tired and had severe headaches. He had to lie down in his drawing room and bathe his head in cold water. His staff probably thought he was trainsick.

Upon his arrival at the White House, Lincoln went to bed, complaining of pain in his head and back, fever and general malaise. The family physician, Dr. Stone, was called. He diagnosed the sickness first as a cold, later as a bilious fever; later still, when the first rash appeared, as scarlet fever. No doubt he gave the patient both time-honored medicines—quinine and calomel.

After two days the fever dropped to normal. At the same time, dusky red spots appeared about the forehead, soon spread over the face and the extremities, and gradually rose to pimples. After two days they developed into the telltale water blisters of the pox, which the vacillating doctor could not fail to recognize.

The blisters were small and widely scattered. This seemed to be a mild case of smallpox, called varioloid. Dr. Stone was apprehensive. He had seen many instances wherein the innocent-looking little blisters had become secondarily infected and filled with pus. Then the fever would rise again and the patient was in danger of blood-poisoning.

Soon the news of the President's illness leaked out and alarmed the nation. Sensational exaggerations of the gravity of his condition appeared in the foreign press. The *London Spectator* went so far as to speculate on the effect the death of the President might have on the outcome of the Civil War. They dug up a brief biography of the virtually unknown Vice-President, Hannibal Hamlin, and concluded with the comment, "Let us hope, however, that there will be no occasion for the curious . . . substitution of a Hannibal . . . for an Abraham."

The President made an uneventful recovery. He got a well-deserved rest without being disturbed by feelings of guilt. Relieved of the swarm of hungry petitioners pestering him for favors, Lincoln smilingly remarked that at last he had something that he could give to everybody. On November 26 he received the heartening news that General Grant had won at Chattanooga. On November 28, Lincoln's recovery was heralded by peeling and itching of the skin, and on December 15 he was back at his official duties.

The epidemic of smallpox which in November 1863 had infiltrated Washington with a few scattered cases, made greater inroads during the winter. Because of its prevalence in January 1864, Lincoln advised his son Robert, a student at Harvard University, against bringing a friend home with him.

During the first chaotic months of the war the inadequacy of the medical service of the Army had been glaringly revealed. To assist the military, benevolent citizens of influence founded in New York City early in 1861 a "United States Sanitary Commission," the efficient predecessor of the American Red Cross. Dr. Clement A. Finley, the current surgeon general and a good army officer, resented the intrusion of laymen into his prerogatives, and refused to cooperate with the civilian commission, in defiance of the President's personal directives. The pressure of public opinion mobilized by the Sanitary Commission forced Congress a year later to pass a bill for the reorganization of the Army Medical Department.

The Sanitary Commission, supported by leading civilian physicians, recommended the appointment of the young assistant surgeon, Dr. William H. Hammond, to the position of surgeon general, and in spite of the vigorous opposition from the medical brass hats the recommendation was followed by the President. Dr. Hammond proved himself to be one of the greatest surgeon generals, but unfortunately he could not get along with the autocratic Secretary of War, Stanton, and resigned two years later. He was succeeded by Dr. Barnes, who also was an able organizer and administrator of the medical department and cooperated well with the United States Sanitary Commission for the duration of the war.

During his Presidency Lincoln was the target of innumerable threats of assassination. Again and again threatening letters were sent to the President, eighty of which he carefully collected and put in a separate file. His family, friends, and members of his Cabinet begged him not to expose himself unnecessarily in public without an adequate bodyguard. Lincoln could not be dissuaded from meeting daily face to face a multitude of unknown people. Up to the last few months he walked at any time, day or night, alone or at best with a friend, unguarded through the streets of Washington. One dark night, as he was returning from the Soldiers Home on horseback, his top hat was shot from his head, pierced by a bullet.

To the entreaties of his advisers Lincoln replied that even with the most elaborate precautions anyone could take his life who was willing to give his own life in turn. Paraphrasing Shakespeare, he said, "If I am killed I can die but once; but to live in constant threat of it, is to die over and over again." Early in 1865 he finally consented to accept the questionable protection of four guards serving in three shifts.

The miracle of his emergence from anonymous obscurity to his elevated position of importance and power, a career which he could not have foreseen or planned, fortified Lincoln in his philosophy of fatalism and the belief that he was born a man of destiny. His rise from a small-town politician to the world's standard-bearer of democracy and the savior of the Union convinced him that he was a divine instrument and that his life was in the hands of God. In the back of his mind the conviction persisted that he was not destined to live through his second term; and he faced this prospect with equanimity. In a conversation with Harriet Beecher Stowe he had said, "Whichever way the war ends, I have the impression that I shall not last long after it is over."

When General Early threatened Washington in July 1864 in a diversional Confederate offensive, Lincoln made an inspection of Fort Stevens, the most exposed sector of Washington's defense perimeter, lying within the rifle range of Early's skirmishers and well pinpointed by the Confederate artillery. Ignoring personal danger, he, the Commander in Chief, watched a counterattack of General Wright's division while standing on the parapet, a gigantic target elongated by his top hat. He was induced to take cover only after a medical officer three feet away had been shot down.

Against all rules of common sense, he insisted upon visiting Richmond the day after it had fallen, and boldly challenged fate by making his way slowly through the narrow streets between the burned-out shells of houses behind which still smoldered the hot embers and the seething hatred of the inhabitants.

On his return voyage from City Point to Washington, the President read aloud from *Macbeth* to his companions:

> Duncan is in his grave;
> After life's fitful fever he sleeps well;
> Treason has done his worst; nor steel, nor poison,
> Malice domestic, foreign levy, nothing
> Can touch him further.

A few days later the Speaker of the House, Schuyler Colfax, scolded Lincoln for his foolhardiness, saying that many people had been worried about the President's exposing himself to violence at Richmond. Lincoln answered, "Why, if anyone else had been President and gone to Richmond, I would have been alarmed, too, but I was not scared about myself a bit."

The fact that he had escaped unscathed from the lion's den convinced Lincoln that his time had not yet come, and he grew even more careless about his personal safety. It is well known that his assassination by a paranoic actor was only possible because the most elementary precautions to safeguard the President were neglected on that occasion. Lincoln had even sent away his constant companion, his devoted friend and self-appointed bodyguard, the husky Ward Hill Lamon, on a confidential mission to Richmond.

There was no guard, not even a locked door, between Lincoln and his assassin on the night of Good Friday, April 14, 1865, at Ford's Theater. The assassin was able to approach him unnoticed from behind and fire a half-inch-caliber bullet at close range at his head. Lincoln slumped unconscious in his chair without a moan.

The first doctor to reach the President was twenty-three-year-old Charles Leale, assistant surgeon of the United States Volunteers, who loved and admired Lincoln. He took temporary charge of the patient and remained faithfully at his side to the very end, nine hours later. At first, the President was in a death-like shock. The pulse could not be felt. Opening the eyelids, Dr. Leale saw the pupils fixed and of unequal size, the right one dilated, the left contracted—a sign of brain injury. Lifting his head, he felt warm blood on his hands, indicating the location of the wound. During his examination, he incidentally loosened a blood clot at the wound opening which had obstructed the flow of blood. Thus the pressure on the vital centers of the brain was momentarily released, the patient started to breathe at irregular intervals, and the pulse became palpable. By this time two other doctors, Charles Taft and Albert F. A. King, had arrived and started artificial respiration on the stricken President, who had been lowered to the floor.

It was obvious from the first that the injury was fatal and death was only a question of hours. In this condition it was inadvisable to transport the President to the White House, and four soldiers were summoned to carry their dying Commander in Chief to the Peterson house across the street from the theater, where they placed his long frame diagonally across the short bed. The doctors had the legs covered with warm blankets, and applied a large mustard plaster to the body in a futile attempt to draw the blood away from the brain.

Soon Surgeon General Barnes, Dr. Stone, the family physician, and several other prominent doctors appeared on the scene. The surgeon general was requested to take charge of the President. He had the patient turned on his side and the thick dark hair cut away around the bullet hole in the back of the head. (This shock of hair is still preserved in the Army Medical Museum of Pathology.) Without benefit of modern antisepsis, several of the doctors in turn probed the wound channel with their fingers. Dr. Barnes eventually used a special metal probe designed for the removal of foreign bodies. It passed in a slightly diagonal direction through the left lobe of the brain up to a depth of four inches, where it met an obstruction. The doctor slowly turned and withdrew the formidable instrument in the hope of catching and extracting the bullet, without success. After a second fruitless attempt with the probe it was decided that any further effort of the kind would be useless.

In hopeless silence the doctors sat around the bed watching

the pulse and respiration which would periodically change in rhythm and volume. At intervals a blood clot would form, stopping the discharge of blood from the wound. The dammed-up blood would then press against the nerve centers regulating the circulation and cause the heartbeat to become slow and pounding. Eventually the blood clot would be dislodged either spontaneously or by probing the wound; then the pulse would again grow faster and weaker.

The breathing, irregular and labored from the start, took on the Cheyne-Stokes pattern, indicating an impairment of the normal automatism of the respiratory center. There would be ever-recurring periods of one to two minutes duration when the rhythm of breathing would go through a full circle from an almost complete standstill to a climax of frantic inspirations and expirations to diminish and fade out again in a pause of silence. This pattern of breathing continued for hours. Both eyes of the President were swollen and bloodshot, the lips were blue, the cold legs could not be warmed by blankets.

The pitiful figure of the President's wife was huddled on a sofa in the adjoining room in stunned despair, supported by Miss Harris, her guest at the play, and Laura Keen, the star. When, from time to time, she was led to the bedroom, her eyes searched the doctors' for a ray of hope. Looking at her unconscious husband, she would rend the stillness with hysterical shrieks, disturbing the dignity of death, and would have to be carried out in a faint. Robert, the President's eldest son, tried in vain to comfort his mother; most of the time he stood immovable at the head of the bed gazing silently at the pale face of his father. He was blaming himself for not having accompanied his parents to the theater where he probably would have been seated between the open door of the box and his father.

In the succeeding weeks Robert often sat alone in the President's box in the abandoned theater, dreaming for hours of how he might have saved his father's life. By a strange coincidence, he who watched his father die was to stand at the bedside of the two other assassinated Presidents—Garfield sixteen years, and

McKinley thirty-six years, later. He was Secretary of War under the former, and the latter's guest of honor. Also, Surgeon General Barnes held his position long enough to attend to the fatal wound of President Garfield.

As the night passed and the first light of a dismal day grayed the curtains of the death chamber, the President's breathing became labored and stertorous; the bleeding from the wound ceased entirely. During the last half hour the breathing would pause for almost a minute at a time, then resume with convulsive effort. Each time the breathing stopped for a longer period, the doctors would take out their watches to note the exact time of death.

Lincoln drew his last breath at twenty-one minutes and fifty-five seconds past seven o'clock on the morning of April 15, 1865. His last heartbeat was felt at twenty-two minutes and ten seconds past seven A.M.

The body was taken to Lincoln's bedroom in the White House where a postmortem examination was performed at noon by the assistant surgeons of the American Medical Corps, Drs. J. J. Woodward and E. Curtis. The official report of Dr. Woodward stated that the lead bullet had entered the back of the skull between the spine and the left ear, one inch to the left of the midline. It penetrated the bone, opened a large venous sinus, shattered the brain in its course, and came to rest in the left frontal lobe behind the left eye. Strangely, Dr. E. Curtis, the second autopsy surgeon, insisted that the lead bullet was found not behind the left but the right eye socket. This would be more consistent with the clinical findings, the dilatation of the right and contraction of the left pupil, and the hemorrhagic swelling of the right eye preceding the bulging of the left eye.

The ball carried with it several small pieces of bone, and by its indirect action fractured the bony roof of both eye sockets, pushing the fragments up toward the brain. A lead bullet of low velocity, it had a limited penetrating power which spent itself within the bony cavity of the skull, acting like a dumdum bullet with explosive power.

In retrospect it can be stated that all the miracles of modern brain surgery could not have saved Lincoln's life. In contrast, the wounds which killed Garfield and McKinley were not fatal in themselves. Both could have possibly been saved by modern surgical methods.

Andrew Johnson

(1808 — 1875)

GOSSIP has branded President Andrew Johnson as a drunkard, an accusation that has echoed down through the history books in spite of the fact that closer scrutiny has revealed the rumor as false. His enemies stymied and defeated Johnson's national politics and, as victors always do, wrote most of the contemporary records which became the reference material of later historians.

It is true that Johnson was under the influence of alcohol when he made his rambling inauguration speech as Vice-President. But it was on the advice of his doctor that he had gulped down a tumblerful of whisky, because he felt faint with diarrhea and cramps on that morning. He had been suffering from a chronic gastrointestinal infection during the previous five months. Sick and weary, he arrived in Washington to be sworn in on the Senate floor. His weakened condition made him particularly susceptible to the effects of alcohol, which he usually drank in moderation, in much smaller amounts than the average Southern gentleman of that time, who often drank himself to sleep with mint juleps or straight whisky.

A day or two after Johnson's inauguration, Lincoln said to William B. Fessenden, his Secretary of Treasury, "I have known Andy Johnson for many years; he made a bad slip the other day, but you need not be scared; Andy ain't a drunkard."

Unfortunately, the American public was not as broad-minded and understanding as Lincoln. And Andrew's political foes didn't miss the chance to keep reiterating that he made a fool of himself at his inauguration and had disgraced the dignity of his office. They branded him forever as a drunkard, not fit for the position of Vice-President; certainly not in the office of President.

Andrew Johnson, born of Southern poor whites in a log hut in Raleigh, North Carolina in 1808, nursed a deep and abiding resentment of the rich and patrician classes of the South. He was left fatherless at the age of three; was apprenticed to a tailor at ten; and learned to read without formal schooling. At eighteen, Andy opened his own tailor shop at the mountain town of Greeneville in eastern Tennessee. In the following year he married Eliza McCordle, who taught him to write. A bright pupil, he continued to educate himself, and developed a flair for oratory and politics. At twenty-two he became mayor of the town; at twenty-seven assemblyman, and, soon after, state senator. In 1843 he was elected to Congress on the Democratic ticket and served for ten years.

While in Congress he broke his right wrist in a railroad accident. He was treated in a hospital in Philadelphia, but the fracture was badly set, making it painful for him to do any writing thereafter. This probably accounts for the fact that the drafts of so many of his messages are not in his handwriting. His critics and historians erroneously concluded from this evidence that all his state papers were composed by others.

From 1853 to 1857 Johnson was Governor of Tennessee, from 1857 to 1862 Senator of the United States. He was the only Senator from the South who dared to take a determined stand against secession and for the preservation of the Union. For his position he was vilified and stigmatized as a traitor, and on several occasions almost lynched by his hysterical countrymen.

What made Johnson feel so strongly that the Union was his real homeland was the lofty democratic tradition of the United States which had fostered the emergence of a Jackson and a Lincoln from the same social stratum to which he also belonged, while his political associates from the class-conscious South, many of whom pretended to aristocracy, made him feel like an outsider.

Johnson never could overcome his hypersensitivity concerning his lowly origin. Like certain members of minority groups, he again and again introduced himself to his audience as a descendant of a despised group, the poor. With masochistic self-abasement, he would bare to the public the painful scars of his wretched youth, preferring to do himself injury and anticipate the stings of humiliation to being hurt by others with thoughtless or intentional remarks.

In 1862, while Johnson was serving in the Senate in Washington, rebel soldiers invaded his home in Greeneville and drove out his wife and his youngest boy of eight, both of whom suffered from tuberculosis. Undergoing great difficulties, the fugitives reached the house of relatives miles away. Young Frank recovered from his consumption, but Mrs. Johnson remained an invalid all her life.

Later in 1862, Lincoln appointed Johnson military governor of Tennessee with the rank of brigadier general, taking him from his safe shelter in the Senate into the very furnace of the war in Nashville. There, at last, he could rejoin his family. His two older sons were stationed not far away in army camps. Charles, a physician, served as army surgeon, and Robert, a lawyer, as colonel in the Union Army. Unfortunately, army life contributed to the habitation of both sons to whisky, the curse of the South.

In January 1863, Charles was thrown from a horse and killed. He was his parents' favorite, and they never fully recovered from the shock. The eldest daughter, Martha, who married Judge D. T. Patterson, took her ailing mother's place as mistress of the household. The younger daughter, Mary, was married to Colonel Dan Stover, who in 1863 died of consumption.

As military governor, Johnson ably organized the defense of the capital, which on several occasions was threatened by the Confederate armies, and succeeded in raising, in Tennessee, twenty-five regiments for the Union army. He was working twelve to fourteen hours a day, and "sleeping on a bed of revolvers and bayonets" at night. Besides his military duties, Johnson worked hard on the re-establishment of a loyal democratic government in Tennessee, which he accomplished in 1864.

His most frustrating task was providing food, clothing, and shelter for the thousands of fugitives streaming into the city from the war-ravaged countryside, and arranging for the care of the countless victims of epidemics of dysentery and typhoid that took the lives of civilians and soldiers alike.

After four years of fighting for the Union, and two years of toiling for his home state, Johnson was close to collapse. In one of his letters he wrote, "My mind is tortured and my body exhausted. Sometimes, I feel like giving all up in despair." Lincoln acknowledged Johnson's great services and sacrifices when he answered some of his critics, in June 1864, as follows: "No man has the right to judge Andrew Johnson in any respect who has not suffered as much and done as much as he for the Union's sake." On another occasion, he called him a man "to whom the country owes a debt of gratitude it can never repay."

As a reward for Johnson's loyalty and as a conciliatory gesture to the South, Lincoln requested to have him put on the Union ticket as Vice-President in 1864. Shortly afterward Johnson broke down with high fever, followed by diarrhea, the beginning of the long siege of sickness that led to the fateful incident during his inauguration.

On the eventful fourteenth of April, the Vice-President had also been marked for assassination by John Wilkes Booth, but George E. Atzerodt, whose assignment this was, got lost in the fog of a tavern. On the morning of April 15, Johnson, shocked by the murder of his idol, was sworn in as President, and started on his thorny path of four years of vilification and humiliation culminating in his impeachment trial for "high crimes and misdemeanors."

He tried to follow the conciliatory and sensible program of reconstruction of the South advocated by Lincoln. But he did not have the flexibility and strength of his great predecessor nor his infinite patience and ingratiating humor.

Unlike "Father Abraham," Johnson was of medium size and squarely built. There was no twinkle in his dark deep-set eyes; the continuous struggle since childhood had frozen in his face the grim lines of stubborn determination. Above all, Johnson lacked the great prestige and popularity of Lincoln.

As President he was the proverbial man sitting between two chairs. The Northern Republicans hated him as a former Southern Democrat, and his Democratic countrymen considered him a renegade and traitor. Both agreed in calling him a drunkard. The bitter fratracidal war had aroused in the people of the Union a hysteria of hatred and vengeance against the South, preventing a sensible approach to the difficult problem of reconstruction. The public cry for punishment of the rebels was so loud that only a few congressmen dared to ignore it.

Only a master politician and popular hero like Lincoln could possibly have soothed the waves of fury against the prostrate South. Now the radicals had been strengthened a thousand times by the public reaction to the assassination of the President, and were better organized than they ever had been throughout the war.

The radical press, appealing to mob psychology, kept undermining the President's prestige by calling him "the drunken tailor" who had "only reeled" into the Presidency, and pouring on him a flood of epithets such as "the beast," "the dirty dog," "the sot," and "the damned traitor."

Chronic dysentery had left Johnson with a sensitive and irritable intestinal tract. He suffered from cramps and diarrhea. He is also reported to have been tortured by kidney stones, which occasionally blocked the urinary flow, doubling him up in pain.

The leader of the radical Republicans in Congress, and Johnson's archenemy, was the bitter, seventy-three-year-old Thaddeus Stevens, who ruled the House with an iron hand. He could never forgive the world that he had been born with a clubfoot, and was quivering with hatred and vengeance toward anyone who disagreed with him.

Johnson has often been blamed for signing the writ of execution of Mrs. Mary Suratt for conspiracy in Lincoln's assassination, whose guilt has never been proven beyond a reasonable doubt. She was convicted solely on circumstantial evidence, the possible victim of a judicial murder. The President was sick in bed with an acute attack of malaria when he was rushed into signing the writ. The recommendation for clemency had been withheld from him, probably through Stanton's connivance, and a score of petitioners for Mrs. Suratt's release had been refused admittance to the White House.

In Johnson's own Cabinet, Edwin A. Stanton, who had attempted to play the strong man in Lincoln's administration, secretly plotted against the new President. He acted his dual role with sadistic finesse worthy of a Shakespearean villain. Betraying the confidence of his Chief, he would assist the radicals in concocting their drastic legislative acts, which were hurriedly railroaded through Congress. Then he would calmly turn about and compose the President's veto messages, masterpieces of cold legalistic logic, knowing they would be overridden by Congress. Stanton played this fantastic game of double-dealing for two years until he was exposed and had to come out into the open.

The President tried to discharge him from his Cabinet, but was prevented from doing so by the notorious Tenure of Office Act passed by a hostile Congress in order to trap the President and drive him out of the White House.

Johnson's refusal to yield his obvious constitutional rights as Chief Executive was then used by his foes as their main argument in the impeachment trial by the Senate, which he won by a single vote.

There was one consolation for the harassed President. He lived in the midst of his devoted family in the White House, and could attend to his ailing wife, to whom he was deeply attached, bedridden as she was and suffering with cough and fever. In return she gave him comfort by sharing his frustrations and humiliations. Because she was able to make only one public appearance as First Lady, the eldest daughter, Mrs. Patterson, acted as the hostess of the White House and managed the large household, which included several grandchildren. She purchased two Jersey cows, kept them on the premises, and supplied the family with milk and butter of questionable sterility.

When Andrew Johnson left the White House in 1869, a lonely figure without a party, he was not content to return home to Tennessee to lick his wounds. Though he was past sixty-two, his inflexible stubbornness, which was his strength and his weakness, was as mighty as ever. He continued fighting up to the last breath for the vindication of his administration. He could never be satisfied with a mere verdict of acquittal. He demanded complete exoneration and endorsement of his policies.

Shortly after returning to Tennessee, he suffered from a flare-up of his old malaria. Immediately after his recovery, he took the stump for Governor Senter, who sympathized with his ideas of reconstruction as applied to Tennessee. Johnson was called home by the sudden death of his son Robert, a suicide at thirty-three. The sensitive young man could not endure punishment of the kind his tough-fibered father had taken: eight years of exile, war, and ostracism. Vainly he had tried to find escape in the dull dream-world of alcohol, to awaken again and again with a hangover of remorse and despair, until at last he found the stress of his conflicts unbearable.

The grief-stricken father did not allow himself to indulge in sorrow for long; after a few days he returned to the political scene to continue his efforts for the restoration of Tennessee as a model of reconstruction for the other Southern states, as he had planned.

In 1873 an epidemic of Asiatic cholera swept over Tennessee. There were nearly a hundred cases in Green County. Everyone who had the means fled from the stricken countryside. True to his character never to run away from danger, Andrew Johnson chose to remain in Greeneville, helping the best he could the victims of the dread disease, and sustaining the morale of his neighbors. Inevitably, Johnson was victim of the contagion to which his weak gastrointestinal tract was particularly susceptible, and for a time his life was despaired of. In fact, he never recovered completely. Death spared his life for a while, but had robbed him of his former strength and vigor. Sometimes his heart troubled him, and he probably suffered from high blood pressure. Yet he kept on fighting for his cause.

In 1874 Andrew Johnson ran an exhausting race for re-election as Senator from Tennessee, and had the great satisfaction of winning on the fifty-fifth ballot; the only former President to be elected to the Senate. He used the sounding board of the Senate in 1875 to make his last great speech to a national audience, defending his cause and attacking the vindictive and corrupt administration of Grant.

On July 30, 1875, he visited the country home of his daughter, Mrs. Stover. During the noon meal he participated in a spirited conversation. Shortly afterward, he went to his room for a rest, accompanied by his granddaughter, Lillie Stover. He talked a few minutes to her, seated in his armchair. As she turned to go out, she heard a crash. Her grandfather had fallen forward on the carpet and was lying helpless, his left side paralyzed. He remained conscious and able to speak, and sternly forbade the family to get a physician.

They put him to bed, but he could not rest. His mind wandered into the past. All bitterness was gone as he talked of his youth, his tailorshop days, his struggle to the top. Next day he had another stroke that paralyzed his whole body and blacked out his consciousness. Physicians were summoned. Bleeding did not affect the rapidly progressing brain infarct. In two hours Johnson was dead. According to his wishes, the family did not call in a minister.

In one of his speeches, Andrew Jackson had once made the melodramatic but sincere declaration: "When I die I desire no better winding sheet than the Stars and Stripes, and no softer pillow than the Constitution of my country." His wish was granted. They buried the old warrior wrapped in the flag he had loved so much, pillowed on the Constitution he had defended so well.

Ulysses Simpson Grant

(1822 — 1885)

WHILE Andrew Johnson was unjustly accused of alcoholism, it was never denied that the life and career of Ulysses S. Grant was deeply influenced by excessive drinking. Alcoholism usually seems to be rooted in a hereditary tendency and generated by personal maladjustment. People drink because they are dissatisfied, though they may not be aware of the cause of their discontent. They drink to blunt the stings of frustration, defeat and fear, to escape from the dullness and boredom of their lives and from the prison of their inhibitions.

To understand Grant's maladjustment it is necessary to go back to his childhood. His father, Jesse Root Grant, was a cocksure, dogmatic busybody who dominated his family. His mother showed no affection which the sensitive child needed for his normal development. She had retired from the world of her boastful, egotistical husband into the shelter of Methodist mysticism, and apparently extended the rejection of her husband to the children he had fathered. In awe of his father and unloved by his mother, from whom he had inherited his introversive bent of character, Ulysses became a shy, awkward boy.

As he grew to adolescence his shyness increased. He was poor company, too slow in repartee to participate in the laughing conversations and banter of his age group. The people of Georgetown, where he grew up, considered him dull and stupid and occasionally made him the butt of their practical jokes. The smart alecks of the town pretended not to be able to pronounce the name with which his grandmother had handicapped him, and called him "Useless" Grant. This nickname stuck to him until his father took him out of the stifling atmosphere of his home town by procuring for him an appointment at West Point.

Grant, like anyone else, craved love and longed for power in some form. Rejected by his mother, unappreciated by his age group, he transferred his love to animals, especially to horses, which gave him the companionship and the sense of power he hungered for. Thus, he spent all his free time with the horses on his father's farm, and soon became an outstanding horseman.

Looking at pictures of the young Grant before he disguised his face with his famous beard, one is astonished how soft and feminine-looking his features were. There was a broad streak of femininity in his make-up, a characteristic he had in common with other great generals of history, such as Alexander the Great, Frederick the Great, and even Napoleon. With Alexander the Great he also shared a love of horses and alcohol.

In his youth, Grant's face was like a girl's, with a rosy complexion and curved outlines. He was small and slender. As a young lieutenant, before the Mexican War, he was called "The Little Beauty" by the officers of his regiment. His voice was soft and melodious, and all his life he was never known to use a swear word, except on one occasion when, during the Wilderness campaign, he came upon a teamster beating his horses in the face; then the quiet man who loved horses exploded in a violent outburst, to the astonishment of his staff. He had the offender severely punished.

All his life Grant had the physical modesty of an old maid. In contrast to his fellow officers, who usually took their morning ablutions naked in front of their tents, Grant would take his bath in the privacy of his tent with the flaps tightly closed. Not even his orderly was admitted to see him naked. When he was close to sixty, he declared once that no one had ever seen him naked since his childhood.

After his unhappy youth in Georgetown he fared not much better at West Point. He remained shy and afraid of people. In four years he never went to a dance, nor ever entered a private home as a guest. He was constitutionally weak, always tired and in need of much sleep. He was not of healthy stock. There was tuberculosis in his father's family, two of his brothers having died of this disease. A brother and sister of Ulysses also died of it. Ulysses himself, for six months before his graduation, had a severe cough accompanied by loss of weight. This unquestionably represented an active phase of latent tuberculosis which eventually became arrested.

His physical weakness and chronic fatigue may be blamed in part for the lack of interest he showed in his lessons and textbooks. As a cadet he spent most of his time sleeping, daydreaming, or dozing over novels. His lack of energy probably explains his apparent diffidence and apathy, which brought him numerous demerits for slovenly habits of dress, for having his coat not properly buttoned, his clothes not brushed, and his shoes not shined—habits which he continued in later military life.

His need of a great deal of sleep is probably why he was frequently late and even absent from reveille and roll calls. The only two subjects he excelled in at West Point were mathematics and horsemanship. He won all competitions in steeplechases, hurdling the highest obstacles. In 1843 he graduated, twenty-first in a class of thirty-nine; in conduct he rated 156th among 223 in the entire corps.

Grant applied for a commission in the cavalry, but no vacancy could be found in the only cavalry regiment then in existence. He then asked for a position as a teacher in mathematics in the military academy, with the same negative reply. The best horseman and one of the best students in mathematics at West Point was not employed in the cavalry, nor in the corps of engineers, but was relegated as second lieutenant to the 4th Infantry Regiment, stationed near St. Louis.

There he met Julia Dent, daughter of a successful farmer. He became engaged to her the next year, and married her four years later. She had plain features and was cross-eyed, but had a sweet disposition and was devoted to Ulysses. Later, as first lady, she considered an operation to correct her eye defect, but

the President did not permit it. He liked her, he said, as she
was and would not have her different.

In the Mexican War, 1846-1848, Grant served as regimental
quartermaster and on several occasions showed personal courage
and initiative. He was with General Scott's army when it took
the coast city of Veracruz, in March 1847. They hurriedly left
the city and marched inland to avoid the yellow fever which
yearly visited the port and was more dangerous than the bullets
of the enemy.

After the excitement of fighting came a long period of idle-
ness during the occupation of Mexico City. There were gay celebrations which Grant disliked, and bull fights which made him
sick because he could not bear the sight of animals bleeding and
dying. (All his life, Grant had a phobia regarding the sight of
blood. His steaks had to be burned practically to charcoal, to
the despair of his cooks.) His puritan temperament forbade his
seeking the company of women.

In wartime, a soldier naturally seeks relief from boredom,
loneliness and fear by drinking. Lieutenant Grant acquired a
taste for alcohol in the course of the campaign. In Mexico City
he changed from a social to a solitary drinker. Drinking was his
only outlet, and he preferred solitude, feeling uncomfortable in
the company of his fellow officers because of his lack of conver-
sational fluency and inaptitude for jesting. Social drinking makes
most people talkative and gay; solitary drinkers, on the other
hand, usually become sad and silent. Grant appeared morose
and downcast when he drank alone, thus cutting himself off
from the chatter and gaiety he could not share with his com-
rades. This withdrawal into alcoholic seclusion appears to have
been the psychological counterpart to concealing his nakedness.

After returning from the Mexican War, Grant married and
moved with his wife into the bare-walled military barracks at
Sackett's Harbor, New York. There the young husband, full of
good intentions, joined the Sons of Temperance, the Alcoholics
Anonymous of the time. However, his daily routine as a quartermaster did not occupy him enough to fill the emptiness of his

life. Moreover, he lacked the inner resources of philosophy and religion. Not balanced by the weight of other interests, his craving for alcohol soon broke its bounds and swept away his temperance pledge.

After two years of dull garrison life in the East, Grant's regiment was ordered to Fort Vancouver, on the Columbia River near the Pacific Coast. Grant had to leave his wife with one young son and expecting another. During the crossing of the Isthmus of Panama an epidemic of cholera killed one-seventh of his regiment. He spent two lonely years on the Pacific Coast, finding his only solace in alcohol. His promotion to captain at Humboldt Bay, California, did not raise his morale; in fact, his drinking made him at times forget the elementary rules of military discipline in which he had been trained for fifteen years. On several occasions Grant appeared dead drunk before his company, until finally, his colonel asked him to resign from the army.

He returned to his family in the Middle West, and for four years managed his wife's farm. In his memoirs he claimed to have got along quite well until 1858, when he had a severe attack of malaria, a recurrence from his boyhood in Ohio. This time he was ill more than a year, an unusually long time for a malaria seizure, especially since it was treated with quinine. It is not too far-fetched to assume that the malaria temporarily reactivated the tuberculosis in Grant's lungs, incapacitating him for the strenuous farm labor and forcing him to sell his holdings. Thus, if we believe Grant, his failure as a farmer was due to sickness and not due to lack of aptitude, as the legend has it.

Tired and discouraged, he tried his hand at selling real estate in St. Louis, an occupation for which he was not fitted. Failing in this attempt, he took as a last resort a position as clerk in his father's leather store in Galena, Illinois, under his younger brothers. By this time he appeared to be a hopeless failure to his relations and acquaintances. He was thirty-nine years old, practically penniless, and barely able to make enough money for the upkeep of his family. His only solace remained liquor, and this was cheap.

The outbreak of the Civil War gave the discontented clerk a chance to escape his rut. He eagerly offered his services to drill a company of Galena volunteers. This was gratefully accepted, there being a dearth of West Point-trained officers. It was a welcome relief for the discharged captain to regain a position of importance and authority, after having been for years looked down upon as a failure. This time he knew that he had to make good, and he applied himself with all his heart to his new position. Feeling himself once more on familiar ground and in a position of responsibility, the diffident little man changed almost overnight into a competent officer and disciplinarian. Now a colonel, he needed money to buy a uniform and a horse. Luckily, a Galena businessman came forward and advanced the money for the necessary equipment. Within a few months he was appointed brigadier general and, during the next year, major general.

As a general, there is no doubt that on a number of occasions Grant displayed a genius for strategy during the Civil War. Military science has been unduly glorified through the ages. It is more of an art than a science, more dependent on native instinct than intellect. Too much imagination and deliberation are handicaps for a general. What he needs is primitive cunning, a realistic mind, and a good deal of ruthlessness. Even Napoleon, for all his versatility in other respects, won his greatest battles by the unexpected simplicity and directness of his plans.

Grant's mind was unsophisticated and matter-of-fact, uncluttered by theories. Andrew Johnson called him "a dullard, whose brain could have been compressed within the periphery of a nutshell." But Johnson was prejudiced by his hatred. The fact is that Grant, after leaving West Point, had never opened a textbook on strategy. He approached his strategic problems with practical directness, unencumbered by reflection and vacillation. In addition, he possessed an unswerving doggedness in pursuing his plans. He had a superstitious aversion to turning back from a line of advance once chosen, according to his own admission.

In one respect Grant had the edge over most other famous generals—his practical training as quartermaster, obtained during the Mexican War. His intimate acquaintance with the supply problems of an army enabled him to execute the unconventional strategic maneuver at Vicksburg.

Grant not only had military ability—more important, he had good luck as a general. In his very first engagement in the Civil War at Belmont, he escaped unharmed when his horse was slain under him. According to a number of experts, he won the bloody battle of Shiloh in 1862 purely by an exceptional streak of good luck. As a consequence of several blunders he had committed, his army was on the verge of defeat on the afternoon of the first day of the battle. It had been pushed back and was all but trapped in the sharp angle between the Tennessee River and Snake Creek. True to his character, the commander had made no preparations for a retreat.

At the crucial moment his able opponent, General Albert Sidney Johnson, personally led a brigade to administer the knockout blow, when he received a flesh wound in his thigh. Blood gushed from the wounded leg; the main artery had been torn. Only a short time before, the general had sent away his staff surgeon to take care of a group of wounded. No one had the presence of mind to stop the hemorrhage with a tourniquet. Within a few minutes the commander of the Confederate army bled to death; his command fell to General Beauregard, a more deliberate soldier, who did not press the attack and let the chance of victory slip away. During the night, fresh divisions reinforced Grant's army and, on the following day, overwhelmed the outnumbered enemy. Had General Johnson not been killed at that critical moment it is quite possible that U. S. Grant would have joined the large club of defeated and discarded Union generals.

On the second day of the battle Grant himself was the target of close-range fire. He was luckier than his opponent had been.

The scabbard of his sword was shot off and the horse of a colonel of his staff was killed, but Grant remained unscathed.

In the choice of his subordinate officers and his staff, Grant as a general was not only lucky but showed unusual good judgment of the military ability of his associates. By contrast, in his career as President, he seemed to lack completely any judgment in the choice of his Cabinet and his Secretaries.

The most fortunate appointment Grant made was that of John A. Rawlins, a friend from Galena, as his chief of staff. This country lawyer with limited education had a clear, strong and relentless mind. He was thin, ascetic-looking, and a teetotaler. The first thing he did on accepting his position was to exact a pledge from the General to refrain from liquor for the duration of the war. And Rawlins never hesitated to remind his Chief in unmistakable terms of his pledge when he broke it, as he did a number of times. Rawlins had the same qualities as Grant's father. He was self-assured, opinionated, aggressive and the General both feared and admired him.

At Grant's headquarters, Rawlins bossed everything and everybody, including his soft-spoken Chief, whom he cursed on occasions when Grant did something wrong. According to General James A. Wilson, it was Rawlins who was the driving force behind some of the rapid, aggressive moves for which Grant got the credit. Out of their collaboration grew the legendary military figure which has passed into history under the name of Ulysses S. Grant. Grant's contribution to the teamwork was his native strategic instinct combined with a driving competitive spirit, frustrated and hidden beneath a sluggish appearance. Just as he, as a horseman, could clear a hurdle the higher the pole was set, as a general he had the capacity to grow with his obstacles and surmount them. It was comparatively easy for him to defeat mediocre adversaries like Beauregard, Pemberton and Bragg. He found his master in Lee and was able to develop into a great general by competing with him.

In order to keep Grant from drinking, Rawlins categorically banished hard liquor from the headquarters and gave secret orders to all the lower staffs not to offer the General any drinks when he was visiting. Neither Grant's pledge nor his fear of Rawlins could always suppress his craving. From time to time, when his guardian was not watching, the general got hold of a bottle and went on a spree. Unfortunately, when under the influence of liquor he liked to go horseback riding and indulge in his favorite sport, obstacle hurdling, putting his precarious equilibrium to a dangerous test. Except for sprains and bruises, he never received any serious injuries, which could be attributed to a state of alcoholic relaxation.

A few days before the battle of Shiloh, his horse had fallen on Grant, causing a painful swelling of his ankle. This accident accounts for his absence from the camp on the morning of the battle when he was resting in a village miles behind the front. However, Rawlins emphatically denied that Grant had been intoxicated on this occasion, and blamed the deep mud as having caused and cushioned the General's accident.

The greatest of Grant's military achievements and a classic of bold strategy was the Vicksburg campaign, which showed the combination of boldness and relentlessness at its best. For a time during this movement his troops were huddled on a levee ten to fifty feet wide, suffering severely from typhoid and dysentery. In addition, an epidemic of smallpox broke out, with a terrifying daily death toll. The newspaper correspondents, whom Grant despised, called the campaign a failure. He would not give up. To add to all his worry and dismay, he lost his false teeth, which a careless servant emptied from a washbowl into the river. It was necessary to summon his dentist from the North. New dentures were hurriedly made, enabling the General to eat solid food once more.

Gritting his new teeth, Grant succeeded in getting his army across the Mississippi, and won several battles resulting in the investment of Vicksburg. The siege was uneventful and dreary. Flies and mosquitoes made everyone's life miserable. Grant started drinking again. And once, during an inspection tour, he almost fell into the hands of the enemy while lying insensible in a small steamboat, unable to give the order to turn back.

Following this escapade, Rawlins gave Grant a severe calling down, reminding him of his pledge not to drink any more, and that the success of his recent campaign was solely due to his abstinence.

The remorseful General solemnly renewed his pledge. He did not keep his word for long. Celebrating the surrender of Vicksburg with several brother officers in New Orleans, he is reported to have "fallen ill" on several occasions. In one instance his horse fell with him, landing with its whole weight on Grant's leg. Again, there were no broken bones, but severe sprains. The commander of the army of the Mississippi had to be carried on a litter to the St. Charles Hotel, where he remained in bed for two weeks.

The next episode of heavy drinking was rumored to have occurred in 1864, during the Wilderness campaign when Grant was brooding over his failure to defeat Lee's army. It was whispered that his friend General Butler surreptitiously supplied him with alcohol against the stern orders and behind the back of his watchdog Rawlins. It was strange enough that Grant appointed the incapable Butler to the important command of the army of the James. He was given the task of attacking Richmond from the east front, which was practically unguarded, while Grant was holding Lee's army in the north. The plan was well conceived and offered the opportunity to take the capital with comparatively small losses. Butler delayed and bungled his attack, either because of cowardice or incompetence. He was defeated and bottled up by inferior forces led by General Beauregard. Despite this failure, Grant did not discharge Butler on the spot, as it was his custom with other incompetent officers, but retained him until the following year.

Exasperated by his inability to defeat Lee by a strategy of maneuvering, Grant resorted to brutal frontal attacks against strongly fortified positions at Cold Harbor, where his losses were enormous. According to some accounts, he ordered these assaults against the violent protests of Rawlins, who called such tactics a "murderous policy of military incompetence." The enemies of Grant maintained that he was under the influence of liquor and deaf to any advice when he resorted to this strategy of slugging.

The final victory made Grant a national hero and, like most people, he was spoiled by his triumph. With his success grew his ambition. According to Gideon Welles, he became secretly jealous of his great good friend Sherman, with whom he had to share the limelight of public adulation. The glittering lure of the Presidency pulled him over to the side of the radical Republicans and made him betray his trusting friend and chief, Andrew Johnson. He was showered with gifts of houses and money, the possession of which aroused the greed for more.

Like every general who won a war, he could have received the nomination for President from either party. He accepted the nomination from the Republican Party as the more promising, although he had voted as a Democrat before the war.

As a President, Grant was a pitiful failure. His general's uniform, even when it was unbuttoned and dirty, had given him the sense of being the wheel of a great machine, a part of a powerful organism. Without the uniform he felt naked and forlorn, once more reduced to insignificance. He was again the meek little clerk from Galena, flattered to be hobnobbing with the rich and powerful men of his time.

As a general, Grant had been guided by the fatherly authority of his Commander in Chief, Lincoln, whom he respected, and by Rawlins who had advised and encouraged him. Now he experienced a secret resentment against his former chief of staff, because he knew that he owed him his rise to fame. Only after long hesitation he made Rawlins his Secretary of War, but felt too self-important to seek his advice.

Grant was too realistic and unimaginative to believe in divine guidance. And guidance he needed desperately, taken as he was out of his accustomed military surroundings into the unfamiliar atmosphere of politics. He felt at a complete loss without a commander in chief, a chief of staff, and the military cohorts who had advised and admired him.

Thus, Grant returned to his old father for advice, and substituted his family, together with some old cronies, for his military staff. Unfortunately, there were no Shermans or Sheridans in the new circle of civilians who surrounded the President, but people like his brother-in-law, A. R. Corbin, who accepted a large bribe for using his influence on the President, and his private secretary, O. E. Babcock, who became implicated in the revenue frauds of the notorious whisky ring.

Under these auspices Grant's administration became a sink of corruption. Participating in the million-dollar thefts were not only Grant's relations and friends, but also several Cabinet members and the Vice-President. The President himself derived no profit from these gigantic blunders, though he showed a naïve incomprehension of his moral responsibility, and made a last-ditch stand for his venal associates even after their guilt had been exposed. And he had no qualms about accepting gifts of money or other gratuities from his supporters, and returning their favors in the form of government offices or even memberships in his Cabinet.

Andrew Johnson asserted that President Grant's Cabinet "was a sort of lottery, those getting the best places that paid the most." Offices were "disposed of at various prices from $65,000 down to a box of segars." It shows the doglike loyalty of the voters to their hero that they elected Grant to a second term in spite of the stench that emanated from the White House.

The health of the President was good. He was wined and dined by his rich friends without ill effects except for the acquisition of an unmilitary paunch, which made it impossible for him to enjoy any more his favorite sport of horseback riding. Instead, he took up buggy racing. He had new stables built on the White House grounds where he kept a number of fast-stepping ponies. Racing through the streets of Washington, he was once arrested by an over-zealous policeman for speeding.

After becoming Chief Executive, Grant is reported to have

stopped his excessive drinking. The opiate of power took the place of intoxication by alcohol. The taste of power is like the taste of a habit-forming drug. After Grant had become accustomed to it for two terms, his craving persisted and he sought renomination for a third term. Failing this, he attempted to gain power in another form, through the most elementary medium, money.

He was fifty-nine and had enough to live comfortably, but he wanted to compete with his rich New York friends, the Vanderbilts and the Pierponts. Again he demonstrated that while he was an excellent judge of horses and soldiers he could not fathom the subtlety of people engaged in the stealthy struggle for power going on below the surface of the world at peace. His military cunning had failed him in the wilderness of politics; it was also too primitive for the intricacies of big business. He opened an investment firm, choosing a slick promoter as his partner. By wild speculations his associate lost not only Grant's fortune but also the savings of thousands who had staked their faith on the name of Grant.

Grant, disgraced and penniless, was once more the pitiful failure he had been before the Civil War. As W. E. Woodward expressed it, "The great adventure of Ulysses Grant . . . the epic of the marching men . . . the triumphs and the adulation . . . all had come to an end in poverty and despair."

But now the cruel irony of fate gave the old warrior a last chance to redeem himself and live up to the legend of a hero. His new enemy, the most formidable he had ever faced, was a cancer of the throat. And in his last struggle against pain and death, he rose to his greatest height as an indomitable fighter.

The history of the cancer goes back to an incident twenty-three years before. Long after the war, Grant stated to General Horace Porter that he had been a light smoker previous to the attack on Fort Donelson. Describing this victory, newspaper reporters publicized the General as calmly smoking a cigar in the din of the battle. Enthusiastic fans, thinking that tobacco was his chief solace, sent him hundreds of boxes of the choicest cigars. Not wanting to waste any, Grant smoked more than he was accustomed to, and continued the habit ever since. There is no question that his heavy smoking over the years contributed to the growth of the cancer at the root of the tongue, an area over which the irritating tobacco juice and smoke had passed for so long. Periods of heavy drinking added to the chronic soreness of the throat.

The first symptom of the cancer was a sharp cutting sensation at the base of the tongue, which the General felt while eating a peach. He did not pay much attention to it. At the time he was too much worried about the financial catastrophe which had befallen him and the number of tearful letters he received from defrauded investors. He was accustomed to the chronic inflammation of the throat which every heavy smoker has, and thought he had perhaps a cold in addition.

The usual home remedies did no good and the soreness gradually became more acute. Finally, after several weeks, Grant was prevailed upon to have his throat examined by a specialist. The doctor found an ulcerated lesion at the back of the tongue. Cocainizing the surface, he cut out a small piece for microscopic examination; the pathological diagnosis was carcinoma. Other consultants could only confirm this diagnosis, and the news soon appeared in the daily papers. In 1884 surgery for carcinoma located at the back of the tongue was not practiced, although it had been used successfully for early lesions at the tip of the tongue. The back of the tongue is one of the most unfavorable locations for cancer surgery. Even today statistics indicate that in this area it is incurable by surgery and only a small percentage of patients can be saved by irradiation therapy.

Grant's dream of power and glory had faded away. There was only one interest left to him—the devotion to his wife who had stood by him through thick and thin, with no reproach. In order to provide for her, the General began his memoirs for the publishing firm of Mark Twain. And, under the pressure of necessity, the taciturn and apparently inarticulate soldier suddenly unfolded a hidden talent for writing, characterized by the simplicity and directness of his personality and an unusually accurate memory.

The General sat in an armchair in his library and dictated to his stenographer in a husky voice. Swallowing became more and more difficult, and even liquids caused pain in passing over the ulcerated area. Grant grew thin and emaciated; the suffering cut deep lines in his face. Even talking was painful. Now and then he had to stop dictating to rest his throat and use a soothing mouthwash. The cancer crater grew larger and deeper, and soon became secondarily infected by a proliferation of bacteria in the oral cavity. Quantities of foul-smelling pus accumulated in the patient's throat and he had to spit continually. The germs caused fever and chills, and the sufferer had to huddle ever deeper in his chair, covered with shawls and blankets.

After two months of dictating Grant's voice failed; the cancer had spread to the vocal cords. Thereafter he sat with his writing pad on his lap and scribbled with a pencil on large sheets of paper. To withstand the agony, he was kept constantly sedated with cocaine and morphine.

Grant knew that the writing of his memoirs was a race with death. There were long hours when he could do nothing. His eyes, dimmed with resignation, seemed to stare into space, waiting for death. Then he would stir and start writing again with a trembling hand. He had to finish his book to earn enough money for his wife to live on after he had gone.

The General accomplished his last mission and died peacefully a week after the completion of his last chapter. The fortune that Grant had been so eager to make in the world of business materialized after his death. Mark Twain sold 300,000 copies of the memoirs and paid out $450,000 in royalties to the General's widow.

Rutherford Birchard Hayes

(1822 — 1893)

RUTHERFORD B. HAYES was one of the five Presidents who served in the Civil War and reached the rank of general. He was the only one who was wounded, and would have been entitled to wear the purple heart with three clusters. Also, four horses had been killed under him. He received his most serious wound in the battle of South Mountain, September 14, 1862.

As commander of the 23rd Ohio Infantry, he was ordered to dislodge the enemy from a vital gap by a frontal attack. His men were loath to leave their sheltered position without the personal example of their commissioned officers. This pattern of herd psychology explains the high percentage of casualties among officers in all battles. In more recent wars, officers from majors upward were not expected to lead their troops personally, while in the Civil War even generals were heading decisive attacks, often on horseback, just as Alexander the Great, Adolf of Nassau, and Marlborough had done, making themselves ideal targets for the enemy.

Hayes was then a lieutenant colonel. While urging his men on, he was struck by a bullet below the left elbow. The ball carried away skin and flesh, splintering one of the two forearm bones and tearing a major blood vessel. The shock made Hayes faint and fall to the ground. He lay there vomiting, but had the presence of mind to ask a soldier to twist a handkerchief around his arm, stopping the hemorrhage. After a while, he recovered somewhat, and, seeing the enemy massing for a flanking attack, he struggled to his feet and ordered an officer to bring up reinforcements. Then he fell back again and remained for twenty

221

minutes helpless on the ground, exposed to enemy fire. Gradually his own regiment was forced back and Hayes found himself abandoned by his retreating men. With his last strength he shouted, "Hello, Twenty-third men, are you going to leave your colonel here for the enemy?" Ashamed, six soldiers sprang to save their commander.

He was brought to the regimental surgeon, who temporarily released the tourniquet, dressed the wound, gave him an opium pill for the pain and some brandy as a bracer. Thus reinforced, Hayes was able to drag himself half a mile to an ambulance, which took him to Middletown, Maryland. Somehow, his brother-in-law, Dr. Joe Webb, arrived in time to take personal care of him. This lucky incident possibly saved Hayes from a dangerous wound infection.

In the vast majority of open comminuted fractures such as Hayes suffered, the chance of fatal blood poisoning was so great that, theoretically, it seemed safer to perform a primary amputation of the shattered limb than to wait for the almost inevitable bone infection to develop. In the Crimean War, six years previously, amputations on exsanguinated, exhausted men, performed with contaminated instruments, had shown an even greater mortality than the nonoperative treatment of compound fractures. Similar conditions prevailed in the Civil War. A typical example was the case of General Stonewall Jackson, who lost his life in spite of primary amputation of his crushed arm.

On the other hand, the conservative treatment of such severe injuries took more time and aftercare than the few surgeons could spend on the overwhelming load of serious casualties that piled up outside the operating tents during bloody battles like Antietam, Gettysburg, and Cold Harbor. Lack of antiseptic and aseptic techniques made surgical treatment of abdominal wounds impossible. They had to be treated conservatively, with almost 100 per cent mortality, when the intestine was perforated. Attempts to treat chest wounds surgically were hardly ever made, and the mortality rate of the conservatively treated was almost 60 per cent. In wounds of the head, efforts were made to remove loose pieces of bone and foreign bodies, but the probing with unsterile fingers or instruments contributed to fatal infection in most of those cases.

The main surgery performed in field hospitals consisted in amputations of extremities which took very little time. The primitive technique is graphically described by General Carl Schurz:

> Most of the operating tables were placed in the open where the light was best, some of them partially protected against the rain by tarpaulins or blankets stretched upon poles. There stood the surgeons, their sleeves rolled up to their elbows, their bare arms as well as their linen aprons smeared with blood, their knives not seldom held between their teeth, while they were helping a patient on or off the table or had their hands otherwise occupied. . . . As a wounded man was lifted on the table, often shrieking with pain as the attendants handled him, the surgeon quickly examined the wound and resolved upon cutting off the injured limb. Some ether was administered and the body put in position in a moment. The surgeon snatched his knife from between his teeth . . . , wiped it rapidly once or twice across his bloodstained apron, and the cutting began. The operation accomplished, the surgeon would look around with a deep sigh, and then—"Next!"

Ninety-four per cent of all reported wounds in the Civil War were produced by rifle bullets, only 5½ per cent were caused by artillery fire and less than one-half per cent by saber or bayonet. In contrast, more than 72 per cent of all wounds in the last three American Wars were caused by fragmentation shells. The Federal soldiers received more than 71 per cent of battle wounds on arms, hands or feet, and only 18 per cent on the torso. The great majority of these wounds were light, without injury to arteries or bones and most of them healed in spite of the lack of sterile technique. All these facts accounted for the comparatively good statistics, revealing that only 14 per cent of all wounded died from their injuries. In comparison, the statistics of the American army covering the Korean War showed a mortality rate from wounds of only 2.4 per cent, notwithstanding the severer type of most wounds.

The only real advance of surgery in the 1860's, compared with the war surgery practiced during the Revolutionary War, and the art of the barber surgeons in the Middle Ages, was in the use of effective anesthetics and improved analgesics. The chief anesthetic of the Civil War was chloroform, which had been first tried out in 1847 by the Scotch surgeon James Young Simpson. It was used in 76 per cent of some 80,000 anesthetics, administered by federal surgeons; in 14 per cent they employed ether, introduced in 1846 by the American dentist William G. T. Morton, and in 9 per cent a mixture of both anesthetic agents. The use of these anesthetics humanized surgery and expanded its scope. The employment of better pain-killing drugs eased pain and speeded recovery.

Opium pills were most widely used against pain. Early in the Civil War, morphine powder was commonly dusted or rubbed into the wounds in considerable quantity. Satisfactory results were reported by the proponents of this method, unquestionably less by the local anesthetic effect than by the systemic absorption of the drug through the wound surface. At the beginning of the war the hypodermic syringe was little known but eventually came into wider use when it was found that morphine by injection was more reliable and effective.

Because Lister published his first papers about antisepsis in 1867, it is usually assumed that antiseptic chemicals were unknown during the Civil War. Actually, the surgeons of the time were already familiar with carbolic acid, alcohol, and other disinfecting agents like iodine, bromine, chlorine and bichloride of mercury and used them in solution or powder form in the treatment of wounds. But before the discovery of the bacterial origin of wound infections, on which Lister's method was based, antiseptics were improperly administered. The fundamental error consisted in employing them when infections had developed to their full bloom, instead of using them for their prevention.

During the Crimean War, Florence Nightingale had proved the value of hospital cleanliness for prevention and control of epidemic diseases. During the Civil War the doctors realized that cleanliness of the surroundings was equally important to reduce the spread of wound infections. Believing that the infective agents were transmitted in some mysterious manner through the air from the outside, they attempted to purify the hospital atmosphere, floors and bedpans by the use of the most powerful germicides. Strangely enough, no one thought of including hands, surgical instruments, and dressings in the cleansing procedure.

In order to remove the infectious elements from the wounds, they were washed with water, then covered with dressings to protect them from secondary infection. Maggots wriggling about in the wounds worried soldiers and surgeons alike. They were considered an infection of the worst type, and were destroyed by pouring chloroform into the wound.

At Chattanooga, Union surgeons worked side by side with Confederate surgeons in charge of the prison stockade. But on account of a shortage of dressing material, the Confederates were denied bandages and lint, and their wounds were left uncovered and exposed to flies.

A miracle happened, the maggot-infested wounds of the prisoners became clean and odorless, while the barracks of the Union wounded reeked with the smell of pus and gangrene. Some of the Confederate surgeons continued for the remainder of the war with the open-wound treatment, inviting the growth of maggots, while the Northern surgeons, unwilling to accept anything new they did not understand, refused to believe their own eyes.

The maggots in a wound perform a scavenging job, eating only bacteria and necrotic tissue, leaving it cleaner and healthier. This observation had already been made and described by the great French surgeon Larrey during the Napoleonic Wars, but was disregarded by other surgeons. Its rediscovery in the Civil War was also ignored by the medical profession at large.

Its final rediscovery in World War I led to the artificial breeding of maggots for use in the treatment of bone infections. This method has been superseded by the discovery of the modern antibiotics, which to some extent work in a similar manner.

One of the greatest scourges of pre-Listerian surgery was "hospital gangrene," which was not the same as "gas gangrene." The latter infection, the deadly plague of World War I, is produced by gas-forming bacteria, which grow in soil highly fertilized by animal manure, like the unrelated, even more deadly germs of tetanus (lockjaw). The type of gas gangrene that killed thousands on fields of France was apparently unknown to the Civil War surgeons and they reported only the comparatively small number of 505 cases of tetanus.

The difference of the wound infections that prevailed in the two wars can be accounted for by two factors: One was that the Civil War was fought for the most part on virgin soil. Second, that 94 per cent of the wounds were inflicted by smooth rifle bullets and not by ragged fragments of shells, which explode on the ground and carry dirt into the wounds. Hospital gangrene was probably a mixed infection, produced by pus germs combined with a gas-forming bacillus. Its mortality rate seems to have been lower than that of gas gangrene. Both infections manifest themselves in a rapidly spreading putrefaction of the tissues. The high contagiousness of hospital gangrenes was early recognized and its victims isolated. Even after the dreadful infection had once started in a patient it seems to have been amenable to local treatment with the antiseptic bromine. This was applied as powder or in solution after surgical removal of the dead tissue, while the patient was kept under an anesthetic.

The wound of Hayes was treated conservatively because his brother-in-law, obviously a progressive surgeon, could give it special care. The wound being wide open and the bullet having passed through it, the use of unsterile metal probes and contaminated fingers was superfluous. At the time Dr. Webb examined the patient, the bleeding had most likely stopped spontaneously through the formation of blood clots. Otherwise, it would have been necessary to tie off both ends of the severed artery with a thread of silk, linen or cotton, which would have been left long, hanging out of the wound, to be removed as soon as it became loose. The wound was washed out with a sea sponge, using unboiled water from a basin.

As the good healing in Hayes case indicated, the water and sponge used could not have been contaminated with virulent bacteria. The wound was covered with lint, kept in place with a linen bandage or strips of adhesive. It is not reported whether the dressing was kept moist with cold water, a method often used at the time. Unquestionably Dr. Webb applied a splint to keep the broken bone at rest and the patient from pain. He probably used one of the available splints of perforated zinc, which could be molded to the shape of the broken bone after it had been set. In a pinch, field surgeons utilized pieces of board, bundles of straw or bark for splinting. The splint was padded with lint and bandaged to the arm. Later in the war, cotton frequently took the place of lint.

Hayes must have possessed rare powers of recuperation and an extraordinary resistance to the common type of wound infections. The healing of his shattered arm took an unusually short time even by modern standards; also, he received excellent care in the home of a family in Middletown. His wife was permitted to visit and nurse him, and three weeks later he was able to celebrate his fortieth birthday by walking with Mrs. Hayes over the battlefield where he had received his wound. Not many weeks later he was well enough to rejoin his regiment. It is only natural that his left arm was still weak, easily hurt and for a good while longer limited in its mobility, but as far as we know, it eventually recovered its normal function.

We cannot estimate the extent to which individual immunity against infection is inherited or acquired. But we know that good nutrition, the avoidance of deleterious substances like tobacco and alcohol, and good physical condition can contribute a great deal to the systemic resistance against infection and to the power of recuperation. Hayes at forty was in excellent general condition. From his early youth he had learned to take care of his health and had built up his body by systematic training.

As a baby, he was so feeble that it was feared he would soon follow his father, who had died three months before his birth from an acute infectious disease, typhoid or malaria. His mother was too much beset by Puritan inhibitions to give him the warmth of affection a sickly baby requires to thrive, as much as a plant needs sunlight. His older sister Fanny took his mother's place and sustained the infant with the loving care it needed to grow up into a delicate boy.

His uncle, whose name, Birchard, became Rutherford's middle name, took his father's place and the boy spent most of his youth at the spacious estate of his kinsman. The healthy farm life there helped the youngster to grow stronger. A little older, he became a crack shot and spent much of his time in the healthful sports of hunting and fishing, swimming and skating. In all these activities he showed an extraordinary perseverance and in time developed unusual strength and muscular coordination, growing up into a broad-shouldered, well-built man of middle size. He was champion runner at Kenyon College, Ohio, where he graduated in 1842. Against the wish of his mother, who wanted him to become a minister, he studied law, at first in a lawyer's office, then at Harvard. There, while playing baseball on the school team, he injured several fingers—no gloves were worn in those days—and gave up the game.

After an unusually sturdy adolescence he suffered from a severe cough when he was nineteen years old. At twenty-five, as a practicing lawyer, he had recurrent attacks of tonsillitis, which kept him from volunteering in the Mexican War. Finally, in 1849, he developed "quinsy," a peritonsillar abscess. Rest, cathartics and cod-liver oil were used as the time-honored remedies, and the abscess broke spontaneously, as it usually does.

In 1852, Hayes married Lucy Webb, the first college graduate to become a President's wife. Like the king and queen of the fairy tale, they had seven sons and one daughter. The sister survived all her brothers and lived until 1950, eighty-three years old.

Besides the wound Hayes received in 1862, he had another close call in the battle of Cedar Creek, in 1864, during which a second future President, William McKinley, served as his aide-de-camp. During this seesaw battle he was reported as missing or killed in action. Eye witnesses saw him galloping down a steep grade, when suddenly his horse was shot from under him and he was hurled violently to the ground, where he lay motionless. They did not know that he was only knocked unconscious by the impact. After a while, he rallied and dragged his bruised body to some nearby woods, mounted his orderly's horse and returned to his brigade.

Soon after, he was elected to the House of Representatives, but took his seat only after the end of the war. Re-elected in 1866, he resigned from Congress to become Governor of Ohio. In this position he gave evidence of the same courage he had shown as an officer during the war. He openly challenged the traditional practice of stuffing the ballot boxes and exposed the professional racket of collections for charitable causes. However, in 1872, loyalty to his party and his own political ambition for once overcame his personal integrity and he vigorously campaigned for the re-election of President Grant, despite the notorious scandals of his administration that had tarnished the shining armor of the war hero.

In 1875 he accepted the nomination as Governor of Ohio for the third time and won the election with such a majority that he became a national figure. His stature in the Republican Party was enhanced by his firm stand for "sound money," which helped him to obtain the nomination for the Presidency at the party convention in 1876 over the perennial favorite James G. Blaine.

On the morning after the presidential election Hayes' Democratic opponent, Samuel J. Tilden, was the winner according to the electoral and popular vote. But by some fancy maneuvering of a congressional committee elected to investigate voting irregularities in the South, the result was reversed two days before

Hayes' inauguration. The decision was bitterly resented by the Democrats, who claimed that Hayes had stolen the election from Tilden by a deal with the Southern states. Actually, a bargain had been made between Republican leaders and Southern Democrats that the three Southern states carried by Tilden would throw their electoral votes to Hayes, provided the occupying federal troops would be withdrawn. Hayes had nothing to do with the deal, but faithfully kept the agreement.

As a consequence of the general bitterness aroused by Hayes' election, a number of threatening letters arrived at the White House which President Hayes ignored—until one evening, while the family sat at dinner, a bullet crashed through the window, passed through two rooms, and lodged in the wall of the library. No one was hurt, but thereafter, the President made his husky second son Webb his personal bodyguard, and let the proud youngster carry a revolver for his father's protection.

The President in his middle fifties was an imposing, soldierly figure. Since the Civil War, no razor had touched his full beard and its silver-gray radiance lent a patriarchal dignity to his calm, handsome face. He still watched his physical condition by going to bed early and getting up with the chickens, which had free run of the White House gardens. Every morning he did his gymnastics, followed by a brisk walk. He restricted himself to one cup of coffee for breakfast, a cup of tea for lunch, and never used tobacco or alcohol. A whisky distiller's son, he, like his wife, were protagonists of national prohibition and never served alcohol in the White House. The guests had to quench their thirst with lemonade and spiced oranges.

The Women's Christian Temperance Union made Lucy Hayes their patron saint and presented her with her portrait in oil, which still hangs in the White House. The Washington sophisticates called her "Lemonade Lucy" and insinuated that she was not only mistress of the White House but also the power behind the President's chair. On one occasion, when she took a trip west, a newspaper commented: "In the absence of his wife, Mr. Hayes is acting President."

Whatever influence his wife exerted on the President, it was certainly a good one. He not only freed the enslaved Southern states, but personally visited their most desolated sections. Withdrawal of the forces of occupation brought Hayes in sharp conflict with many leaders of the Republican Party, who apparently intended to disavow the promise of their election committee, being afraid that by relinquishing the military rule they would lose their grip on the South completely.

The President realized that by the pursuit of his principles, in opposition to the short-sighted selfishness of the politicians, he made himself unpopular and unelectable for a second term. Without regrets he supported the presidential nomination of his friend Garfield, who, he knew, had a political philosophy similar to his own. In the spring of 1881 he returned from Washington to his home in Spiegel Grove, Ohio.

After his retirement Hayes, accustomed to a busy schedule, continued to follow a self-imposed, rigid daily routine which left him no time to brood. He worked for prison reform, and acted as trustee of several educational funds and universities. In spite of all the care which Hayes continued to take of his health, heredity prevailed over all precautions which are supposed to prevent hardening of the arteries: moderation in eating, avoidance of smoking, enough sleep, physical exercise, mental composure.

In his late sixties, symptoms of hardening and narrowing of the blood vessels of the brain developed, gradually interfering with the blood supply to the delicate higher nerve centers, and leading to their degeneration. A loss of memory, typical of senility, resulted, characterized by the forgetting of recent events while remembering past ones. At the same time, a hereditary form of nerve deafness increasingly interfered with Hayes' hearing and in time reached the critical point when the understanding of words became too strenuous for him; he gave up listening and withdrew into himself. The sense of isolation and inadequacy caused by the loss of hearing led to regressive changes. The less he could understand what people were talking about, the more suspicious he grew that they were whispering about him.

In 1889, his wife died of a stroke, worn out by the toil of bearing and bringing up eight children and the grief of losing three of them in infancy. Lucy's death left the old man lonelier than ever. He might have abandoned himself to his grief, ready to join his wife, had it not been for his children and his friends and the many interests which still bound him to the world.

On Sunday, January 8, 1893, Hayes drove in a sleigh to the cemetery to visit Lucy's grave. "My feeling was one of longing, to be quietly resting in a grave by her side," he wrote in his diary that evening. The next day he went to Columbus to attend a meeting of the board of trustees of the State University. He also called on his old companion in arms, the later President McKinley, then Governor of Ohio. From there he took a train to Cleveland to look after the affairs of the Western Reserve University. On the draughty train he caught a bad cold and a cough. A few days later, while waiting for another train to take him home, he was suddenly stricken with severe chest pain, accompanied by nausea and shock. His son Webb got him a glass of brandy, which somewhat relieved the pain, described by Hayes as being as bad as the pain from the bullet that had crushed his arm at South Mountain.

Webb urged his father to return to the home of his hostess where he had been visiting, but he refused. "I would rather die at Spiegel Grove," he declared, "than live anywhere else." Made comfortable in his drawing room on the train, he arrived at his home station safely, still in great pain, and was taken to his beloved home and helped into his own bed. There, the family physician relieved him with an injection of morphine. The old doctor realized that his patient was suffering from a heart ailment and treated him for the next few days with injections of camphor and a concoction of digitalis leaves. Like his contemporaries, he knew little about the pathology of the heart and did not fully realize the seriousness of his patient's condition.

Today, every medical student would recognize the symptoms

and course of Hayes' disease as being typical for a coronary thrombosis, an occlusion by a blood clot of one of the arteries feeding the heart muscle, and a complication of hardening and narrowing of these blood vessels. However, Hayes' family physician showed more common sense in the treatment of his patient than a surgeon general showed thirty years later with a similar condition of President Harding. The good old doctor insisted on complete bed rest for his patient, whereas Harding was permitted to walk around the day after his first attack.

After several days, Hayes felt a little better. He grew restless and began to get out of bed. During the night of January 17, the undulating curve of the disease took a sudden drop. The damaged heart, exhausted, stopped beating.

James Abram Garfield

(1831 – 1881)

THREE American Presidents have been assassinated—Lincoln, Garfield and McKinley. Three unsuccessful attempts have been made on the lives of Presidents—Andrew Jackson, Harry Truman, and President-elect Franklin Delano Roosevelt. Theodore Roosevelt also was wounded by an assailant's bullet, though not while he was in office.

Garfield was born in Ohio, the home state of six other Presidents. He served with great distinction during the Civil War and was breveted major general at thirty-two for outstanding bravery. During the rout of Chickamauga in September 1863, Garfield served as chief of staff of the army of Cumberland. He personally tried to re-establish communication with the left wing of the army commanded by General Thomas. As he rode toward the sound of the cannons, accompanied by an officer and two volunteers, they happened unaware upon some hidden Confederate pickets, who fired at them at close range. One orderly fell dead, one horse was killed, and Garfield's horse was wounded. Garfield escaped unhurt and successfully fulfilled his mission. It is a curious coincidence that he was to die on the eighteenth anniversary of the Battle of Chickamauga.

Garfield entered practical politics at the age of twenty-eight, when he was elected to the Senate of his home state. The Civil War interrupted his career, but at Lincoln's request he resigned from the army late in 1863 to serve as a Republican representative from Ohio. He distinguished himself as a hard worker in committee and as speaker for his party on the floor, and continued in this office for seventeen years, when, in 1880, he was elected President.

On Saturday, July 2, 1881, President Garfield was up early. He was looking forward eagerly to his vacation, which was to start with a visit to his beloved alma mater, Williams College, in Massachusetts. There, he was to deliver the commencement address and continue his holiday jaunt along the Atlantic coast, where his wife was recovering from malaria. Garfield's first four months as President had been strenuous. He had been incessantly badgered by office seekers and politicians demanding political favors in reward for their support.

Strangely enough, two days before his departure, the President had asked Robert Lincoln, his Secretary of War, to tell him all about his father's assassination. Stranger still, Robert Lincoln, who had kept the death watch at his father's side, was to stand again at the bedside of the mortally wounded Garfield, as he was to witness also the assassination of McKinley twenty years later as his guest of honor in Buffalo.

On this July morning, Garfield's spirits were high; in spite of his fifty years, he accepted the dare of one of his boys to jump over his bed. Garfield and his party reached the depot at 9:20 and headed through the waiting room on the way to the train. There were only a few people in the room, and only one policeman on hand to guard the President.

One of those present was Charles Guiteau. He was a man of thirty-eight who for fifteen years had led the shiftless, aimless and friendless life typical of many schizophrenics. A childish egocentric, devoid of judgment, taste and moral sense, he had written a number of bad poems and committed other petty crimes. In the spring of 1880, Guiteau had switched from the pulpit of an itinerant evangelist to the soapbox of a street-corner politician. He had composed some incoherent pamphlets and made unsolicited and ineffectual stump speeches in favor of Grant for President for a third term.

After Garfield received the Republican nomination, Guiteau went over to him without any qualms and supported him in his meddlesome manner. Following Garfield's election, Guiteau deluded himself that it was his pamphlets and speeches which had decided the issue, and that he deserved, for his invaluable services, either the consulship in Paris or the ministry in Austria.

For months he made daily attempts to approach the President and the members of the Cabinet, and deluged the government officials with demands for a reward. On a few occasions he succeeded in cornering James G. Blaine, Secretary of State, and once even the President, but was brushed off politely. He soon found out that the staff of the White House had been instructed not to let him in.

Guiteau gave up at last, but his frustration and anger led him to regard Garfield as the ungrateful villain who deserved punishment. As an echo from his earlier preaching, the delusion reverberated in his brain that all his acts were inspired by God, who now commanded him to "remove" the President. And, in order to justify his act before the world, he borrowed from the political enemies of Garfield the charge that the President was splitting and betraying the Republican Party by opposing the wing of the "stalwarts" led by the notorious political boss, Roscoe Conkling. Guiteau felt therefore that he had to sacrifice himself for the good of the party and the nation, by eliminating the President. Once this obsession had taken hold of his sick mind, he proceeded to execute his plan with the single-minded determination and cunning of the paranoiac.

On July 2, 1881, the nattily dressed little man, five feet, five inches tall, was standing behind a bench in the waiting room, a broad-brimmed black hat pulled low over his eyes, like the badman of the storybooks. He drew his revolver, rushed up within a few feet of Garfield, and shot him in the back.

"My God, what is it?" the President gasped, flinging up his arms and staggering. Guiteau stepped closer and fired again. The second bullet passed harmlessly through Garfield's sleeve. The assailant was seized before he could empty the five-chambered, fully loaded English Bulldog 44-caliber revolver.

The President slumped to the floor and was placed on a mattress, on which he was carried to a room on the second floor of the station. A number of doctors were summoned. Dr. D. W. Bliss, a prominent surgeon of Washington, D. C., took charge of the patient. According to his report, he found the President lying on his left side, in a semiprone position. His face was a ghastly white; large beads of perspiration stood out upon his forehead, his hands and forearms. His respiration was slow and sighing; the pulse exceedingly feeble and rapid. The symptoms indicated a state of shock and internal hemorrhage.

The first doctor to arrive had given the patient half an ounce of brandy and a dram of spirits of ammonia, which had been promptly vomited. The President complained of a sense of heaviness and numbness in the legs and genital region, which was soon followed by tingling and pain.

Dr. Bliss found the point of entrance of the bullet four inches to the right of the spinal column at the height of the eleventh rib. According to the approved surgical practice of the time, he tried to determine the course and location of the bullet by introducing a probe, turning it around to find the place of the least resistance. He used the so-called Nélaton probe, the same type of instrument with which Lincoln's wound had been probed. It was a device tipped with rough porcelain, which was supposed to catch and remove a foreign body, such as a bullet, as it was withdrawn.

Unfortunately the channel carved by a bullet changes its course according to the position of the victim, the activity of the muscles, and with inspiration and expiration. Garfield, a muscular man, was shot in the back while walking briskly. Now he was lying on his left side, his muscles relaxed. We cannot blame Dr. Bliss for not finding the course of the channel with his cumbersome tool. As he probed around in the wound, suddenly the instrument slipped downward and forward. Under the impression that he had found the bullet track, the doctor pushed the instrument farther, three and one-half inches through the muscles of the back, into what he thought was a cavity. As he tried to withdraw the probe, it became stuck between the shattered fragments of the eleventh rib, and was liberated only with difficulty, causing the stoic patient to wince with pain.

Not satisfied with this attempt, the eager surgeon kept exploring the wound with the little finger of the left hand, which he introduced to its full extent, and followed up with a long flexible silver probe which he pushed all around. He was finally convinced that the bullet had entered the liver and that further exploration would not be warranted.

In retrospect, we must assume that the surgeon inadvertently burrowed a false passage during his first attempt with the heavy Nélaton probe, leading through the muscles of the back into the retroperitoneal space. This artificial channel was inevitably dilated by the additional probing with finger and silver probe sound until it resembled a real bullet track, to deceive not only Dr. Bliss but all other surgeons subsequently called in consultation. The wrong impression regarding the course and location of the bullet was reinforced on the following day by the appearance of a black and blue spot on the right side of the anterior abdominal wall opposite the supposed site of the bullet.

The unfortunate procedure of assiduously probing wounds for foreign bodies has been employed since antiquity and continued up to the end of the nineteenth century, when bacteriological studies revealed its dangers and the discovery and perfection of the X-ray made it largely unnecessary.

Dr. Bliss does not report what method he used to cleanse his instruments and hands, though he does mention dressings with the antiseptic carbolic acid and irrigation of the wound with carbolic acid solution. Bacteriologic studies in more recent times have revealed that even under the most perfect conditions of surgical sterility, repeated probing of a wound may introduce bacteria from the deeper layers of the skin and disturb the natural defense mechanism of the tissues against infection.

In 1881, surgical antisepsis was still in its infancy in America, though Lister had advocated carbolic acid solution for systemic surgical use as early as 1867, and had tirelessly led the crusade for his gospel of antisepsis, against the determined opposition of his reactionary confreres. Lister came to the United States in 1876 to preach his new method, but was received with polite coolness by most of his American colleagues. As late as 1885 the great American surgeon, William Stewart Halsted of New York and Johns Hopkins, had to perform surgical operations in a large tent on the grounds of Bellevue Hospital in New York, having found it impossible to carry out antiseptic precautions in the amphitheater of the hospital where the anti-Listerian surgeons predominated.

After Dr. Bliss had concluded his examination, he applied a dressing. The President, at his urgent request, was cautiously transferred to the White House by horse-drawn ambulance over cobblestone streets. Late in the afternoon his wife arrived from the sea coast and exchanged words of restrained affection with her husband, whose face was deathly pale but whose mind remained clear. In the course of the evening, the signs of internal hemorrhage became more and more alarming, reaching the climax at 11 P.M., when the pulse rose to 158, the respiration to 35; at the same time the temperature fell to 96.5°. The patient was in deep shock, extremely thirsty but unable to retain fluids.

The attending doctors feared that the President might not survive the night. To their astonishment the rugged patient rallied; around midnight his pulse slowed down to 120, respiration to 20, and his temperature rose to 98°. The hemorrhage had apparently stopped spontaneously when the blood pressure had fallen to shock level. Later during the night the President was able to retain sips of water, and appeared stronger.

Early next morning a consultation was held in the White House at which the Surgeon General J. K. Barnes and his assistant, J. J. Woodward, who had attended the dying Lincoln sixteen years previously, participated. The patient had visibly improved but still complained of pains in the legs, for which he was given a hypodermic of morphine.

On July 4, two well-known surgeons, Dr. D. Hayes Agnew of Philadelphia and Dr. Frank H. Hamilton of New York, arrived as consultants. They could not understand how a bullet which was supposed to have taken a direction forward and downward toward the lower abdomen could cause numbness and pain in the legs and scrotum. Such symptoms pointed to a spinal injury. In their search for a bullet track which would explain the mysterious neurological symptoms, the consulting surgeons also explored the wound with metal probes, followed by digital examination. Their attempts were futile; they could not locate any other channel than the one Doctor Bliss had found. One consolation was that intestine and kidneys had been acting normally; there was apparently no injury to them. Then, on the evening of the same day, the unexplained pains in the legs diminished and the patient was able to retain some food.

It was hot and sultry that summer in Washington. The feverish President suffered acutely from the heat. To make him more comfortable, well-meaning folk recommended and sent all manner of gadgets to cool the air in the White House. The basement became cluttered with boilers, steam engines, pipes and hoses. Eventually, an ingenious apparatus was put together in which the air passed through a large iron chamber containing three thousand feet of turkish toweling, hanging in layers and saturated by constantly dripping salted ice water. A fan drew the cooled air into a second icebox filled with charcoal to purify and dry it, and from there it was blown through a pipe into the President's room. This complicated system proved quite efficient and kept the air in the sickroom cool and comfortable.

The patient continued to improve, with slight fluctuations, up to July 23, when he suffered a severe chill followed by a temperature of 104°. The attending surgeons found that a pus sac had formed in the direction of the false channel. Pressure on the right side of the abdomen caused discharge of pus through the wound, and in order to facilitate better drainage, the opening was enlarged by a small incision. When the high fever continued, the cut had to be extended and a small piece of fractured rib removed. All this was done without anasthesia. Thereafter the doctors tried to keep on evacuating the pus from the wound cavity to prevent its systemic absorption, by irrigating it twice a day through a catheter, using the mildly antiseptic solution of potassium permanganate.

The failure to locate and remove the bullet which was supposed to be the focus of the infection continued to worry the attending surgeons. It began to disturb the American public, who were kept informed by daily bulletins. Dr. Alexander Graham Bell, inventor of the telephone, had a brain storm. He rigged up an electrical induction system connected with a telephone. In laboratory experiments he found out that a piece of metal, like a bullet, brought in close proximity between the primary and secondary coil, would cause a slight disturbance of the balanced circuit, manifested by a faint hum in the telephone receiver.

The idea was ingenious, and was later put to practical use in a more elaborate form for the detection of land mines. But Bell's first improvised instrument was not sensitive enough to locate a relatively small, deeply buried bullet. Bell, however, was convinced of the efficiency of his invention, and asked for the opportunity to locate the bullet in the President's body. Full of confidence, he appeared at the appointed hour in the White House, accompanied by an assistant.

The President was propped up in bed and watched the proceedings with great interest. Bell stood behind the patient, holding the telephone receiver, while the assistant moved the coils around the abdomen and back. When the circuit crossed the black-and-blue spot on the abdomen under which the bullet was supposed to lie, Bell's face lighted up. He thought he heard a slight hum in the receiver. The experiment was repeated several times, once with Mrs. Garfield at the telephone. She also imagined she heard the faint hum when the black spot was approached. Bell decided that the bullet was actually located below the black spot at a depth of four and one-half inches. It was the consensus of the attending surgeons that it would be too hazardous to try removing the bullet from its supposed lodgment behind the abdominal viscera.

On August 8 a renewed rise of the temperature necessitated

once more an exploration of the wound. The previous incision was enlarged, outward and downward. For the first time ether anesthesia was employed for this operation. On the following day pulse and temperature dropped to a lower level and, on August 10, Garfield felt strong enough to sign an official paper, the first since his illness.

Three days later a new relapse occurred, with nausea, vomiting and general prostration, indicating a further spread of the infection. Vain attempts were made to nourish the patient by enemas containing eggs, beef extract and whisky. At that time the fact had not yet been established that hardly any calories, but only water, electrolytes and certain drugs can be absorbed by the rectum. The method of introducing water, electrolytes and other vital substances by the intravenous route is only some fifty years old.

On August 18 a swelling of the right parotid gland was noted, accompanied by restlessness and wandering of the mind. These were ominous signs, indicating that the septic bacteria had broken into the blood stream, producing blood poisoning. The right side of the face became paralyzed by the pressure of the swollen gland on the facial nerve. During the next two weeks several small incisions were made in the gland in the effort to drain the accumulated pus.

All this time the wound track in the back was kept open by daily irrigations for which carbolic acid solution was now used, alternating with potassium permanganate. During the latter part of August a number of pus blisters appeared in both axillae and in other parts of the skin, a further manifestation of bacterial dissemination.

When the President had left the White House on July 2 on his vacation, he had looked forward to getting away from the tropical heat of Washington and enjoying the sea breeze of the New Jersey coast. Now, he begged the doctors to let him be taken from the cheerless sickroom to the sea shore. The attending surgeons realized that the President was in a critical condition. There was serious disagreement among them about the

advisability of such a move; the more so because of signs of a
spreading bronchitis and congestion of both lower lobes of the
lungs.

On August 28, the abscess of the parotid gland suddenly broke
and was freely discharged through the right ear and the mouth.
Another period of subjective improvement followed. The President insisted with the stubbornness of a dying man to be taken
to the sea shore, and finally the surgeons consented to have him
removed to a cottage by the sea at Elberon, New Jersey. The
trip was carefully planned and accomplished on September 6,
by train and carriage, with the least possible inconvenience to
the patient. On September 8, the President could hear the
church bells ringing, summoning the people to prayer for his
recovery. He was cheerful and happy to have reached the sea
shore where he could see from his bed the faraway horizon
across the water.

The deceptive calm in the course of the illness lasted until
September 17, when at 11 A.M. a severe chill of a half hour's
duration occurred, raising the temperature to 102°, and the
pulse to 120. The chill was accompanied by a sharp pain in the
middle of the chest. For the next two days the same sequence
of chills, fever and chest pain recurred several times. During
these spells the President's mind slipped off into unconsciousness. On September 19, shortly before ten o'clock at night, he
fell asleep, to be awakened a few minutes later by a sudden excruciating pain which made him utter a loud cry of agony. He
died at 10:35 P.M.

On the next day an autopsy was performed which showed that
the surgeons had been far astray in their notion of the direction
and site of the bullet. It was not lodged in the right lower quadrant behind the abdominal organs, as they had assumed, but on
the opposite side, ten inches away and higher up, behind the
peritoneum. Alexander Graham Bell's much-touted induction
balance device had proved to be no more accurate than a divin-
ing rod.

The bullet had taken a direction at a right angle to the one

assumed by the doctors and had pierced the first lumber ver-
tebra, causing a temporary pressure on the spinal cord. It had
continued its course toward the left, behind the pancreas, where
it was found to be encapsulated. On its way it had torn a large
rent in the splenic artery, a major abdominal vessel, producing
the severe internal hemorrhage which had almost been fatal during the first day. After the bleeding had stopped spontaneously,
the clotted blood around the vessel had become encapsulated by
a sac of scar tissue resulting in a so-called traumatic aneurysm.

The continuous and increasing pressure of the blood flowing
through the center of the sac had gradually caused a fissure between the layers of organized blood clots and surrounding scar
tissue, which had been softened by the spreading infection.

The terrifying episodes during the last two days had been
caused by preliminary spells of leakage of blood into the tissues
around the injured artery, self-limited by the automatic fall of
blood pressure and the continuous process of clotting, until
finally the dam of scar tissue had burst wide open, the blood
pouring out into the retroperitoneal space as a lethal hemorrhage.

Leading from the wound entrance, forward and downward,
the large pus pocket was found which the surgeons had repeatedly incised and drained. The pus had spread far down behind
the peritoneum into the pelvic cavity. A second large abscess,
connected with the pus pocket, was discovered between the
lower surface of the liver and the transverse colon.

It is easy today to criticize the surgeons of 1881 for their wrong
diagnosis and management of the case. But even if they had
known the site of the bullet, under the surgical handicaps of
the time, it would have been extremely difficult and dangerous
to remove it from its hiding place in the posterior abdominal
wall behind the pancreas. It is probable that the wound infection causing the blood poisoning was introduced, or at least
aggravated, by the repeated probings and explorations. But such
was the surgical practice of the time.

Even today, in a well-equipped hospital, the removal of a

bullet from behind the pancreas would be technically difficult. However, under modern conditions, Garfield could have been saved. The primary shock would have been combated with massive blood transfusions, and the patient brought into a condition to be operated on at a fair risk. X-ray studies would have determined the exact location of the bullet. With modern surgical technique and good lighting, the rent in the splenic artery could have been found and repaired, or the vessel tied off and the spleen removed. The infection would have been controlled by antibiotics.

Enraged by the cold-blooded murder of the President, the American public and their representatives on the jury rejected the plea of insanity which the defense made for Guiteau. Public opinion cried out for retribution, insisting that Guiteau was sane when he shot the President and that he was merely a disappointed office seeker who wanted revenge. The people demanded a change. They would no longer tolerate the system of patronage by which public offices were doled out as spoils for political services without regard to the character and fitness of job seekers.

Garfield was considered to have been a martyr of the vicious spoils system which he had so vigorously opposed during his short administration. Under the irresistible pressure of the voters, Congress, in January 1883, passed the National Civil Service Law, long overdue, which has since become the basis for the progressive improvement of the mechanics of American government. Thus the assassination of a President had a far-reaching political consequence for the nation's welfare.

Chester Alan Arthur

(1830 — 1886)

CHESTER ALAN ARTHUR was born in Fairfield, Vermont, on October 5, 1830, the eldest of seven children of Reverend William Arthur, a Scotch-Irish Baptist clergyman. He was a bright, active boy and leader of his group. At eighteen, he graduated at Schenectady College, New York, then taught school, studied law, and established a successful law practice in New York. He married at the age of twenty-nine and had two sons and a daughter. One son died in infancy, his daughter married the famous detective Allan Pinkerton.

Arthur became early associated with the anti-slavery movement and the Republican Party, making a name for himself by successfully arguing a case against the Fugitive Slave Law and obtaining a ruling for equal treatment of the Negroes on the New York railroads.

In 1861, his political patron Edwin D. Morgan, the wartime Governor of New York, appointed him quartermaster general of the State of New York. The largest group of war volunteers came from the Empire State, and Arthur showed outstanding ability as organizer and administrator in his responsible position. After the Civil War he became a satellite of Roscoe C. Conkling, notorious boss and Senator of New York, and founded the Grant for President Club. As reward, President Grant made him Collector of Customs of the Port of New York in 1871, and for seven years he was responsible for the bulk of the customs revenues of the United States.

Trained in the school of practical politicians, Arthur administered his office according to the practices of the spoils system, but without making any personal profit. In fact, he ran the custom house as honestly and efficiently as it could be run, over-staffed as it was with a swarm of employees who had been paid off with government jobs for their services to the Republican Party. President Hayes, who tried to eradicate the flagrant abuses of the patronage system, had the New York custom house inves-tigated. After a bitter inter-Republican controversy, Arthur was discharged for using the large government payroll of his office in the interest of the New York Republican machine. His dis-honorable discharge left the smudge of corruption on his con-temporary and historical image which the disclosure of the real facts could not erase.

In the compromise preceding the nomination of Garfield for President, a deal was made with the powerful Conkling that he could name his candidate for the second place. He had his front man Arthur nominated, never dreaming that Arthur would be in the White House in less than a year, championing reforms he had been briefed to oppose.

Up to the point of his sudden conversion, Arthur had occu-pied less important political positions in which he could follow the covetous practices of the spoils system without feeling any personal guilt. Even so, he had revealed his secret sense of shame by boasting about his cynical attitude. The minister's son had lost the literal faith of his fathers, yet their stern moral code remained ingrained in him. The impact of presidential respon-sibility, unexpectedly thrust upon his shoulders, made the self-assured politician pause and grope for guidance, which he found in the still, small voice of his conscience.

Arthur had presidential stature. He was six feet, two inches tall, well built, impeccably groomed and dressed, with an open benign face and dignified bearing. Now he also began acting like a President. He split with Conkling, supported a new civil service law, prosecuted Republican officials accused of graft, and vetoed a pork barrel rivers-and-harbors bill. By breaking with his political past, Arthur rendered himself persona non grata with the Republican machine, as Hayes had before him. As a consequence, his own party turned against him and tried to discredit him as President.

One year before Arthur's election his wife had died. He made his sociable sister, Mrs. McElroy, the hostess of the White House. She made it once more the center of the social life of Washington. The fastidious Arthur could not bear the sight of the run-down interior of the White House that he called a "badly kept barracks." He hired Louis Comfort Tiffany, the originator of the ornate style then in vogue, to repaint and modernize the executive mansion with fancy patterns of golden eagles and flags. More practical improvements were the installation of an elevator, replacement of the old plumbing with new fixtures, and the addition of two tiled bathrooms.

In that age of innocence, when the pleasures of the table were not yet soured by the counting of calories and the bugaboo of cholesterol, President Arthur's dinners were famous for their opulence. He himself loved heavy foods, fine wines and after-dinner liqueurs, disregarding his expanding girth. The diligent application to his official duties and to his social life left him little time for his favorite hobby, salmon fishing.

Overweight, overwork, and too many parties inevitably took their toll. Spring of 1883 found the fifty-three-year-old President thoroughly worn out, and his doctors sent him to Florida to recuperate. On his return trip through the swampy lowlands Arthur contracted a severe type of malaria that quinine did not seem to help. Chill followed chill in quick succession, probably caused by a simultaneous infection with two different strains of malaria germs. He was a very sick man when he reached the White House and took several weeks to recover.

Subsequently, he suffered from frequent painful attacks of indigestion, diagnosed by his doctors as nervous indigestion. Consistent with Arthur's constitutional type and mode of living, his ailment was probably a chronic gallbladder disease, caused in part by precipitation of bile solids into gall stones. These concretions may at times occlude the narrow outlet of the gallbladder, arousing a reflex contraction of the gallbladder muscles in trying to empty the hollow organ. Such spasmodic contractions against an obstruction are the common cause of gallbladder colic, often so painful as to require opiates for relief.

In spite of this condition, the President was ready to serve a second term and was disappointed when his party bypassed him. Regretful, but with a good conscience, he surrendered occupancy of the White House to another minister's son, Grover Cleveland. During the inauguration ceremonies Chester Arthur towered beside the big, broad-shouldered Cleveland, his elegant whiskers and erect carriage in distinct contrast to the bald ruggedness of the new President.

After several weeks of rest the former President returned to his law practice in New York, but retired after a few months because of ill health. His gallbladder ailment became worse and he could not master the self-control to curb his appetite for rich foods, conducive to recurrent colic. Food was for him, as for many fat persons, a substitute for the affection which he unknowingly craved.

Arthur's inner conflicts added to his disappointments as President. His frustration due to forced inactivity and physical suffering culminated in a feeling of hopelessness and morbid pessimism, unexpected in a man who looked like a tower of strength and stability. A long sea voyage served only as a temporary diversion. Arthur's main apprehension was that he would become a victim of Bright's disease, the bane of his family. This did not alter his eating and drinking habits, which sorely taxed his kidneys.

His premonition came true; at the age of fifty-five the former President developed an acute form of nephritis. The diseased cells of the kidneys became unequal to their task of excreting certain toxic end products of metabolism and filtering out of the blood stream sufficient water to maintain fluid balance. The retained poisons caused drowsiness and nausea, and the retained fluid collected as edema, most pronounced in the legs. The condition of the kidneys was aggravated by hardening of the arteries.

The acute phase gradually subsided, leaving the kidneys

scarred and contracted, curtailing their function. The body is geared to compensate for the diminished excretory surface of the kidneys by increasing the muscular tonus of the blood vessels, in this manner raising the pressure in the arterial system and the filtration pressure in the kidneys. The heart, which has to pump the blood through contracted channels, responds to the increased demands with overdevelopment of its muscles. If the damage to the kidneys is irreversible and progressive, as in Arthur's case, the left half of the heart will gradually overwork itself and become flabby, distended and decompensated. The arterial blood will become dammed up in the lungs, congesting them, compressing the breathing space.

In turn, the right chambers of the heart will be unable to overcome the back pressure into the pulmonary circulation and also become dilated and decompensated. Stagnation of the venous circulation follows. The liver becomes congested, fluid accumulates in the legs, and, with the increasing disability of the heart, gradually rises up in the body, collecting in the abdominal and thoracic cavities. In the case of Arthur, the fluid resulting from the decompensation of the heart was superimposed upon the edema, caused by the deficiency of the kidneys.

Arthur was in constant misery. Weary from the labor of breathing, he was unable to lie down and stretch out his tired limbs. Somnolent and restless, he could sleep only with the aid of narcotics. He no longer cared for food. His body was swollen; the weight loss caused by the wasting of fat and muscle tissue was more than made up by the interstitial accumulation of quarts of fluid.

A change of surroundings in June 1886, from the heat of New York to the cooler climate of Connecticut, did not alter the relentless course of the disease. Returned to New York, Arthur said despondently to a friend: "After all, life is not worth living. I might as well give up the struggle for it now as at any other time and submit to the inevitable."

On November 16, 1886, a short improvement occurred. Death granted the condemned man a last respite. For one day the heavy chains of disease were sloughed off, letting him enjoy good appetite for his last meal. Cheerfully he went to bed. During his sleep one of the fragile blood vessels of the brain ruptured. The hemorrhage paralyzed his left side and the centers of his consciousness. He died two days later, on November 18, 1886.

Grover Cleveland

(1837 — 1908)

On JULY 1, 1893, around noon, the yacht *Oneida* was steaming up the East River of Manhattan at half-speed. Sitting on the deck were two men, the owner of the yacht, Commodore E. C. Benedict of New York, and the United States Secretary of War, Daniel Lamont.

They were sitting in silence, eyes fixed on the gangway leading to the quarters below. The steady pulse of the yacht's steam engine and the brisk splash of the waves sent rhythmic vibrations through the ship. On the bridge the captain stood gravely at the wheel, the engineer beside him watching the steam and oil pressure gauges. From time to time a sailor noiselessly crossed the deck.

In the ship's saloon below there was intense activity. The sweetish smell of ether hung in the air. In the center, under the skylight, six white-gowned doctors stood around an operating table upon which lay Grover Cleveland, President of the United States, in the deep sleep of anesthesia. He was being operated upon for cancer of the left upper jaw.

The operation was being performed in the incongruous surroundings of a pleasure yacht because the President and his close political advisers felt that complete secrecy of the President's illness was imperative at this particular time, a crucial moment in the nation's history.

When Grover Cleveland was inaugurated for his second term on March 4, 1893, an economic crisis was sweeping the world. The great nations of the world were engaged in a wild scramble for gold. In the United States business was bad, unemployment was growing. For the first time in fifteen years exports had fallen below imports, leaving a balance of $35 million to be met in gold.

The foreign credit of the United States was tumbling, and European banks were hurriedly unloading American securities which had to be redeemed with gold by the United States Treasury. The gold reserves were dropping rapidly below the critical point of $100 million fixed by law. At the same time a flood of silver was pouring into the national vaults, unstemmed by the safeguards of sound money regulations, drowning the credit of the country. Under the pressure of the silver interests of the Western states, in 1890 Congress had passed the Sherman Silver Act, obligating the United States Treasury to buy four and a half million ounces of silver bullion every month. In spite of this law the value of silver steadily fell on the open market, because the more the Treasury bought, the more the mine owners supplied from the inexhaustible veins of the Western mountains.

Grover Cleveland was known as a staunch advocate of "sound money" and the gold standard, the standard of the great nations of the world. His opponents were isolationists from the agricultural Western states who were clamoring for free and unlimited silver coinage. Their leader was the "silver-tongued orator," William Jennings Bryan, who urged the establishment of a national money structure based on silver and gold at a fixed rate, and claimed that the United States was self-sufficient and did not need any foreign trade. In order to pacify the Western voters, the Democratic Party had chosen for Vice-President Adlai Stevenson of Illinois, who was known to be a silver advocate.

In his autobiography Charles Francis Adams II called the crisis of 1893 "the most deep-seated financial storm in the history of our country." The *Commercial Financial Chronicle* wrote, "Mr. Cleveland is about all that stands between this country and absolute disaster." *The Nation* said editorially, "A great deal is staked upon the continuance of a single life."

During June 1893, the crisis had risen to such a pitch that a national disaster threatened. Grover Cleveland, a slow-moving and deliberate man, saw himself forced to act at once.

Just then he discovered a rough spot at the roof of his mouth. He called Dr. R. M. O'Reilly (later surgeon general of the United States Army), who found a growth the size of a silver quarter on the left side of the hard palate, which appeared to have invaded the bone of the upper jaw. Suspecting malignancy, he excised a specimen of the tissue and, without revealing the identity of the patient, sent it to the pathologist of the Army Medical Museum for microscopic examination.

The pathologist found the specimen cancerous. His diagnosis was confirmed by Dr. William H. Welch, distinguished pathologist of Johns Hopkins Medical School. Dr. O'Reilly advised consultation with Dr. Joseph D. Bryant, eminent New York surgeon and a friend of the President. Dr. Bryant arrived promptly, and carefully examined the suspicious area. "What do you think it is, Doctor?" the President calmly inquired. Dr. Bryant replied, "Were it in my mouth, I would have it removed at once."

This answer settled the matter. Cleveland asked Dr. Bryant to make the necessary preparations, and added that it was absolutely necessary to withhold from the public any disclosure—or even suspicion—that anything serious was wrong with the President, in order not to precipitate national bankruptcy. He did inform his close friend Secretary Lamont, who arranged with Mr. Benedict, also an old friend, to use the latter's yacht for the operation. The President had frequently been a guest aboard the *Oneida* and it was felt that here would be the one place where absolute secrecy could be maintained.

July 1 was set as the earliest possible date for the operation. In the meantime, the below-deck salon of the yacht was prepared; an operating table, instruments, drugs, and dressings were put aboard.

On the afternoon of June 30 the *Oneida* was anchored at Pier A on the East River. During the evening a team of five bearded doctors, whom Dr. Bryant had chosen for consultation and assistance on the operation of his illustrious patient, boarded the yacht.

He had requested the surgical assistance of Dr. W. W. Keen of Philadelphia, one of the great American surgeons of the time. For the induction of the anesthesia and the preliminary dental work, he had asked Dr. Ferdinand Hasbrouck, an expert dentist who had had experience in administering nitrous oxide for the extraction of teeth. The continuation of the anesthesia with ether he entrusted to Dr. O'Reilly. Dr. E. G. Janeway, well-known New York internist, was to give the President a complete physical examination before surgery, and to stand by during the operation. Dr. Bryant's regular assistant, young Dr. John Erdmann, was to serve as second assistant. All the attending doctors had been impressed by Dr. Bryant with the importance of absolute secrecy.

The crew of the *Oneida* had been told that the President was to have two teeth extracted and did not wish any publicity, so that he could rest undisturbed on the yacht. They must have wondered why such extensive preparations had to be made for a tooth extraction, and why so many doctors were needed. But the crew knew the President well from previous cruises and were devoted to him. Not a hint of the secret operation was ever uttered by them.

Late in the evening of June 30 the President was driven to the pier in the company of Secretary Lamont and Dr. Bryant. The President's wife, being in the seventh month of her second pregnancy, was unable to accompany him.

Before leaving Washington that day, President Cleveland had called a special session of Congress for August 7 to repeal the disastrous Sherman Silver Act—which he wanted accomplished unconditionally and without compromise. He had been assured by the optimistic Dr. Bryant that he would have recovered sufficiently at that date to be back in Washington and put his personal weight behind the repeal.

The *Oneida* lay at anchor all night in Bellevue Bay. The President sat on deck smoking a cigar and chatting with the party almost till midnight. Then he retired and slept soundly without a sedative. In the morning the yacht hoisted anchor and cruised slowly up the East River. Dr. Bryant was afraid that some of the interns at the nearby Bellevue Hospital might recognize members of the medical staff on the yacht, and he warned the doctors to remain below deck until the craft was well out of sight.

Dr. Janeway gave the patient a thorough physical examination and declared him in good condition, except for his great corpulence, which increased the surgical risk. Dr. Keen, who was later to describe the operation in detail, confessed that he had misgivings about the hazards of the anesthesia on a patient of fifty-six who was much overweight—and with good reason. Cleveland had a history of gout and represented what used to be called "the apoplectic type," meaning an individual disposed to strokes. Such persons have a tendency to high blood pressure and premature hardening of the arteries. The impaired cardiovascular system might be adequate for the normal demands of life, but unable to carry the added load of a deep anesthesia and the shock of surgery. Another danger in a patient of this type was the possible formation of blood clots, particularly following surgery, which can choke off the blood supply to vital organs. Aside from every other consideration, this patient was the President of the United States, harassed to the point of physical and mental exhaustion by the cares and responsibilities of office.

There is no record that President Cleveland received any preoperative medication such as is customary today. The preparation consisted merely of cleansing the oral cavity with antiseptic mouthwashes. Following this, the President was put on the operating table and Dr. Hasbrouck, the dentist, started the anesthesia with nitrous oxide. A few minutes later the narcosis was deep enough for the extraction of two back teeth close to the cancerous area. Dr. Bryant then made an elliptical incision around the part that was to be excised at the roof of the mouth.

For the radical procedure to follow, the anesthesia had to be deepened by changing from nitrous oxide to ether. It was a challenge to the skill of the anesthetist to obtain with ether the deep level of anesthesia required for a major operation on a man of Cleveland's bulk, and keeping him at this stage for the greater part of an hour. The amount of anesthetic required corresponds to the weight of the patient, and Cleveland then probably weighed close to 250 pounds. With every drop of ether the anesthetist must have shed a drop of cold perspiration.

Another factor added to the difficulty of the narcosis. Since his twenties Grover Cleveland had been accustomed to drinking quantities of beer, nor did he disdain harder liquor on occasion. Alcohol and ether being related in chemical composition and physiological action, the more a person is accustomed to alcohol, the more resistant he is to the effects of ether. This makes it all the more remarkable that Dr. O'Reilly could keep the patient for more than forty minutes at a level of narcosis permitting the extensive operation to be performed without a hitch.

Describing the operation later, Dr. Keen wrote that he had used for the exposure of the operative area a self-retaining cheek retractor that he had brought back from Paris in 1866, and which proved very helpful on this occasion. Dr. Bryant skillfully removed the greatest part of the left upper jawbone with surgical hammer, chisel, and bone-cutting instruments. Dr. Erdmann handed him the necessary instruments, and a boat steward served as circulating "nurse" for the necessary menial tasks. The surgeons arrested the flow of blood by the use of pressure with gauze sponges and an electric cautery powered by a storage battery, coagulating and sealing over the bleeding points. Only one tie of catgut was necessary on a large vessel.

During the procedure the left antrum, the cavity below the eye, was opened. It was found to be filled with a gelatinous mass of undoubted cancerous nature. Because of this unexpected finding, more bone had to be removed than had been anticipated, to ensure the complete removal of the malignant tumor with a margin of healthy tissue around it. All of the left upper jawbone was cut away up to the orbital plate, the lower wall of the eye socket, which was retained. The entire operation was done from within the mouth, thereby avoiding an external scar as visible evidence of an operation.

At the completion of the surgery, the resulting large wound crater was packed with antiseptic gauze to stop any residual oozing of blood. The patient was returned to his bed in excellent condition. "What an intense sigh of relief we surgeons breathed when the patient was once more safely in bed can hardly be imagined," wrote Dr. Keen.

The postoperative course was uneventful. An hour following surgery the patient was given one hypodermic of morphine. According to Dr. Keen, this was the only narcotic which Cleveland required after the operation. From the first postoperative day on, the temperature never rose above 100°; the pulse averaged 90. The President took pain and discomfort without complaining. His speech was labored and thick, though understandable while the wound was packed; however when the packing was removed it became unintelligible, resembling the speech defect resulting from a cleft palate.

Apparently Dr. Bryant was a believer in the early rising of patients following surgery. On the second day following the operation he allowed the President to get up and walk around. Two days later, on the evening of July 5, the *Oneida* steamed into Buzzards Bay and Cleveland was transported by launch to Gray Gables, his summer home. He walked to his house unassisted and without apparent effort.

Back in New York Dr. Bryant examined thoroughly the excised pieces of tissue with a pathologist. They discovered that on one point of the specimen the line of resection seemed to run too close to the malignant tissue, and Dr. Bryant was worried that a remnant of the cancer might have been left behind. He had the courage to reveal his suspicion at once to the President, who had barely started to recover from his ordeal, and to advise him to undergo a second operation as soon as possible. Grover Cleveland took this disheartening news with his usual fortitude.

On July 17, a second operation was performed, again on board the *Oneida* and under the same precautions of secrecy. The wound was exposed, the suspected area removed, and the entire wound surface seared with the cautery. This procedure took only a few minutes and the President stood it well. A week later Cleveland was able to see a few important visitors at Gray Gables. Richard Olney, the Attorney General, was one of the first to be received. Olney found the President changed a good deal in appearance and behavior. He had lost weight, talked with difficulty, and seemed depressed. Cleveland gratefully accepted Olney's offer to help him with his message to Congress, to be delivered August 7, asking for the repeal of the Sherman Silver Act.

The recuperative and healing powers of Cleveland were remarkably good, and he was able to travel to Washington on August 5, as planned, just twenty days after the unscheduled second operation. In the meantime the dentist, Dr. Kasson C. Gibson, had completed a temporary artificial upper jaw for the President, made of vulcanized rubber to be inserted inside the cheek, which gave his face a normal appearance and his voice a natural quality. It must have been very painful to wear on the unhealed, raw wound surface. In Washington the President was personally able to direct the strategy for the repeal of the Sherman Silver Act.

With a majority of more than two to one the House repealed the Act on August 28; the motion had harder sledding in the Senate because of the larger representation from the Western silver states in the upper House. After weeks of filibustering by the Western senators, and much personal prodding by the President, the Act was finally repealed on October 30 by a scant majority of 48 to 37.

By September the wound was sufficiently healed to allow the President to wear the artificial jaw with greater comfort. On September 5 Cleveland opened the Pan-American Medical Congress in Washington. It was reported that on this occasion his voice sounded clearer and more resonant to his doctors than on March 4 when he delivered his inaugural address. Two weeks later he made another speech at the opening of the centennial of the founding of Washington, D.C.

The operative area was so well-healed by October that Dr. Gibson was able to fit the President with a permanent cast of the left upper jawbone, made of hard rubber, which Cleveland wore for the rest of his life. The artificial jaw was fused with an upper dental plate and was inserted and kept clean like any ordinary denture. In a letter of thanks to Dr. Gibson, Cleveland expressed delight with his "new machine," which he said he could wear with the utmost ease and comfort all day long.

On September 9, 1893, Cleveland's second child, Esther, arrived, the first child born in the White House to a President. The baby was delivered by Dr. Bryant, who apparently did not stick to his specialty of surgery but acted as family physician.

By November 1893, Grover Cleveland had won two great victories. He had conquered the malignant tumor which had threatened his life, and had won the battle over the blight endangering the national economy, the Sherman Silver Act. In his account of the operation Dr. Keen remarks, "We can only surmise and shudder over what the national and political consequences might have been if the news of the operation had leaked out."

Apparently keyhole reporters were not snooping around in those days and the operation remained a secret for nearly two months. Then, on August 29, a reporter under the by-line of "Holland"—his real name was E. G. Edwards—wrote in the Philadelphia *Press* a sensational account of the first operation, with uncannily accurate details that only an insider could have known.

The story was vigorously denied by Dr. Bryant. The editor of the Philadelphia *Public Ledger,* L. Clarke Davis, a personal friend of Cleveland, characterized Holland's report as "an infamous exploitation of a toothache," and said he had never seen the Chief Executive in better physical or mental condition. Other newspapers also denied that a major operation had been performed.

By the time the story came out, the appearance of the President seemed to belie it. He had completely recovered, had regained his weight, and was his old self abounding with energy. No scar or deformity was visible. No change in the voice betrayed the defect resulting from the mutilating operation. The sensation aroused throughout the country and the world by Holland's report quickly subsided and was soon forgotten. Dr. Bryant blamed the dentist, Dr. Hasbrouck, for breaking the code of medical secrecy, and thereafter would neither speak nor write to him. He sent Dr. Hasbrouck his $250 fee by a messenger with no note enclosed.

Grover Cleveland's operation remained one of the best-kept secrets in American history. It became public knowledge for the first time twenty-four years later, nine years after Cleveland's death, when Dr. W. W. Keen published his authentic account of the event in the *Saturday Evening Post* in 1917.

The secret operation constituted the most dramatic episode in the life of Grover Cleveland, a life filled with interesting and colorful incidents.

Stephen Grover Cleveland was born in Caldwell in Essex County, New Jersey, on March 18, 1837, the fifth of nine children. His father was Richard F. Cleveland, a poor Presbyterian clergyman of English descent. His mother, Ann Neal, was the daughter of a bookseller of Irish extraction. When Grover was sixteen his father died suddenly at the age of forty-nine, exhausted from overwork and the worry of rearing a large family on a minister's income. He left his wife with seven minor children to look after.

Instead of going to college, as Grover had looked forward to, he had to look for a job. In the spring of 1855 he left New York with the notion of traveling to Cleveland, Ohio, the city which got its name from one of his kinsmen, General Moses Cleveland. It seemed to him a good omen. He stopped off in Buffalo to visit an uncle, who offered him a home and a temporary job until he could find something better.

While living at his uncle's place Grover was stricken with

typhoid fever and was desperately ill for several weeks. He received the best medical and nursing care then known—practiced for centuries—for the treatment of typhoid: It consisted in virtually starving the patient, giving him only water and low calorie liquids such as diluted milk and thin soup. This practice followed the old maxim, "Feed a cold and starve a fever." In typhoid fever there seemed to be some justification for this rule because the most dangerous manifestation of this disease is the formation of multiple ulcers in the intestinal wall.

It was assumed that the passage of food would increase the danger of rupture of an ulcer, a complication occurring spontaneously in 3 per cent of the patients and causing a fatal peritonitis. The modern practice of supplying intravenous calories and electrolytes and highly concentrated liquid foods was then unknown. The forced starvation produced a severe acidosis, greatly diminishing the patient's resistance, with a resulting mortality of 5 to 20 per cent. The patient who survived the average of four weeks of fever and starvation, as Grover did, emerged emaciated to a skeleton and required a long period of recuperation.

In 1859, at the age of twenty-two, Cleveland passed the New York State bar. He had just begun his practice as a lawyer when the Civil War broke out, claiming the services of men of military age. Three of the four Cleveland brothers (the fourth was a clergyman) drew straws to decide which of them should remain at home to support their mother and two minor sisters. The lot fell to Grover. Two years later when the universal draft law went into effect, he hired a substitute for $300, as was the common practice. (Later on in his political career, his opponents never let the voters forget this apparent lack of devotion to the Northern cause.)

His New England ancestry and upbringing as the son of a clergyman had not made a Puritan out of Cleveland. As a young man he enjoyed all the good things of life and was fond of wine, women, and song, and especially of the good German beer brewed in Buffalo. More in accord with the tenets of his Puritan ancestors were his rigid honesty and the need to express his opinions in a straightforward manner, often bordering on tactlessness.

In 1880, Cleveland had become the best known lawyer in Buffalo. He was then forty-three, a large man who apparently never watched his weight and carried the bulge of a hearty beer drinker. His head and face were massive, proportionate to his size. He had a fair complexion and fine brown hair thinning out over a gently curving forehead. The top of his head was bald. His dark blue eyes, inherited from his Irish mother, were bright and direct. The mouth was partly hidden by the huge handlebar mustache of the period, which gave the benign face the deceptively ferocious look of a German schnauzer. On a generous double chin rested a square, determined jaw which in earlier years was well able to take a punch when young Grover got involved in a barroom brawl. His voice was clear and powerful and his enunciation excellent. On the platform he usually stood with his left hand held behind his back, making sparse gestures with his right hand, a mannerism acquired in the courtroom when he addressed a jury at close range.

At the age of forty-four Cleveland was elected mayor of Buffalo, with the mandate to clean up the corrupt and extravagant city government. This he did—literally. He forced the city council to award the street-cleaning contract to the lowest bidder, taking it away from a crooked politician at a saving of $100,000. He made an even greater contribution to the general welfare when he cleaned up the city's antiquated sewer system and water supply. Statistics of the city health department showed that 36 per cent of the total mortality was caused by diseases bred in wells polluted by seeping sewers and privies. Cleveland initiated the construction of a new water-supply system and the closing of the contaminated wells under the supervision of a citizen's committee appointed by him. The following year he was elected governor of New York State, and in 1884 was nominated for the presidency on the Democratic ticket, against the bitter opposition of Tammany Hall. His Republican opponent was the well-known and able James G. Blaine.

Now began one of the most bitter and dirty political battles for the presidency ever waged, with no holds barred. Blaine was accused of political corruption. Cleveland was called a slacker and a lover of the South. A reporter dredged up a sensational scandal for the Republican newspaper headlines which proclaimed that the champion of the moral forces of the country was the father of a ten-year-old illegitimate son. The presidential candidate did not deny the story. The record showed that he had taken full responsibility for the upbringing and education of his son, who had been adopted by friends. Despite the dirty tactics of the opposition, Cleveland was elected, but only by a scant majority.

As President, Cleveland insisted upon giving personal attention to each of the seven hundred medical pension bills for Civil War veterans which Congress had passed during his administration. He had the courage to veto 233 of them for injuries not connected with military service. Among these were claims such as by a veteran who had broken his leg falling into a cellar, or another who had been thrown from a buggy, and by a man killed in a snow slide in Colorado twenty years after the war, and by still another who had been shot by a nearsighted neighbor aiming at an owl. In vetoing these bills the President drew down upon himself the wrath of the Grand Army of the Republic, supported by the Republican press.

In the second year of his first term, at the age of forty-nine, Cleveland married Frances Folsom, the twenty-two-year-old daughter of his good friend Oscar Folsom. The wedding took place in the White House. The marriage was a happy one, blessed with five children—three daughters and two sons. The first daughter was born in 1891 during the interval between Cleveland's two terms of office while he was practicing law in New York. His second and third daughters were born in the White House during his second term. The sons were born after his retirement to Princeton, the younger in 1903 when Cleveland was sixty-six years old.

Cleveland's later life was troubled with gout. At the funeral of General Grant in 1885, Cleveland was observed for the first time limping on his right leg. He had all the characteristics described as typical for most gout victims—corpulence, a sedentary profession, fondness for rich foods and alcoholic drinks.

In 1892 Cleveland was much handicapped in his presidential campaign by repeated attacks of gout and was able to make only a few personal appearances and public speeches. In 1901, at the funeral of President McKinley, he was observed to limp painfully, his right foot swathed in bandages. In a letter in 1907, he wrote that for a change gout had attacked his right thumb.

Cleveland's second administration, so successfully begun, soon became replete with frustrations and disappointments. The only act that brought him general public applause was when he pushed the button that opened the Columbian Exposition at Chicago on May Day, 1893.

After his retirement from the White House Cleveland found a berth at the University of Princeton, renowned for its liberal tradition; it bestowed upon him the honorary degree of Doctor of the Laws, and made him a trustee. Teachers and students esteemed him as a lecturer on public affairs.

Cleveland wrote numerous magazine articles in his spare time, among them several sketches on hunting and fishing, of which he was an enthusiast although overweight and short-winded.

As time went on the American people and the press gradually came to understand and appreciate the aims and achievements of Cleveland during his presidency. He became respected and loved throughout the country. In 1902 he was chosen to speak on the occasion of Woodrow Wilson's becoming President of Princeton University. That year President Theodore Roosevelt, in a nonpartisan gesture, asked Cleveland to serve as mediator in the great coal strike threatening the nation.

Always a devoted husband and father, Cleveland at Princeton had for the first time enough leisure to enjoy his family. Tragedy occurred when his twelve-year-old daughter Ruth died of diphtheria in 1904. The disease at first had been mistaken for tonsillitis but was recognized as diphtheria after four days. Only then was the child given diphtheria antitoxin, discovered by the German army surgoen, Emil von Behring, in 1891. The following morning the child suddenly died, probably resulting from paralysis of the heart muscle caused by the deadly diphtheria toxin, which the treatment with antitoxin was too late to prevent.

The sudden death of his eldest daughter was a great shock to Cleveland, who was deeply attached to the beautiful, bright and charming child. Three days after her death, Cleveland wrote, "I had a season of great trouble in keeping out of my mind the idea that Ruth was in the cold, cheerless grave instead of in the arms of her Saviour."

Cleveland's friends realized how deeply he suffered from the loss of his daughter. They urged him to return to politics once more to take his mind off his grief. In 1904, President Theodore Roosevelt was up for election to a second term. He was immensely popular, and there was no Democratic figure in sight who had a chance to beat him, except Grover Cleveland. Cleveland was adamant in his refusal to run for a third term. However, he was instrumental in the Democratic nomination of the irreproachable Judge Alton B. Parker, sidetracking the political ambitions of William Randolph Hearst.

Late in 1907 Cleveland's health started to decline. In the spring of 1908 he had to take to his bed, crippled with arthritis and a failing heart. He was still under the medical care of his faithful friend Dr. Bryant. During the month of June, Cleveland's condition became critical, and Dr. Bryant called in several consulting physicians. On the twenty-third the patient seemed to rally, but it was the last flicker of life which so often precedes death. The following morning the former President suddenly lapsed into unconsciousness, gasped for breath, and died. He was seventy-one. The immediate cause of death probably was a coronary thrombosis.

Benjamin Harrison

(1833 — 1901)

BENJAMIN HARRISON was the grandson of President William Henry Harrison and the second son of John Scott Harrison, who was Congressman and later governor of the Northwestern Territory. Benjamin was born in 1833 on a farm adjoining that of his grandfather, just below Cincinnati on the Ohio River.

He graduated with distinction from Miami University in 1852. During the following year he married a college friend, Caroline Lavinia Scott, and they had a son and a daughter. Admitted to the bar, he opened law offices in Indianapolis. In the tradition of his family, he became active in the Republican Party and an effective speaker.

In 1862 he helped in raising the 70th Indiana Infantry and became their colonel. As a strict disciplinarian, he made himself unpopular with the men in the barracks, but once in action, he won their respect by personal courage and coolness under fire, worthy of old Tippecanoe. Apparently his grandfather, who had studied medicine before becoming a soldier, had also left a medical tradition in the family, for Benjamin acted as an amateur surgeon in an emergency during the Civil War. It was after the bloody battle at Hope Church in 1864, when the regimental surgeons could not be located. Hundreds of moaning wounded were lying about unattended and the colonel took it upon himself to set up a first-aid station in a small farmhouse. Rolling up his sleeves, he went to work under the light of flickering candles, bandaging wounds, applying and loosening tourniquets, and administering opium pills, until at last the surgeons arrived.

At the age of thirty-two, he belatedly contracted a severe case of scarlet fever, which lasted three weeks, without aftereffects.

Harrison's active interest in politics continued after the war. He ran unsuccessfully for governor of Indiana in 1876, but won election as senator in 1881. In Congress he worked for generous pensions demanded by the veterans' lobby, which were vetoed by Cleveland, whom Harrison defeated in the presidential election of 1888.

Compared with his husky predecessor, the new President was not prepossessing. Only five feet six inches in height, he had a big torso, supported by short legs. His bearded face was plain and square, with white skin that never tanned. The one great asset he possessed was a high, melodious voice whose resonance carried his short, simple and logical speeches to his audience.

Although Harrison was a short man, he was strong and muscular, as he proved during a curious incident when he resided in the White House. One day a crazy young man broke into the executive mansion, threatening the President's life. Two doorkeepers could not subdue the madman, who knocked one of them down. Hearing the crashing of glass, Harrison hurried to the aid of his guards and quickly subdued the intruder by pinning his arms to his sides. He tied him up in a professional manner and handed him over to the police.

Harrison faithfully enforced the laws enacted by Congress. By not assuming personal leadership, and merely executing the resolutions of Congress, he was not burdened by the weight of responsibility. Thus, his store of vitality was not drained and he left office in better health than when he had entered it. However, in the summer of 1892, while living in the White House, Harrison's wife fell victim to a serious infectious disease, possibly typhoid, and died several weeks later.

At that time the White House was still a dangerous place to live in. Later on, in 1901, an effective start was made to drain and canalize the swampy basin of the Potomac. Previously, under Grant's administration, only part of the Tiber Creek, the "indescribable cesspool" stagnating behind the White House, had been filled up and covered. However, beyond the Washington

Monument remained the largest marshes of the district, teeming with mosquitoes and flies.

During Harrison's Presidency, when the disastrous Johnston flood occurred, the Potomac River and its branches overflowed their shallow banks, unprotected by dams. The flood reached Washington on June 2, 1889, carrying with it destruction and disease. In a few hours the greater part of town became half-submerged in the muddy waters. Pennsylvania Avenue, between the White House and the capitol, was transformed into a grand canal on which boats floated. When the sun reappeared, Washington looked like Venice. The old Centermarket stood out as a little island, its venerable church resembling San Marco on its glorious lagoon.

After his term ended, at the age of fifty-nine, Harrison was in good health for eight years. In 1896 he married his wife's niece, who bore him a daughter when he was sixty-four. In March 1901, he caught influenza, which started with the symptoms of a heavy cold. Three days later the infection exploded in a severe chill, followed by high fever and aching all over the body. His family physician prescribed bed rest, analgesics, and steam inhalations.

After two days the patient developed pain in the left side of the chest with rapid, labored respiration and a fast pulse. By tapping the chest with the finger tips and listening to the respiratory sounds with a stethoscope, the doctor found the density of the left lung increased, the bronchial tubes filled with inflammatory exudate, signs of pneumonia (recently renamed pneumonitis). The patient was given the traditional treatment employed until the discovery of sulfa drugs and antibiotics. Stimulants, such as digitalis and camphor, were administered for the heart, weakened by the toxins of the infection and struggling to force the blood through the obstructed channels of the left lung. In order to alleviate the work of the lungs in getting the needed oxygen, and the heart in pumping the oxygenated blood through the body, the President was given inhalation of pure oxygen. It was applied through a face mask from an iron tank, first at intervals, then in a continuous flow.

All efforts were in vain. The strong, sixty-seven-year-old man failed rapidly and died four days after the first chill from an influenza-pneumonitis, possibly complicated by a secondary invasion of deadly streptococci. It is interesting to note that Benjamin Harrison's presidential grandfather, William H. Harrison, had died from a similar type of pneumonitis approximately at the same age.

William McKinley

(1843 – 1901)

SIXTEEN years (four administrations) after Garfield's assassination, William McKinley became President. There are many parallels in their lives and careers. Like Garfield, McKinley was born in Ohio and also served with distinction in the Civil War, being promoted to major at twenty-two.

Both men were professional politicians in the Republican Party. Their careers ran such a similar course that McKinley succeeded his older colleague in some important political positions. At thirty-five, he was elected congressman, serving for twelve years. In 1880 he replaced Garfield as member of the Ways and Means Committee; later on, as spokesman for the party. In 1891 McKinley was elected Governor of Ohio, and in 1896 President of the United States.

Though there were many similarities in their careers, they were different types physically. Garfield at fifty was tall and athletic; McKinley at fifty-five was large, fat and flabby, with an inherent weakness of the cardiovascular system.

Like Garfield, McKinley was shot by a paranoic madman incapable of a real political motive. The name of McKinley's assassin was Czolgosz, who, like Guiteau, was small, slender, and single. He was twenty-eight years old, and up to the age of twenty-five had behaved normally. Then he went through an acute phase of schizophrenia. It changed him from an industrious, average young man into a lazy loafer who always complained of feeling sleepy and sick. As a machinist in his earlier years he had come in contact with socialist and Marxist labor leaders. After the development of his psychosis he came under the spell of the high-sounding phrases of the prophets of anarchism without understanding their meaning, and he conceived the glorious dream of becoming a hero by performing some great feat for the benefit of the working class.

In 1901, the sensational news of the assassination of the Italian King Humbert by an anarchist threw Czolgosz into a state of high elation. He read and reread a crudely illustrated clipping of the shooting. Gradually the idea took shape in his brain that he should assassinate the American President, the equivalent of the Italian king. In time this idea assumed an obsessive compulsive character.

After careful preparation, Czolgosz awaited his opportunity, and found it on September 6, 1901. President McKinley was then visiting the Pan-American Exposition at Buffalo. Against the advice of his staff, he held a public reception in the Temple of Music that afternoon. He was wearing a black frock coat, black tie, white vest and dark trousers. In his pockets he carried a well-worn silver nugget and a battered coin—good-luck pieces. The President was guarded in a haphazard fashion. The neatly dressed, impassive Czolgosz, his right hand wrapped in a white handkerchief, did not arouse suspicion; he had no trouble joining the line to shake the President's hand.

It was seven minutes past four o'clock. The majestic strains of organ music by Bach floated through the high-domed temple when the assassin came face to face with the President. He quickly fired two shots through the handkerchief from a short-barreled 32-caliber revolver, at such close range that the powder scorched the President's white vest. Before he could empty the barrel, Czolgosz was knocked down and disarmed.

A look of incredulous astonishment came over the face of the stricken President. He shivered and straightened up to his full height, then slumped into the arms of his secretary.

He was taken immediately by electric ambulance to the emergency hospital on the exposition grounds, and placed upon the table in the operating room. As he was being undressed for examination, a bullet fell from his clothing. This was the first bullet, which had been deflected by a button and had merely grazed the skin between the second and third ribs. The second bullet was found to have entered the upper abdomen, to the left of the midline.

Dr. G. McK. Hall, who was in charge of the hospital, covered the wounds with antiseptic dressings and had his nurse administer a hypo of morphine, one-sixth of a grain, and one-sixtieth grain of strychnine. Dr. Herman Mynter, a local physician, Dr. Eugene Wasdin of the U.S. Marine Hospital, along with several other doctors, arrived after a short while. All agreed that an immediate operation was necessary. Dr. Matthew D. Mann, an experienced local surgeon, was summoned to perform the surgery. He arrived at 5:10 P.M.

At 5:20 Dr. Wasdin started the anesthetic with ether which he dropped on a gauze mask. While the anesthetic was being given, Dr. Mann, Dr. Mynter, with two other doctors and two nurses who were to assist with the operation, prepared their hands and arms by thoroughly scrubbing them with soap and water, then immersing them in a solution of bichloride of mercury. Rubber gloves were not yet in general use.

President McKinley took the ether well and was under its influence within nine minutes. The abdomen was shaved, scrubbed with green soap, and then washed with ether and mercury bichloride solution. Surgeons and nurses wore steam-sterilized gowns, and the surgical field was surrounded with sterile towels. Dr. Mann carefully probed the wound in the left upper quadrant of the abdomen, and found that it penetrated deeply in a direction somewhat downward and outward.

He made an incision four inches long, downward from the edge of the ribs, across the bullet wound. Below the skin, he found and removed a piece of cloth from the President's coat. The incision was developed through a layer of fat two inches thick, and through the other layers of fascia, muscle, and peritoneum. In the anterior wall of the stomach, close to its inferior border, a small bullet-size opening was visible. It was closed with two layers of silk sutures. A larger hole was found on the back wall of the stomach. In order to get a better exposure of the second opening, the incision in the abdominal wall had to be enlarged to six inches. The lower attachment of the stomach was then divided, the stomach turned over, and the hole also closed with two layers of silk sutures.

Then Dr. Mann introduced his hand up to the elbow in order to palpate carefully all the structures behind the stomach, without locating the bullet or its path. Introducing the hand and feeling around seemed to have an unfavorable influence on the President's pulse, which was already fast and weak, indicating mild shock. Dr. Mann therefore had to desist from further exploration.

The question of drainage was discussed. Dr. Mynter was in favor of putting a gauze drain behind the posterior wall of the stomach and letting it emerge through the skin. However, Dr. Mann and the two other assistant doctors held that drainage was unnecessary.

Before closing the abdomen, the peritoneal cavity was washed out with warm saline solution. As the last stage of the operation, the tissues around the bullet track in the abdominal wall were trimmed, as being potentially infected. The abdominal wound was closed with seven through-and-through silkworm gut sutures. The fascia was joined with a buried catgut suture, and the edges of the skin brought together with fine catgut sutures. The incision was then washed with hydrogen peroxide, covered with an antiseptic powder, and dressed with sterile gauze and cotton, which were held in place with adhesive strips.

The difficulties of the operation were very great. The emergency hospital was not equipped for major surgery and there was a lack of adequate instruments for an abdominal operation. The main handicap arose from the poor lighting of the operating room. A few blocks from the hospital was the chief attraction of the exposition, the Tower of Light, a miracle of the time, exhibiting 35,000 incandescent electric lights invented twenty-two years previously by Edison. But only a few weak electric bulbs had been spared for the hospital. The setting sun shone directly into the room, but not into the wound. The windows were low and covered with awnings.

Fortunately, the President's family physician, Dr. P. M. Rixey, who had arrived shortly after the operation had started, produced a hand mirror with which he reflected the sunlight into the operative wound. The great size of President McKinley's abdomen and the amount of fat present necessitated working at the bottom of a deep hole. Towards the end of the operation the daylight was fading and a red glow from the Tower of Light shone dimly through the windows. Luckily, one moveable electric light with a reflector was found in the hospital. Thus the surgeons were able to complete an accurate closure of the incision.

The operation was concluded at 6:50 P.M., having lasted one hour and twenty-one minutes. At the beginning, the pulse rate had been 84. It rose during the surgery to 124. The patient was given a hypodermic of morphine, and was removed by electric ambulance to the mansion of the director of the exposition, John G. Milburn, at 1168 Delaware Avenue, where a hospital bed had been prepared in a corner room.

During the next twenty-four hours the pulse rose at times above 140; the rectal temperature went up as high as 102.5°, and the respiration to 28, but the general condition was considered satisfactory. The patient was kept comfortable with small doses of morphine by injection, and was given digitalis for the heart. Small retention enemas of saline in water were kept up at regular intervals to supply the necessary fluids. However, the urinary output was insufficient.

During the following night the President's pulse rate ranged between 130 and 140, the respiratory rate was between 24 and 27; the highest temperature was 102.8°. On the morning of the third day, Dr. Charles McBurney, a famous New York surgeon, arrived and examined the patient in consultation with Dr. Mann. He approved the handling of the case and gave a favorable prognosis.

During the day, normal bowel action was obtained with enemas, and the patient received several doses of strychnine by hypo and digitalis by mouth in an attempt to slow up the heart action. In the afternoon the President was given small sips of warm water and retention enemas containing egg, whisky and water. His fluid output was still less than one pint of highly concentrated urine within twenty-four hours, which is about half the minimum requirement.

During the next two days the President seemed to improve steadily. Temperature, pulse and respiration dropped to a lower level, but were still moderately elevated. The so-called "nutritive" enemas were continued and he was given increasing amounts of warm water by mouth.

The outlook seemed so favorable that the mercurial Vice-President, Theodore Roosevelt, who had been called to the President's bedside, hurried off again to go climbing in the Adirondacks.

On the evening of the fifth day, Dr. Mann changed the dressing and examined the wound. It showed some slight discharge, indicating a low-grade infection. Four skin stitches were removed for better drainage, and the remainder of the superficial stitches on the next day, when the improvement seemed to continue. Thereafter the wound was dressed three times a day, irrigated with hydrogen peroxide, and covered with the antiseptic mixture of Peruvian balsam and glycerine.

On the sixth day the President rested comfortably. He was given beef juice in teaspoon dosages, which his stomach tolerated well. The urinary output became more satisfactory. The doctors were overjoyed and believed that all danger had passed. The chief consultant, Dr. McBurney, returned home to New York on the morning of the seventh day. However, the fever chart showed silent forebodings of a relapse to come. The temperature and respiratory rate remained elevated; the pulse started climbing again.

There was a public clamor for an examination of the patient by X-ray, discovered six years before, to determine the location of the bullet. In fact, a cumbersome X-ray machine was hauled to the improvised hospital. But the doctors decided it would be too dangerous to move the patient from his bed and subject him to such an extended and complicated procedure as taking an X-ray picture required at that time. They made the announcement that an X-ray examination was considered neither necessary nor advisable.

In the morning of the seventh day, the President was permitted to take chicken broth, a small piece of toast and a cup of coffee, all of which he relished. The apparent improvement of his condition continued until noon, when the doctors became aware of the ominous rise of the pulse. They resumed dosing the patient with digitalis and strychnine. In the afternoon, McKinley complained of headache, nausea and great fatigue. He was given whisky and water, and then beef juice, but he could not force down the soft-boiled egg and toast offered him. He became more and more drowsy and restless, and his mind wandered at times. The doctors thought the cause might be an "intestinal toxemia" for which they gave the patient calomel and two doses of castor oil, followed by a high enema of ox gall. In spite of good bowel action and repeated doses of digitalis and strychnine, the pulse became steadily faster and weaker.

At 11 P.M. the President was given for the first time a pint of normal saline solution, subcutaneously. At midnight it became obvious that his condition was steadily deteriorating. He received strychnine and whisky at intervals, and hypodermics of camphorated oil.

At 2:50 A.M., of the eighth day, a bulletin was issued declaring the patient's condition as very serious, giving rise to the gravest apprehension. Stimulants were administered, as before. He was given brandy by subcutaneous injections. Also, the newly discovered hormone of the adrenal gland, adrenalin, was injected several times. In the forenoon, about one quart of normal saline solution was given under the skin. Still the pulse grew steadily weaker, and the President became somnolent. At 5 P.M., oxygen was administered.

At 6 P.M., a pint of saline solution containing adrenalin was injected subcutaneously. At 6:35 and 7:40 P.M., morphine by hypo was administered as the President exhibited the frantic restlessness of the dying man who struggled to escape death, unconsciously feeling its approach. The President continued to sink. At 8 o'clock he became pulseless; at 9, the heart sounds were barely audible. The patient was in deep coma. At 10 P.M., the oxygen was discontinued. He died at 2:15 A.M., on September 14.

Autopsy showed that the two bullet wounds in the stomach were well closed. Firm adhesions had formed, reinforcing the suture line. There were no indications of peritonitis. However, the stomach wall around both suture lines showed signs of necrosis. According to the pathologist's report, this might have been the result of autodigestion by the stomach juice, a terminal or postmortem condition.

After piercing the stomach, the bullet grazed the right kidney and injured the right adrenal gland. A large cavity of tissue destruction was found in the retroperitoneal fat, involving part of the pancreas—the large digestive gland behind the stomach.

Microscopic and bacteriologic examination revealed an extensive necrosis of about half the pancreas, but without evidence of bacterial infection. The heart muscle showed fatty degeneration and "brown atrophy."

The main cause of death was the destruction of the pancreas, leading to an overwhelming absorption of toxic decomposition products. The most important contributory factor was the degeneration of the heart muscle.

The autopsy continued for a longer period than was anticipated by those who had charge of the President's body, and the pathologists were requested to desist from seeking the bullet and to terminate the autopsy. Even today such a request is not unusual, the schedule and routine of the undertaker often being considered more important than the curiosity of the pathologist.

It is difficult to estimate whether modern surgical methods could have saved McKinley. Even today, pancreas necrosis produced by trauma carries a high percentage of mortality. It is possible that drainage of the area behind the stomach, as had been recommended by Dr. Mynter, could have drawn some of the toxic material to the outside and prevented its fatal absorption.

By modern standards the postoperative treatment was inadequate. The patient did not receive enough fluids, vitally necessary electrolytes, and hardly any proteins and vitamins, essential to the vital functions and the healing process, which at present can be administered by the intravenous route. It is certain that modern surgical and postoperative methods would have given McKinley a better chance of survival.

The assassination of McKinley and the fact that he was the third of nine Presidents murdered within thirty-six years shattered public illusion that a Chief Executive was necessarily sacrosanct or safe. Apparently a more competent system of protection was necessary.

Soon after Theodore Roosevelt took office, the Secretary of the Treasury directed the United States Secret Service, a section of the Treasury Department, to assume full-time responsibility for protecting the life of the President.

Theodore Roosevelt

(1858 — 1919)

THEODORE ROOSEVELT was the most forceful and aggressive President since Andrew Jackson and equally colorful and popular. Both men were born fighters and leaders of men, who underwent the trial of chronic disease before they matured. Though T.R. resembled Jackson in aggressiveness and temperament, he vied with Jefferson in versatility and variety of interests. Roosevelt himself felt a kinship with the stormy Hickory, the man of the people, but disliked the Sage of Monticello, a man with a background similar to his own. Theodore Roosevelt had no understanding of the agrarian philosophy and the Olympian world view of Jefferson, the exponent of the humanistic renaissance of the eighteenth century. Teddy was the typical representative of industrialized America at the turn of the nineteenth century, which suddenly had grown into a young giant among the world powers, bursting with vitality and self-assurance.

Roosevelt was born in New York City on October 27, 1858, the second of four children of Theodore and Martha Bulloch Roosevelt. Six generations of the Dutch Roosevelts before him were identified with Manhattan, and the most recent of them were well-to-do. Teddy's mother was born in Georgia of Scotch-Huguenot and English extraction. The chance mixture of different racial strains accounted for the multicolored personality of Teddy Roosevelt. Among his inherited characteristics he also displayed certain traits of degeneration such as a congenital form of nearsightedness and a severe bronchial allergy, from which his younger sister also suffered.

He was only an infant when he developed violent attacks of bronchial asthma. This condition is caused by a swelling of the mucous lining of the small bronchial branches with secretion of mucus. Concurrently the air tubes become spastically contracted, impeding the breathing, particularly expiration. The spells are brought on by certain irritating substances, called allergens, inhaled or else carried by the blood stream, such as derivatives from some foods. Nervous and emotional stimuli can also trigger attacks of asthma.

Such episodes occurred during Teddy's childhood at frequent intervals. He would be suddenly aroused from a sound sleep by a feeling of suffocation, gasping for breath, his face a bluish white. He had not even enough breath left for a loud cry. Only a low moan would accompany his wheezing, rattling expiration. His parents fed the frightened child all kinds of soothing syrups which he could hardly swallow; they let him inhale the suffocating fumes of stramonium (Jimson weed) leaves or steam from a kettle scented with aromatics. These medications only resulted in a croupy cough. The exhausted and sleepy little patient could not catch his breath when lying down, and for many nights could only find comfort and sleep in his father's arms.

Roosevelt's asthma continued throughout his childhood and adolescence. The attacks were not limited to the pollen seasons in summer and fall but occurred also in winter and spring. Often they were accompanied by diarrheas, indicating that the intestinal canal was also sensitive to some allergens.

Over the years all kinds of nostrums were tried on the patient. Quacks recommended the smoking of cigars, which made the panting little fellow only more miserable by nauseating him. More effective was the coffee treatment, the caffeine from a strong cup of coffee at times arresting an attack at the cost of a sleepless night.

In 1869 the Roosevelts took a trip abroad, hoping that a change of climate would benefit their two asthmatic children. They visited Paris, the Riviera, Italy, Austria and Germany. For little Ted the journey meant a succession of asthma attacks and diarrheas, relieved by a few breathing spells in mountain resorts, where the air had a lower atmospheric pressure and contained less dust and pollen. A second trip to the dry climate of Egypt and the Holy Land during 1872 and 1873 was better tolerated by Teddy. During the summer of 1873 the four children were left for a while with a German family in Dresden. In the damp old city the boy got another asthma spell and had to be taken to a spa in the hills to recuperate.

Even if these travels in foreign countries did not help Roosevelt's asthma, they certainly left a lasting impression on him, lifting his horizon beyond American provincialism and giving him an awareness of the characteristics of different nations and a foundation for his knowledge of global politics as President.

Compared with Roosevelt's severe allergy, the childhood diseases of chicken pox, measles and mumps were almost pleasant experiences and left no aftereffects. The recurrent attacks of bronchial asthma during his formative years set up a lasting pattern of responses in Roosevelt's personality. The terrifying experience of feeling the invisible constriction in his chest, and the desperate struggle for breath in the dark sickroom, instilled in him a yearning for the outdoors, where he could fill his thirsty lungs with clean drafts of fresh air. It was possibly in reaction to these frightening childhood impressions that Roosevelt as an adult courted danger—as if to prove to himself that he had conquered his deep-seated fearfulness.

Teddy's respiratory and digestive allergies retarded his physical development. He was a pale, thin boy, small for his age, with skinny legs, eager blue eyes and sandy hair. Also, one of the family traits was his protruding teeth; orthodontics was still unknown. In his later life, Roosevelt hid them under his walrus mustache.

His father was a leonine man who encouraged his asthenic son to build up his body by systematic exercise. He installed a private gymnasium on the open-air porch of his brownstone house in New York. There, under the direction of instructors, Teddy applied himself patiently day by day, year by year, lifting the weights, doing pull-ups on the rings, and working out on the parallel bars. In time the narrow-chested youth who looked like a scarecrow transformed himself into a big, muscular, broad-shouldered man.

Another weakness that molded Roosevelt's character was his extreme nearsightedness. Because he was taught by private tutors and did not sit on public school benches, his myopia was not discovered until he was thirteen years old. Before this, his vision served for writing and reading, which he did voraciously. At a distance he could only discern vague outlines of objects, and was a clumsy playmate whom the other children teased. His defective vision was first recognized when he was being taught by his father to shoot a rifle. He could not focus the sights.

Fitted with thick-lensed glasses, Teddy practiced target shooting with double determination until he became a crack shot. To compensate for the humiliation caused by his weakness and awkwardness as a child, he developed a compulsion to excel in games and sports that called for strength, endurance and skill, such as boxing, wrestling, obstacle riding and mountain climbing. Despite the thick lenses and unorthodox style, he even became an acceptable tennis player.

At Harvard, Roosevelt made Phi Beta Kappa, and graduated in 1880 without having decided on a career. History and politics interested him. In 1882 he published his first book, on the naval war of 1812, starting a prolific rather than artistic literary career.

In 1878, his father died from a condition diagnosed as intestinal obstruction by a fast-growing malignant tumor, on which the doctors of the time did not dare to operate.

Following his graduation, Theodore married Alice Lee, who died four years later from unknown puerperal complications following the birth of their daughter Alice. His mother died of typhoid fever only twelve hours after his wife's death. The twenty-six-year-old Roosevelt was left alone with his baby. During the years of his marriage his asthma had much improved and his attacks occurred at lengthening intervals. His profound grief brought on a severe relapse combined with a persistent hacking cough, causing suspicion that he might be developing tuberculosis of the lungs. On the doctors' advice he went west and bought a ranch in North Dakota.

It was with some reluctance that he left, because he had to give up a promising political career as assemblyman of the 21st District at Albany, where he had taken up the good fight against the evils of corruption in government. Soon his love of nature and the wide-open spaces made young Roosevelt feel at home at the ranch. He threw himself enthusiastically into the unaccustomed role of cowboy and in time became an expert at branding the calves and breaking in the horses.

During this period his long history of accidents and broken bones began. He fractured an arm when he was thrown from a bucking broncho, and a few months later a shoulder blade when a rearing horse fell on top of him. Always a Spartan, Roosevelt was undaunted by such trifles and forever retained a glowing memory of his life in the West. With restless energy he wrote thousands of pages about the West and its history.

But he was not satisfied with roughing it on the ranch. Roosevelt occasionally took a vacation and participated in the bone-breaking sport of fox hunting on Long Island. On one occasion the run crossed unusually rough country, with the result that before the contest was over, half the gay party were ready for the hospital. The host had dislocated his knee; a guest had broken several ribs; Teddy's brother-in-law had torn half the skin off his face and been knocked unconscious. As for Roosevelt, his mount struck the top rail of a five-foot fence, fell heavily and rolled over his rider on a heap of stones. The indestructible horseman got up, his face covered with blood from cuts and bruises, his left hand hanging limp from a fractured wrist. He remounted and continued for another five miles, taking twenty more fences and catching up with the survivors of the slaughter. That night he went out to dinner, proudly exhibiting his bandaged head and arm in a plaster cast. The next day he walked for three hours in the woods.

His bones mended, his mind and body refreshed, Roosevelt returned in 1886 to New York and his political career. In the same year he married Edith Kermit Carow. They had four sons and a daughter, whom the father taught from early youth the Spartan principles in which he believed.

In 1889 Roosevelt was appointed Civil Service Commissioner by President Benjamin Harrison. In this position he continued his life-long fight for good government. With his honest efforts he combined a native genius for personal publicity which made him good copy. In 1895 he accepted the position of Police Commissioner in New York and with his usual vigor tackled the unholy alliance of politics, graft and crime, exposing them to the light of day regardless of friend or foe.

President McKinley appointed him Assistant Secretary of the Navy in 1897. Anticipating the Spanish-American War, Roosevelt ordered a crash program of naval target practice. In February 1898, as acting Secretary, he cabled Admiral Dewey exact instructions for offensive operations in the Philippines. After war was declared in May, Roosevelt could not endure sitting behind a desk in Washington letting others get the excitement and glory. He promptly resigned from his office to participate in the combat. Together with Colonel Leonard Wood he organized the first United States Voluntary Cavalry, called the "Rough Riders," and led the famous charge up Cattle Hill at San Juan. As he led the spectacular attack, he was armed not only with a revolver, but also with a dozen pair of spectacles in their metal cases distributed all over his pockets.

The casualties of the Cuban campaign were comparatively small; however, the losses from sickness were staggering. The trouble started at the point of mobilization at Tampa, Florida, where the expeditionary force was severely stricken with food poisoning from spoiled canned rations and with typhoid fever from poor sanitation. In Cuba, sporadic cases of yellow fever and numerous ones of dysentery swelled the sick list. But the most devastating plague was a tropical form of malaria which almost forced the withdrawal of the attacking army from Santiago de Cuba.

After the city was captured, the commanding general begged the War Department in Washington to permit the removal of the army from the pest-ridden area. This request was denied and the forces seemed doomed to be wiped out by the epidemics.

Because General Shaffer could not make the officials in Washington understand the gravity of the situation, Roosevelt, who had no army career to risk, went over the heads of his superiors directly to the press, and by public pressure forced the hand of the War Department, thus saving the expeditionary force from possible destruction.

Like Julius Caesar, Roosevelt was his own press agent and did not understate his own exploits. He returned to the United States like a conquering hero who, singlehanded, had defeated the enemy. Even the kindly McKinley remarked that nobody got so much out of the war as Theodore Roosevelt.

As a public hero he was elected governor of New York in January, 1899. He immediately went to work fighting against the spoils system and for taxation of corporation franchises. Unable to stop the aggressive reformer, who had the public on his side, the special interests and political bosses looked for a way of making him innocuous. They figured that it would be best to kick him upstairs into the silent obscurity of the Vice-Presidency, where the obstreperous hero would have four years of oblivion.

In a political deal, the Republican leaders of New York and Chicago forced him on President McKinley as running mate. The Colonel, as he liked to be called, saw through the scheme, which was meant to be his political grave, and hesitated several weeks accepting the nomination. Finally, popular pressure and party loyalty induced him to bow to what appeared to be the end of his career. But even as Vice-President he succeeded in keeping his name alive by publishing a book of verbose essays and addresses.

The assassination of McKinley hastened the fulfillment of Roosevelt's destiny as President, hurdling him over the entrenched interests. In his inauguration speech he promised to continue the cautious policy of his predecessor. But being the man he was, he could not follow in anybody's footsteps; he had to plot his own course and set his own pace.

His achievements in this direction are history: the enforcement of the Sherman Anti-Trust Law; the regulation of railroad rates; the reclamation and preservation of national resources; and the Pure Food and Drug Act, so important for the public health. In international politics he paved the way for building the Panama Canal; mediated the peace between Russia and Japan; was instrumental in the Conference of Algeciras, postponing World War I for eight years; and truly deserved the Nobel Peace Prize he received in 1906.

In spite of all his hard work as President he still found time to spend two hours every day on strenuous physical exercise. One day as he was boxing with a young captain, his opponent forgot to pull his punches, and hit Roosevelt's left eye. The blow caused a hemorrhage, followed by a detachment of the retina and almost total blindness. Thereafter, the President stopped boxing and took up ju jitsu. A chain of other accidents followed. Once he was almost killed when his horse somersaulted and he landed on his head. Three times during 1904 he injured a leg, once tearing a muscle of his thigh and causing a considerable hemorrhage.

Not all of Roosevelt's accidents came about in the pursuit of sport. Some of them were due to the haste with which he always moved. In 1902 the carriage in which he was riding collided with a trolley car, killing a secret service man beside him and throwing the President forty feet. The severe impact injured one of his thigh bones; an infection followed and necessitated surgical treatment. The leg injury gave him trouble for the rest of his life, flaring up on several occasions.

After leaving the White House in 1909 the Colonel went on an African safari and shot innumerable animals. He described his adventures in voluminous letters and articles in magazines and newspapers. Returned from his trip, he learned of the growing split between the conservative wing of the Republican party toward which President Taft was leaning, and the progressive elements favoring him. Thus it came to a break between the two friends. When the Republican convention in 1912 steam-rollered Taft's nomination for a second term, Roosevelt bolted the party and became candidate of a third, "Progressive," party. From the remark of the former President that he felt "as fit as a bull moose," this ungainly ruminant became the symbol of the new party and gave it its popular name.

In his campaign against Taft, Roosevelt showed the hostility of a bad conscience and stooped to personal invective against his old friend. At times he seemed to be intoxicated by his own oratory and ranted almost incoherently, as if drunk. His enemies made capital of this impression, calling him a drunkard. Actually, Roosevelt hardly ever touched liquor and drank only light wines in moderation. The former President's raving got on the nerves of cultured Henry Adams, in whose veins the acid of his ancestors flowed, and he quipped: "Roosevelt is never sober, only he is drunk with himself, and not with rum."

During the campaign Roosevelt was shadowed by a paranoiac, John Schrank, whose sick brain created a drama in which he was to be the hero. The spectacular T.R. was the most publicized figure at the time, and stalking him gave the shy little man a feeling of self-importance. To shoot him down would give him for one moment the sense of ecstatic power and make the world take notice of him at last. In John Schrank's dream-world delusions, the ghost of McKinley appeared to him, pointing to Roosevelt as his, McKinley's, murderer and asking him to avenge his death. To rationalize his crime, he convinced himself that it was his sacred duty to uphold tradition against a third term, which his villain was flouting. His mental regression was also evident in the banal poems he wrote, which were almost as incoherent as those of Guiteau, Garfield's assassin.

His opportunity came on the evening of October 14, 1912, in Milwaukee, when he could approach his target at a distance of six feet, in front of a hotel. He had a .38 Colt, which could not fail to hit Roosevelt as he stood there waving at the crowd. The Colonel felt something hot strike his chest, without being aware of much pain. The impact made him stagger back but he braced himself and did not fall. Before Schrank could fire a second shot he was bowled over by Roosevelt's secretary, a former college football tackle.

The bullet had struck Roosevelt in the right breast close to the nipple and passed upward and medially about four inches, fracturing the fourth rib but not entering the pleural cavity. As the madman was being dragged away, the Colonel put his hand to his lips and coughed. Not finding blood on his fingers, he knew that his lungs were not injured and the wound was not critical.

A Colt fired at such short range has great penetrating power and the bullet would certainly have torn the lungs and probably the large vessels of the heart if it had not been impeded by the contents of Roosevelt's bulging breast pocket. The bullet pierced one of his numerous metal spectacle cases, then passed through the manuscript of his prepared speech that was loosely folded to fit the pocket, serving as a bulletproof vest. Unquestionably it was the most effective speech of Roosevelt's career.

Always an actor, Roosevelt rose to the occasion. He insisted upon being driven to the auditorium instead of the hospital and to deliver his scheduled speech. As he opened his coat to take out the bullet-pierced manuscript, his blood-soaked shirt became visible, arousing a wild frenzy among the large audience. In his excitement Roosevelt hardly looked at his script, but extemporaneously delivered a rambling address lasting fifty minutes, directing his blasts at random against the trusts, the Standard Oil Company, and the Republican bosses.

During the harangue the speaker's friends formed a circle around the podium ready to catch the bleeding Colonel in case he collapsed. Exhausted, but still on his feet, he was finally prevailed upon to end his speech and be taken to the hospital. There, several doctors examined him, among them Dr. Joseph C. Bloodgood of the Johns Hopkins Hospital, who happened to be in the audience. Roosevelt knew the doctor, greeted him warmly and asked him to look after him. "I do not want to fall into the hands of too many doctors and have the same experience that McKinley and Garfield had." Dr. Bloodgood expressed his regret at not being able to treat the Colonel, since he was not on home grounds. He advised him to take the short trip to Chicago and entrust himself to the famous surgeon John B. Murphy.

Roosevelt agreed. Dr. Bloodgood personally called John B. Murphy's home and arranged for the examination. In the meantime, three other well-meaning friends of Roosevelt had called their own favorite surgeons—Drs. Bevan, McArthur, and Ochsner, all of whom were waiting at the railroad station to receive the illustrious patient at the scheduled time.

By some curious mixup Roosevelt arrived on a special train three hours earlier and was met by Dr. Murphy, who took him to his own hospital without notifying his colleagues. This questionable behavior of Dr. J. B. Murphy, who was not noted for consideration toward his confrères, led to serious charges against him before the American Medical Association. He was accused (but afterward exonerated) of "stealing" the patient and deliberately seeking notoriety.

Contrary to the surgical practice used with disastrous consequences on President Garfield, Dr. Murphy did not probe Roosevelt's wound, thus avoiding the risk of carrying bacteria from the outside into the wound. He took X-ray pictures which revealed the location of the bullet outside the pleura, imbedded in the fractured fourth rib. He decided not to attempt removing the bullet by surgery unless an infection set in making it necessary.

The patient received a prophylactic injection of tetanus antitoxin, in general use since the end of the nineteenth century, introduced by Emil von Bering, who also had discovered the diphtheria antitoxin. The fractured rib caused pain in breathing, which was relieved by strapping the chest, bed rest and mild sedatives. No complications occurred. The external wound healed promptly. After a week, the patient felt so well that he could leave for his home in Oyster Bay, Long Island.

Just two weeks after his injury, Roosevelt made two major campaign speeches before capacity crowds in Madison Square Garden. The American people admired Teddy's pluck, but at the polls they elected Woodrow Wilson, the Democratic candidate, over the split opposition. Roosevelt carried the lead bullet in his chest for the rest of his life. It became well encapsulated and never troubled him.

Roosevelt took his defeat in good grace and looked for other outlets for the overflowing energy that could not be contained in a life of leisure. This in spite of a chronic rheumatoid arthritis from which he had been suffering for years. Now, at the age of fifty-four, it crippled him a good deal, and often prevented him from doing his daily stint of exercises. As a consequence, he became too fat around his waistline but was not Spartan enough to control his gargantuan appetite.

According to a friend he ate like a trencherman. It was not unusual for him to consume a whole chicken with trimmings all by himself, and wash it down with four big glasses of milk. He also drank great quantities of coffee and tea. He had his special coffee cup, described as being more like a bathtub. Its contents required five to seven lumps of sugar for sweetening. Eventually, Roosevelt made the usual show of reducing by substituting saccharine.

Though overweight and rheumatic, he retained great endurance in all physical activities. In 1913 he was invited on a lecture tour to South America and wanted to use the occasion for undertaking a spectacular geographical exploration, to satisfy his spirit of adventure and his craving for the limelight. Aside from these motivations, he was all his life genuinely interested in natural science, geography, zoology and botany. He selected as his goal the River of Doubt, one of the tributaries of the Amazon River, whose origin and course had never been mapped. With the support of the Brazilian government he rashly organized an expedition which was supposed to last some six weeks, but took almost eight months.

Different versions of the adventure have been given, the most credible one by his son and faithful companion, Kermit. From the start the party was beset by bad luck and illness. One man was drowned; a second went berserk and killed a member of the party. The journey took much longer than expected. A third of the food supply was used up with only one-sixth of the distance covered. For forty-seven days they did not meet another human being. They lost part of their baggage and were left without clothes except what they wore, daily drenched by the tropical rains then steamed dry on their backs. Occasionally the rains kept up and they had to lie all night in their soaking-wet clothes.

Roosevelt developed a tropical fever resembling the malaria he had contracted fifteen years before in Cuba, resistant to quinine. One day, in his weakened condition, he jumped into the rapids to save two canoes from being smashed against the rocks. He was banged against a sharp stone and received a deep gash, on the same thigh he had injured eleven years before. The wound became infected, the leg started to swell and drain pus, either from a new or a reactivated infection of the thigh bone. A veritable plague of deep abscesses developed, probably from a spread of the infection through the blood stream, and was followed by symptoms of dysentery.

For days he lay in his boat, floating down river half dead in the blazing sun. Fortunately, the toxins from the severe infection eased his torture by numbing his brain with the fog of delirium. To the surprise of his companions he survived and was carried on a stretcher out of the jungle, after the expedition had almost been given up as lost.

The damaged leg never healed. The suppuration of the bone recurred at intervals, with the separation of little sequesters of dead bone and the formation of draining fistulas which often had to be reopened when they closed up. In addition to his infected leg, the penetrating dampness of the jungle had aggravated Roosevelt's chronic rheumatism. His only reward was the honor of having the River of Doubt named for him—the Rio Roosevelt.

In February 1918 the crippled Colonel contracted a severe throat infection that spread to both middle ears. He was taken to the Roosevelt Hospital (also named for him) in New York. The admitting diagnosis was "bilateral acute otitis media, inflammatory rheumatism, and abscess of the thigh." The pain in both ears was getting worse, the fever climbing, and it was necessary to pierce both ear drums to release the pus which had formed behind them. After ten days, the right ear was drying up, but the left ear continued discharging pus. X-ray pictures showed that the suppurative process had infiltrated the cavities of the mastoid bone behind the ear.

At that time, as today, the accepted treatment for mastoiditis with pus formation was surgical opening of the bone for better drainage. In Roosevelt's case the physicians in charge did not perform this operation, with the consequence that the left ear continued running, without completely draining the pus, which was what gradually destroyed the middle ear. Thus at the age of sixty, Roosevelt was deaf in the left ear, in addition to being blind in the left eye.

There must have been some reason why the undoubtedly competent doctors did not advise simple mastoidectomy, the opening and direct drainage of the bone. They must have suspected that the rheumatic ailment of the patient was not rheumatoid arthritis, but recurrent rheumatic fever with silent involvement of the heart. Any major surgery under such conditions might have stirred up a progressive inflammation and destruction of the valves of the heart. The physicians preferred not to take such a risk and treated the running ear conservatively with gentle irrigations and instillations of weak antiseptic solutions.

As Roosevelt's health improved, his old wanderlust awakened once more. He returned to his beloved Middle West. The unavoidable motion and friction of his chronically infected thigh during the journey brought on a severe infection of erysipelas, a type of streptococcus that spread through the subcutaneous tissue, producing a rose-colored swelling and blistering of the skin. Before the discovery of the sulfa drugs and antibiotics, it used to carry a considerable mortality by causing blood poisoning. Roosevelt recovered, however, to receive a few weeks later the crushing news that his youngest son, Quentin, serving in the Air Corps in France, had been shot down and killed shortly before Armistice.

Roosevelt's grief aggravated the pain in his muscles and joints, which became so severe that he had to be readmitted to the hospital with the diagnosis of inflammatory rheumatism.

The current attack caused him more pain than ever before, particularly in his lower back and his legs. After a while his condition improved and he was discharged in time to celebrate Christmas with his family in his beloved refuge at Oyster Bay. For ten days he felt better and his old cheerfulness returned.

On January 5, 1919, he wrote an editorial for a newspaper, spent a comfortable day, went to bed at eleven o'clock. At four o'clock in the morning, an attendant who occupied an adjoining room noted that the Colonel was breathing strangely. He called the day nurse, but by the time she reached his bedside Roosevelt was dead. No postmortem was performed. The clinical impression of three doctors who had treated him was that death had come from a coronary occlusion by a blood clot. They believed that the patient's recent attack of inflammatory rheumatism had not directly contributed to his death.

Chronologically, Roosevelt's life lasted only some sixty years. By the tempo of his life it compressed within its span the experiences, activities and accomplishments of a score of lives of ordinary mortals.

William Howard Taft

(1857 – 1924)

WILLIAM H. TAFT was the largest of all Presidents, standing six feet two inches and weighing 330 pounds. He was the only American to attain the Presidency and the office of Chief Justice of the Supreme Court. Taft's real avocation was the law. His grandfather had been a judge in Vermont; his father served two terms on the Superior Court in Cincinnati, Ohio. The roots of the Taft family were anchored in the soil of New England. His mother, Louisa Maria Torrey, was his father's second wife; she, also, was descended from an old New England family.

Young William was a plump, healthy, fair-haired boy with blue eyes. He had an accident when he was nine; the family horses had run away down a steep hill, upsetting the wagon with the boy. He was thrown out on his head, the skin badly cut and the skull apparently slightly fractured. Bill was at the head of his class at the age of twelve; at seventeen he entered Yale. He had an unusually quick perception and a correspondingly retentive memory; learning was more play than effort for him. He graduated in 1878, second in a class of twelve, and gave the class oration. In 1880 he received his law degree from the Cincinnati Law School and was admitted to the Ohio bar.

At that time he was described as a big, good-natured young man, with a charming smile that lit up his face, possessed of every qualification for becoming a successful lawyer and an outstanding public figure. His one weakness, in common with the average person when confronted with difficult problems, was to procrastinate. Like Abraham Lincoln, he was an effective orator, despite his tenor voice that at first startled audiences who expected a deep bass from so big a man.

Only twenty-three years old, he was elected speaker for the Ohio Republican Committee. In the following year he was appointed assistant prosecuting attorney of Hamilton County, and shortly afterward, director of internal revenue for Cincinnati.

Though he was only twenty-five, he showed that he was a man of principle by resigning from a lucrative position rather than give in to the arbitrary pressure of his superiors to oust several of his best employees for political reasons. However, in 1884 he took active part in the campaign to elect James G. Blaine for President against the Democratic candidate Grover Cleveland. Two years later he married Helene Herron. They had five children, of whom three survived. In 1887 he was appointed and, in 1888, elected judge of the Superior Court of Ohio. Shortly thereafter, President Benjamin Harrison made him Solicitor General with offices in Washington. From 1892 to 1900 he served on the Circuit Court of the 6th District. Offered the presidency of Yale in 1899, he refused on the grounds that he was a Unitarian and that in other respects he did not feel qualified for the post.

In 1900 President McKinley asked Taft to become chairman of the civil commission for the pacification and administration of the newly acquired Philippine Islands. Here Taft's conciliatory attitude came into immediate conflict with the military mind of the commanding General Arthur McArthur. The continuous friction ended only with the general's recall the following year, when Taft was appointed Civil Governor of the Islands. He worked at his job conscientiously and with great fairness toward the natives, and soon won the respect and affection of the pacified majority of the population.

The Governor was always a heavy eater and continued this lifelong habit in the tropics. However, he hardly touched alcohol and did not smoke. He was accustomed to taking a daily nap after lunch. His only exercise was a short walk before dinner. As a result, his weight rose to more than 300 pounds.

Unwisely, he chose the month of August 1901 for an inspection trip to the remote mountain region of Luzon, where he suffered severely from the heat. The shocking news of President McKinley's assassination reached him when he returned.

His faith in the Filipinos was put to a severe test when 50 American soldiers were slain in an ambush. Physically and mentally exhausted, Taft was stricken in October with an intermittent fever associated with intense pain all over his body. Doctors diagnosed his illness as "dengue" or "breakbone" fever, a self-limiting disease of about a week's duration, caused by a virus transmitted by a tropical mosquito.

In Taft's case the fever did not subside, but kept rising and the pain became localized in the region of the perineum. An abscess developed and broke through the skin near the rectum. It probably originated from a fistulous tract that had developed from an ulcer in the wall of the rectum. An extensive operation under ether anesthesia became necessary, to open and drain a spider web of pus-filled ducts and pockets undermining the skin. A month later, a second operation was required to open residual pus pockets about the rectum. On Christmas Eve he was so far recovered that he could start on a return trip to the United States, to recuperate and report to the Senate about his activities.

At home, a new assignment awaited him. The Vatican had asked the American government for compensation for the millions of acres of land which the Church had acquired in the Philippines during the Spanish rule and which had been taken over for distribution among the inhabitants. Roosevelt commissioned Taft as his representative to Rome. Before Taft could leave, a third fistula operation was necessary. Taft then went abroad and settled the claims of the Church for several million dollars.

Eagerly he returned to the mission nearest to his heart, the rehabilitation of the Philippines. On his arrival he found that during his absence two catastrophes had stricken the struggling country—the rinderpest, which had carried away 75 per cent of the livestock, and Asiatic cholera, which threatened the human population of the Philippines. It was difficult for the new government to enforce the necessary measures of quarantine and sanitation among the illiterate, superstitious people.

One outbreak of cholera near Manila had been traced to a "sacred" spring supposedly containing waters with miraculous healing powers. A multitude of natives had flocked to it, drinking it and carrying it home in bottles for the cure of all kinds of ailments. The health officers, puzzled by the sudden outbreak of the epidemic in the vicinity, had found that a contaminated sewer drained into the spring. Stern measures of the administration succeeded in stamping out the plague.

In March 1903, Taft, finally cured of his rectal ailment, contracted the inevitable amebic dysentery endemic in the tropical islands. This kind of dysentery acts usually in a less fulminating, but more insidious and stubborn manner, than the bacterial types. Alarmed by the news of the Governor's sickness, his department chief, Secretary of War Elihu Root, sent him a telegram inquiring about his condition. The patient received the cable at a mountain resort to which he had retired, having been able to travel the last part of the journey on horseback. He replied that he was on the way to recovery and closed as follows: "Stood trip well, rode horseback 25 miles to 5,000 ft. elevation." Root, visualizing his 330-pound Governor on a panting pony, cabled back: "Referring to your telegram—how is the horse?"

In 1904, when his chief resigned, Taft was appointed Secretary of War in his stead. In this position he served on several occasions as trouble shooter for the impulsive President Roosevelt, who sent him to Panama to organize the construction of the canal, and in the following year to Cuba to pacify a brewing revolution.

In his responsible office Taft found that his overweight handicapped him, making him sluggish and drowsy. He embarrassed his wife by falling asleep at the most inopportune occasions, such as sitting in the front row at public affairs. He seriously attempted to lose weight, riding horseback almost daily, but unfortunately giving the horse more exercise than himself. In December 1905 he finally got down to the hardest but only effective method of reducing—a low caloric diet. For this he had the supervision of an English doctor. Starting at 326 pounds, he got down to 250 by next summer and felt considerably better.

Much against his personal liking, but groomed by Roosevelt and prodded by his ambitious wife, he accepted the Presidential nomination in 1908. He won easily over the clownish Democratic opponent, Bryan, who was in the same weight class with him. After moving into the White House, Taft found to his dismay that there was no bathtub large enough to accommodate him. Then, when along with his increasing worries his girth grew bigger than ever, he actually got stuck a few times in the bathtub and had to be rescued. An extra-large bathtub was ordered specially for him; it was the size of a small swimming pool. A picture of it shows four men comfortably seated in it.

Two months after Taft's inauguration, his forty-eight-year-old wife fainted during a boat trip and developed a paralysis of her right side. The President, who had been married to her twenty-five years, was stunned. According to his secretary, Archie Butt, he "looked like a great stricken animal, I have never seen greater suffering . . . on a man's face."

At first the doctors thought the paralysis might be only a functional disturbance of hysterical nature. However, the existence of a speech defect and the slow recovery indicate that a cerebral thrombosis must have been the cause. It is the more remarkable that, after her recovery, Mrs. Taft lived thirty more years, surviving the President by thirteen.

President Taft lacked the political instinct, the showmanship and leadership of Roosevelt, and by superficial comparison appeared to be a failure as chief executive. Actually, he made valuable contributions to the international relations and the national economy of the United States. For instance, he was more active—if less noisy—than Roosevelt as trust-buster.

What made him seem a disappointment to his contemporaries was the complete failure of his promise to lower the tariff, a perilous issue on which a number of former Presidents had become shipwrecked and which clever politicians like T.R. had steered clear of.

The uncongenial office of President became even more onerous to Taft when the liberal wing of the Republican Party, under the leadership of his old friend Roosevelt, turned against him with a vengeance. With his disappointments nagging at him, his desire for the elementary solace of food increased accordingly. His weight mounted to 332 pounds. Taft was the first President to play golf, a game supposed to reduce weight and divert the mind. But playing eighteen holes in the fresh air made him all the more ravenous and the game failed to quiet his nerves. Like the ordinary kind of golfer, the placid-looking President was known to have lost his poise on occasion and after a bad shot tossed his club after the ball with an appropriate curse.

As much as Taft disliked being President, stung by Roosevelt's invective, he desperately fought back in the campaign for his re-election. In an address he once expressed his profound bitterness in the following words: "I am a man of peace and I don't want to fight. But when I do fight, I want to hit hard. Even a rat in a corner will fight."

Following Wilson's election in 1912, Taft experienced the deep satisfaction of being able to return to his true element, the law. His alma mater, Yale, appointed him professor of constitutional law. In 1921 he reached the ultimate goal of his life when President Harding named him Chief Justice of the United States.

He felt so much happier as a judge that he tried again to take better care of his health and to reduce. He struggled down to about 250 pounds, which his doctors considered fair enough for a man his size. Modern statistics prove that this weight is about fifty pounds too much for the most favorable life expectancy.

In his fifties Taft developed signs of hardening of the arteries accompanied with a rising blood pressure. During the last decade of his life he was also suffering from a chronic bladder ailment, probably a hypertrophy of the prostate gland which increasingly interfered with normal urination. The glandular swelling partially blocked the outlet of the bladder and after a while urine could only be forced out in a thin trickle. Soon the bladder could not be emptied completely. The stagnant urine became a ready culture medium for bacteria, resulting in a chronic cystitis.

In December 1922, Taft was briefly hospitalized to have "gravel" (small concretions of urinary sediment) removed from his bladder. Unquestionably he was examined and treated with the cystoscope, a slender telescopic instrument, introduced through the urethra and used to illuminate and treat the inside of the bladder. The modern cystoscope had been invented in the 1880's and was in general use in 1920.

The accepted treatment for hypertrophy of the prostate during the last seventy years has been the surgical removal of part, or all, of the obstructing gland. But this procedure carried a considerable mortality in fat, arteriosclerotic patients of Taft's type. During the 1920's the modern, less drastic method of electrosurgical resection through a special operating cystoscope was not yet practiced. Also the efficient new chemical and antibiotic antiseptics were unknown. The conservative treatment was to administer antiseptics by mouth, to drain the bladder through a catheter and to irrigate with mild bactericidal solutions.

During 1923 and 1924 the Chief Justice began to suffer from "digestive disturbances ... which affected his heart," most likely symptoms of narrowing of the coronary arteries of the heart. He developed the "effort syndrome—" pain in the chest, shortness of breath and heart consciousness after physical exertion, typical for angina pectoris. In May 1924 he had to forego a planned trip to England and even missed the commencement exercises of his beloved Yale. He went for a long rest to the seashore. On advice of his doctors he intensified his efforts to keep his weight down and faithfully followed a strict diet for several months, even refusing dinner engagements.

Still the progress of the degeneration of his cardiovascular system could not be arrested and gradually also affected his brain. In 1925 he complained that he could not write as rapidly as he used to, and three years later that his memory was growing ever poorer.

In March 1929, Taft, as the Chief Justice, administered the inaugural oath to President Hoover; the proceedings were broadcast over the radio for the first time. On this occasion he forgot some of his lines and had to improvise.

In December of the same year his half brother Charles P. Taft died. All his life Charles had been William's adviser, assisting him with sage counsel and financial support when needed. Against the advice of his doctors Taft attended the funeral. The emotional and physical strain aggravated his poor general condition; he became depressed, and his urinary difficulties increased to such an extent that he had to undergo hospital treatment for several weeks.

Taft kept hoping that he would recover sufficiently, so he could end the dream of his life at the Supreme Court bench and die with his robe on. However, his condition became so bad that on February 3, 1930, he had to resign from the Supreme Court. Two doctors issued the following bulletin: "For some years, Chief Justice Taft has had a very high blood pressure, associated with general arteriosclerosis and myocarditis. Together with these conditions he had a chronic cystitis. He has no fever and suffers no pain. His present serious condition is the result of general arteriosclerotic changes."

Further medical consultation could not change the unfavorable prognosis. The toxic waste products of his cells, insufficiently drained, accumulated and gradually smothered the flame of his life. For days the patient lay unconscious and could be aroused only with difficulty to swallow a few sips. The doctors tried to prolong the vegetative processes of living by administration of sugar solutions by rectum and intravenously. Late in the afternoon of March 8, 1930, William H. Taft expired in deep coma at the age of seventy-two.

Woodrow Wilson

(1856 — 1924)

WOODROW WILSON was born in 1856 in Staunton, Virginia, the first son and third child of Dr. Joseph Wilson, Presbyterian minister. He was named Thomas Woodrow after his maternal grandfather. Two years later, his father's brilliant oratory won him the pulpit of the aristocratic First Presbyterian Church of Augusta, Georgia.

In 1860 the Civil War tore asunder the close-knit clans of the Wilsons and the Woodrows. Though born and raised in the North and the son of an abolitionist father, Dr. Joseph Wilson had to pay lip service to the cause of his Southern parishioners and preach war against his own people. He felt uprooted and homesick, isolated from his brothers and sisters. In his son he saw the closest link with his kin, and Tommy became his little brother and confidant. To his delight he found in his son a deep sensitivity and a keen receptive mind that was a joy to cultivate.

Feeling deeply ashamed that he could not attack the unChristian institution of slavery, the minister impressed all the more emphatically on his son the tragedy of principles compromised. The influence of his father on Woodrow Wilson lasted throughout his life; he remained for him the image of God, whom one loves, respects, fears, at times resents, but never questions.

Tommy wore glasses from the age of eight, was light blond, thin and freckled, with a long narrow head. He received his early education from his father and had little contact with boys his own age. His mother and two elder sisters hovered over him until he was ten, when a second son arrived.

At eleven Tommy was sent to a select "classical school" to study Latin, history, writing and bookkeeping. Accustomed to the stimulating discussions with his father, he was bored by the dry methods of his new teachers and became more interested in the normal activities of boyhood he had missed so long. Although lack of physical strength and skill at first prevented him from becoming a big wheel in his group, the need to be a leader asserted itself. The boys of his circle soon responded to his precocious articulateness, his superior intelligence and imagination.

At seventeen Wilson spent a year at the poorly endowed Davidson College in North Carolina. Here the food was inadequate for an adolescent boy and no physical exercises were included in the curriculum as an outlet for the fermenting aggressiveness of his age. Frustrated aggression added to malnourishment resulted in "nervous indigestion," consisting of discomfort, heartburn and nausea after eating, and irregular bowel action. Later in life Wilson often suffered from similar gastrointestinal episodes, brought on by emotional upsets probably combined with an allergy to certain foods.

His poor physical condition in turn decreased his resistance to the emotional conflicts of adolescence. They became magnified into neurotic introspection, feelings of guilt and self-reproach. The religious figures, so familiar to the minister's son, were readily transposed into the daydreams of his neurosis. He identified himself with the tortured Job, who had to choose between God and the Devil. Occupied with himself, he was unable to continue his studies and retreated into the safe shelter of his home.

After a breathing spell of a year he enrolled as student at Princeton University, where he graduated with honors. Here he discovered his singular interest in constitutional law and wrote an article, "The Cabinet Government of the United States," which was published in the *National Review*. Convinced he was destined to become a statesman, he chose the study of law at the University of Virginia, where he excelled as a speaker and writer of magazine articles on Bismarck and Gladstone. Full of enthusiasm, Wilson overworked, didn't sleep enough, and gulped down ill-prepared foods. As a consequence his gastric ailment recurred, this time not combined with mental indigestion but with symptoms of respiratory allergy, sneezing and coughing.

Once again he took refuge in the healing warmth of the family hearth and remained there a year and a half. Here he could concentrate on his studies. In 1882 his alma mater awarded him the degree of L.L.B. in absentia. A month later he passed his examination as a lawyer with flying colors.

He was now twenty-six years old and at last felt enough self-confidence to sever the cord of dependence with his family. As a sign of his independence he dropped the diminutive Tommy and became Woodrow Wilson.

Ripe to fall in love, he was still shy and awkward with girls, self-conscious at social functions. Once, entering a long drawing room, he slipped on a treacherous small rug, skid over the polished floor and almost bowled over his hostess. For years he could not forget his humiliation. Wilson's first love fastened upon a girl within his close proximity—his cousin, Harriet Woodrow. However, she was incapable of seeing the man Wilson through the surface of awkwardness and reserve, and rejected him, which hurt him deeply.

Wanting to prove himself, Woodrow opened law offices in Atlanta, Georgia. However, the city had a lawyer for each 270 inhabitants, and he soon recognized that he was not able to elbow his way through the dense competition. And he discovered he did not care for the commercial aspects of law. With great relief he retired into the ivory tower of academic life. This time he enrolled at Johns Hopkins University and wrote several noteworthy books that secured him a fellowship in their history department and a Ph.D. degree.

In 1885 he married Ellen Luise Axson, who loved and admired him. In the following years his childhood experience of being surrounded by adoring females repeated itself, with his three daughters and their mother worshiping him. From 1885 to 1890 he taught at Bryn Mawr and at Wesleyan. Then his old college, Princeton, called him as professor of jurisprudence and political economy.

He was a born teacher with the gift of clarity; his lessons were interesting, and he was more concerned that his students understood the facts than memorized dates. In 1902, in acknowledgment of his outstanding qualifications, he was unanimously elected president of Princeton.

One morning in May 1906, Wilson, then fifty years old, awoke and found that he couldn't see out of his left eye. During the preceding month he had been suffering from neuritic pains in his left shoulder and leg, and his right hand had been handicapped by a condition like writer's cramp.

Two specialists diagnosed the blindness of his left eye as caused by a thrombosis of the sclerotic ophthalmic artery and recommended three months' rest. Not satisfied with their advice, Wilson consulted a famous doctor in Edinburgh and asked him whether he should continue with his arduous duties. The wise old man answered that if everyone stopped working because of such a condition as Wilson's, a good many of the world's tasks would remain unfinished. He probably thought of Pasteur, who after suffering a stroke at forty-six made his greatest contributions in the following twenty-seven years; and of Charles Darwin, who completed his books on evolution in spite of lifelong delicate health. Wilson's eye improved somewhat but always remained half-blind. In the following years an involuntary muscle-twitching developed around the eye, possibly as an unconscious attempt to get a sharper focus.

In 1910 Wilson resigned from Princeton to be elected Governor of New Jersey. As a politician, Wilson made good use of his genius and training as an educator, to clarify his issues and present them in a convincing manner to the electorate, thus creating favorable public opinion. As Governor, he made such a name for himself by his reforms in a few months, that in the following year he was nominated and elected President of the United States.

One of his physicians, the famous neurologist Dr. S. Weir Mitchell of Philadephia, expressed his doubts that Wilson could stand the strain of the strenuous duties of Chief Executive, which Wilson himself once said required "the constitution of an athlete, the patience of a mother and the endurance of an early Christian."

The new President inherited from his predecessor, as White House physician, a young officer of the Navy Medical Corps, Dr. Gary Grayson. Taft introduced him to Wilson, saying, "Here is an excellent fellow that I hope you will get to know. I regret to say that he is a Democrat and a Virginian but that's a matter that can't be helped."

Dr. Grayson took the new President's medical history and found out that his patient had brought along his own stomach pump which he had learned to use himself. In fact, he used it almost daily—in the way some people take enemas. Wilson also had a history of habitual headaches for which he medicated himself indiscriminately with all kinds of headache powders. Most of them probably contained aspirin and contributed to his chronic gastritis, for which he used the stomach pump. Dr. Grayson won his fellow Virginian's confidence and took over his treatment on a more professional basis.

In April 1913, President Wilson appeared before both Houses of Congress to deliver his first message, thus reviving a custom that Jefferson, a poor speaker, had discontinued. By personally addressing Congress, he availed himself of his persuasive rhetorical powers, outlining his legislative recommendations in a terse speech that received thunderous applause. Before the first impetus of his leadership had spent itself and the spokesmen of reaction in Congress recovered, he had whipped an unprecedented number of new laws through Congress: the Federal Reserve Act, a lower tariff, an effective amendment of the Anti-Trust Law, a child labor law, the creation of the Federal Trade Commission.

It was a mockery of destiny that Wilson, with his profound understanding of the history and the internal problems of the United States, was called as President to give his chief attention to international affairs, less familiar to him; and that he, a convinced pacifist, was forced to lead his country into a war generated by European power politics which he detested.

During the first week of August 1914, when the sound of the guns of Liége reverberated around the world, Wilson's devoted wife, Ellen, died from chronic nephritis. The President had to face the hate-ridden world without her love and encouragement. The President's daughters kept house for him, but their filial affection could not compensate for the companionship his dependent personality required.

In the following year he married Edith Bolling Galt, a beautiful widow, who soon became his indispensable companion. Supported by her devotion, Wilson kept his physical and mental balance up to his final breakdown. Edith Wilson carefully supervised the diet for the President's sensitive stomach, as outlined by Dr. Grayson. To relieve the tensions which often brought on her husband's headaches, she took him whenever possible to musical comedies and vaudeville shows, his favorite entertainment.

Rather than any physical support, there was a vision that sustained Wilson during World War I—that with American help the war could be won to end all wars; that out of the holocaust a lasting peace would emerge in the form of a league of nations dedicated to peace.

On December 3, 1918, the President started on his eventful trip to Paris, accompanied by his wife, with the intention of exerting his personal influence on the foreign statesmen to accept his blueprint of a league of nations. At the time of departure he appeared to be in unusually good condition, weighing more and looking stronger than ever. Only the tic around his left eye remained, a reminder of the latent pathologic condition.

His health, that had so well withstood the stress of war and had been buoyed up by the final triumph, soon deteriorated under the strain of irreconcilable conflict at the peace table. The Allied politicians, led by Georges Clemenceau, "The Tiger," clamored for a peace of revenge and punishment, scorning the viewpoint of the American President, who preached a lasting peace of moderation and justice. The European statesmen's sullen refusal to learn from the lessons of history infuriated Wilson almost beyond self-control.

Bitter resentment and frustration made him "bilious" and nauseated; his indigestion and "heartburn" intensifying his irritability and impatience. It was inevitable that the tension at the conference table stirred up the President's tension headaches, painful spasms of the head and neck muscles. Wilson himself attributed one of these headaches to "bottled-up wrath at Lloyd George."

Worn out by his unrewarding efforts, Wilson insisted on working as many as eighteen hours a day, determined to have at least the Covenant of the League of Nations inserted in the peace treaty. The strain not only tightened up the muscles of the neck, it also contracted his usually relaxed facial muscles into sharp ridges of hostility. His features became haggard, the lid of his half-blind eye fluttered at an alarming rate.

On April 3, 1919, Wilson finally broke down with fever, profuse diarrhea and a convulsive cough, followed by a congestion of the lungs and difficulty in breathing. It was weeks before he recovered somewhat from the complex of symptoms, labeled by Dr. Grayson at first as food poisoning, then as influenza. When the President returned to the conference table he could no longer control his irritability and impatience; he was quarrelsome, and suspicious even of his closest friends.

Present-day views are that these changes were based on brain damage, probably caused by arteriosclerotic occlusion of blood vessels. Another sign was his increasing insomnia, for which Dr. Grayson had to prescribe increasing doses of barbiturates. It is well known that intractable sleeplessness is often caused by cerebral arteriosclerosis with hypertension. Wilson's sleep was also occasionally interrupted by attacks of bronchial asthma, a new manifestation of his allergic tendency.

When the President returned to America in July 1919, he did not resemble the man who had left barely seven months before, radiating strength and self-confidence. His shoulders sagged, weariness and anxiety had deeply gnawed into his face that looked gray and drawn. The weaker the old lion appeared, the louder became the jackal clamor in the Senate chamber.

One of their leaders, Hiram Johnson of California, called the League of Nations a gigantic war trust. The resistance of the American Senate against his plan deeply disappointed the President and aroused a bitter resentment in him. Stubbornly, he refused to give an inch or to listen to friends' advise to compromise in order to preserve at least the substance of the covenant.

Historians have often expressed wonder that Wilson, who had made so many concessions to statesmen abroad, would not even sit down at the conference table with his domestic opponents. Evidently he considered them hopelessly ignorant or wicked. Perhaps there was a physiological barrier: the increasing occlusion of the arteries of his brain, impairing its elasticity. The progressive degeneration of the central nervous system induced a rigidity of mind. The less sympathetic features of the old schoolmaster came to the surface—an air of authority and superiority, no longer censored by the weakened superego. His apparent arrogance embittered Wilson's antagonists and estranged some of his lukewarm supporters in the Senate.

In a last desperate attempt to win his battle for the League, the President decided on a speaking tour across the nation, counting on his personal persuasiveness to bring the American public over to his view. He closed his ears to the entreaties of his wife, his doctor, his Cabinet, not to undergo the ordeal. "I don't care," he said, "if I die the moment after the treaty is ratified."

Woodrow Wilson's last mission to save the American people from another war proved to be as futile as a similar pilgrimage of Andrew Johnson half a century before, when he appealed for a peace of reconciliation following the Civil War. Both Presidents were statesmen with greater vision than their myopic opponents. They failed utterly because they were unable to compromise.

At eleven o'clock on the night of September 2, 1919, the President boarded the special train which was to carry him to the people. With him were Mrs. Wilson, Dr. Grayson, and Tumulty, his faithful secretary. The latter reported that he had never seen the President look so weary. The tour had barely started when Wilson was stricken by severe headaches, which interfered with the preparation and delivery of scores of speeches he had planned.

The pall of tobacco smoke in the ill-ventilated halls made him sneeze and cough. The hot, dry air of Montana brought on an attack of bronchial asthma. Dr. Grayson often had to spray the President's aching throat during the night. It became necessary to nurse his sensitive stomach with nourishing liquids and predigested foods.

In Seattle, worn out as he was, Wilson spoke five times in one day. Radical labor leaders had arranged a public demonstration against the President. He invited them to a personal interview and shamed them into silence while he spoke to them in a strained voice, his hands shaking, face twitching, eyes closed. In addition to these inauspicious events in Seattle, accidents occurred which a Plutarch would have interpreted as evil omens. While the President was reviewing the Pacific Fleet his launch collided with other boats, shipped water and listed badly. A day later, during a sightseeing tour, an automobile in the Presidential party was struck, killing a popular newsman and injuring another.

The worst shock came on September 15, at Portland, when it became public that Secretary of State Robert Lansing had privately stated that the League of Nations was a fraud and should be defeated. Broken-hearted but determined, Wilson proceeded to California, where he made four addresses in two days. The audiences received him with great enthusiasm. Dead tired from banquets, parades, and blaring bands, the President dropped into a chair and moaned: "They mean it so well but they are killing me."

Revived in spirit but physically exhausted, Wilson turned back East to complete his circuit. His private train was badly ventilated. In the Sierras the gas fumes in the long tunnels and the smoke of forest fires choked his sensitive lungs. The sudden change of altitude oppressed his heart. Crossing the desert, heat and dust engulfed the train. And then the President received the news that his vindictive enemies in Congress had introduced a resolution for an investigation of an alleged "shower of gifts" received by the Wilsons in Europe.

In the stale air of the packed Tabernacle at Salt Lake City, Wilson could hardly finish his speech, and lost his temper—and his audience—when he replied sharply to a heckler. In Pueblo, Colorado, Wilson made his last speech to the American people, expressing the hope that eventually the world would find a lasting peace. Tears were in his eyes and the eyes of the audience when he ended his valedictory.

His headaches had mounted in intensity throughout the journey. Their character had changed also. Formerly they had been located mainly in the back of his head; now they had shifted more to the inside, making him feel as if his brain were congealed. During the night, after leaving Pueblo, his wife found him moaning beside the bed, his head resting on the back of a chair. She called Dr. Grayson, who observed a curious drooping at the left side of the President's mouth and a trace of saliva trickling out—sign of a stroke, caused by a progressing thrombosis.

For Mrs. Wilson, this was the longest night of her life. Nothing the doctor could do gave relief. Finally the President got up and dressed, as if he wanted to run away from the iron grip that tortured his brain. While the train rushed through the darkness, the President walked restlessly from one end of his private car to the other. Finally, at 5 A.M., he fell asleep seated in a chair.

Next day, the President resigned himself to the verdict of his doctor and his wife, that he was too ill to complete his tour. With shades drawn, the train roared on to Washington, arriving there forty-eight hours later.

The President made a pitiful effort to hide how badly he felt; meanwhile the pathologic process was relentlessly progressing. On the evening of October 1, he read aloud a chapter from the Bible before retiring. He wound up his watch but forgot to take it to his room. When he awoke the next morning, his left hand hung helplessly at his side. Soon the paralysis spread to his left leg. Helped to the bathroom, he collapsed and lost consciousness. He was lifted into the big bed that once had been Abraham Lincoln's.

Specialists were summoned. The consensus was that a thrombosis had produced an infarct of the right side of the brain controlling the motion of the left side of the body, and by indirect pressure had blocked out consciousness. For days Wilson's life hung in the balance; then, dimly, consciousness returned, to dwell on what had obsessed him before his collapse—the League of Nations.

Dr. Francis X. Dercum of Philadelphia, the chief consultant, gave stern instructions to keep all disconcerting news and visitors away. On his orders Mrs. Wilson and Dr. Grayson guarded the President like dragons. Hardly any news seeped in or out of the sickroom.

The less the public knew, the more gossip was invented. It was whispered that the President had a venereal disease, even that he was insane. The rumor in medical circles was that Wilson's left knee had been deformed by Charcot's disease, a consequence of locomotor ataxia.

One reason for all these dark rumors was that, around the middle of October, the limousines of several new medical consultants were observed in front of the White House. A serious complication had arisen. A prostatic obstruction was blocking the bladder. On October 17, Dr. Hugh Young of Johns Hopkins, the best known urologist of the time, was summoned in consultation with five other doctors. He made repeated attempts to dilate the contraction and insert a catheter, but was unable to overcome the spasm of the closing muscle. He concluded that the bladder, distended with urine, could not be drained without surgical procedure.

The other consultants were in agreement with Dr. Young. The alternative appeared to be a progressive urinary poisoning, followed by irreversible uremia and death. On account of the great risk of surgery on a patient in the President's condition, the decision was left up to Mrs. Wilson.

She, however, could not make up her mind. Wilson's temperature rose; his pulse became slow and bounding; he became increasingly uncomfortable and restless. The nurses continued applying hot packs to the distended bladder, the doctors sat around waiting for Mrs. Wilson to make the decision. More than two hours had passed, when suddenly the muscle relaxed, allowing the urine to pass.

Thereafter improvement set in and progressed at a slow but steady pace. By the end of October the President could again read the papers; by November he was able to dictate three to four letters a day. In the meantime the wheels of government had almost ground to a halt. Letters sent to the President's sickroom did not come back; even emergency communications vanished. No pardons were signed, no proclamations issued. Bills became law without the President's signature.

Finally, a committee of Senators was delegated to investigate the President's condition and judge whether he was mentally able to continue as Chief Executive. One of the delegates was the oily Senator Albert B. Fall, whose dislike of Wilson was heartily reciprocated. The stage was well set for the reception of the visitors. The President was propped up on pillows, his left arm hidden under the covers. Edith Wilson sat in a chair opposite the bed, ready with pencil and notebook to record the conversation and guard against any misquoting of her husband.

The discussion was lively. The crippled President was still able to parry his opponent's clumsy blows. In parting, Senator Fall leaned over the bed and pressed the sick man's hand between his own and said: "I have been praying for you, sir." For a moment the President's face turned purple; then he replied: "What way, Senator?" This rejoinder stopped unctuous Albert B. Fall in his tracks and ended the Senate investigation of Wilson's mental disability.

After a few months the invalid gained a measure of control of his paralyzed limbs and finally learned to walk, with a shuffling gait, when supported on both sides and leaning on a sturdy cane. At the same time the President recovered some of his power of decision and action. However, he showed marked emotional instability, which made rational cooperation with his staff and his Cabinet almost impossible. After a while, one after the other of his aides and Cabinet members could no longer take their chief's emotional outbursts and deserted him.

In one point only the President remained consistent. He categorically declined to sign a peace treaty, including the Covenant of the League of Nations, with any reservations whatsoever, even if the Allied nations would accept them for the price of American adherence to the League. Because of Wilson's compulsive rejection of a peace treaty with modifications, the divided Senate could not muster a two-thirds majority to ratify any treaty whatever.

After the end of his second term Wilson quietly moved with his family to a house on S Street, where he lived in seclusion. Oblivious of her husband's mental condition, Mrs. Wilson had arranged for him a partnership in a commercial law firm in downtown Washington, and had furnished a beautiful suite of offices. Wilson went to his law offices only once.

He refused innumerable tempting offers to write his memoirs, or newspaper columns and articles. Apparently he felt that the span of his attention had become too short, his mind too easily fatigued for consistent effort. He preferred to play games of solitaire, read detective stories or the novels of Scott and Dickens, and to see vaudeville shows—things he had enjoyed all his life but never got enough of.

The twilight of Wilson's life was brightened by visits from Georges Clemenceau and Lloyd George, who, like himself, had been discarded after the war. The old Tiger came bouncing upstairs to embrace the prophet whose gospel he had ridiculed at the conference table. Lloyd George, who visited him a year later, was shocked by Wilson's physical and mental decline. The President's conversation consisted of fragmentary recollections and plans for a future which was never to come.

At times, Wilson was aware of the hopelessness of his condition and of the fact that his life's work would remain unfinished. Then, tears would roll down his cheeks. Only his unshakable faith in the omnipotence and goodness of God saved him from utter despair.

In January 1924, Dr. Grayson took a much needed vacation. During his absence the patient behaved like a lonely child who misses the comforting presence of his father. Toward the end of the month Wilson seemed to feel that his end was approaching. On January 28, Dr. Grayson was called back by telegram to keep his last vigil at his patient's bedside. On February 1, Wilson lapsed into unconsciousness. Yet he rallied once more, to everyone's surprise. According to his daughter, Eleanor McAdoo, on the following morning, he prophesied in a clear voice that the time would come when this country would join another League of Nations, which would work effectively. On February 3, 1924, Wilson died from a massive infarction of the brain.

Warren Gamaliel Harding

(1865 — 1923)

THE famous heart specialist and uncanny diagnostician, Dr. Emmanuel Libmann of New York, met President Harding at a dinner party in the fall of 1922. Next day he called up a friend and expressed his private opinion that the President was suffering from a disease of the coronary arteries of the heart and would be dead in six months.

The President died eight months later from the effects of an acute occlusion of his narrowed coronary arteries. As an expert on heart disease Dr. Libmann was far ahead of the practitioners of his time.

The disabling and often fatal pathologic condition of the coronary arteries of the heart had been sporadically recognized by a few outstanding physicians during the second part of the eighteenth century. Keen pathologists and clinicians of the nineteenth century observed that the coronary arteries of older people often were scarred and narrowed by disseminated "atheromatous plaques" of cholesterol and calcium surrounded by thin-walled capillary vessels and repair cells. This condition they called "coronary sclerosis."

Only since the beginning of the twentieth century has the pathological picture of coronary sclerosis been coordinated with clinical observations, and it has been shown that the perceptible symptoms depend mainly on the degree to which a segment of a blood vessel feeding the heart muscle has been narrowed by the process and by possible vascular spasm.

Transient oxygen deficiency of part of the heart muscle causes a peculiar pain usually localized beneath the breastbone, the

323

upper abdomen, left shoulder and arm, combined with a sensation of constriction of the chest. From this sense of oppression the medical term "angina pectoris" has been derived, meaning literally "strangling of the chest."

Longer-lasting deficiency of arterial blood leads to the death of a patch of heart muscle, a condition called "cardiac infarction." In the majority of cases this condition is caused by a mechanical obstruction of one of the coronaries by a blood clot, or "thrombus."

The subjective symptoms of coronary occlusion are similar to those of angina pectoris, except that they are usually more severe, persistent and shocking.

The modern treatment aims to aid the healing of the damaged area by bed rest and to prevent an extension of the thrombosis by thinning out the blood with anticlotting drugs.

Atypical forms of occlusion and infarction are also known, with the pain referred to the jaw or only the abdomen, and some are almost painless and "silent." However, the resulting pathological changes and potential complications are the same.

The greatest contribution to the study of heart disease, especially coronary sclerosis, was made by the Dutch physiologist, Willem Van Einthoven, who invented the electrocardiograph in 1903. Its essential part is a delicate, very sensitive string galvanometer capable of recording on film the minute electrical impulses generated by the action of the heart. Painstaking studies over the years have revealed that the character of these tracings varied with the different pathologic changes of the heart, making an accurate clinical diagnosis possible.

The first demonstration in the United States of the value of the electrocardiogram for the diagnosis of acute coronary occlusion was made in 1918. Yet in 1923 no electrocardiogram was taken of the stricken President Harding during the six days of his illness. Nor were his five doctors able to coordinate the clinical signs and symptoms presented as components of the picture of coronary occlusion. They considered them separately and offered to the public a motley assortment of symptoms and diagnostic impressions as definite diagnoses in the official bulletins: "Hypertension . . . Angina pectoris . . . Acute gastrointestinal attack . . . Crabmeat-copper ptomaine poisoning (although the President had not eaten any crabmeat) . . . Gallbladder disease . . . Pneumonia . . . Circulatory collapse . . . Apoplexy. . . ." Take your choice!

The bewildered public did not know what to think, and was left with the suspicion of foul play by poison, or of suicide. This impression was deepened by the stern refusal of Mrs. Harding to permit an autopsy. In spite of the lack of a definite postmortem diagnosis, in retrospect there is hardly a doubt that nothing was strange about the death of President Harding. We inevitably arrive at the diagnosis of coronary sclerosis with final occlusion if we follow the clues from the President's symptoms, and review his medical history which is inseparably interwoven with the history of his life.

It is a much-debated medical question whether the accumulation of nervous tension, excitement and worry, such as Harding was subjected to, can contribute to hardening of the arteries, and in particular to coronary sclerosis. Statistically there is no definite proof for this general impression.

The most important factor in the tendency to hardening of the arteries appears to be heredity. Overeating and overweight seem to favor the deposition of cholesterol, believed to be the cornerstone of arteriosclerosis. And there is a school of research that blames animal fats as the source of cholesterol. Another fact can be statistically proved: that people who keep in good physical condition through their occupation, or systematic exercise, are less prone to develop coronary occlusion than those in sedentary occupations.

However, when hardening of the coronary arteries has once developed to a certain point, physical and emotional stress and strain tend to aggravate the condition. For instance, they may bring on spells of angina pectoris, each of which adds its bit to the damage of the heart.

It is also well known that an extraordinary mental shock or

unusual physical strain can initiate an acute coronary occlusion. The completion of such an occlusion and consequent infarction of the heart may take minutes, hours, or days, and only then do the acute symptoms manifest themselves.

Because of the scarcity of medical data, it cannot be determined if any of the earlier Presidents died of coronary occlusion. Besides Harding in more recent times, Rutherford B. Hayes, Grover Cleveland, Theodore Roosevelt, and Calvin Coolidge died under circumstances and with a history suggesting coronary obstruction.

We can assume that Harding's coronary sclerosis dates long before he became President. He was not only fond of liquor but also of rich food, and carried around with him the unsound overweight of the successful politician of his time. During his administration Harding had more than his share of emotional stress and strain to tax his coronary arteries to the limit.

Harding never wanted to be President. He was a handsome, affable, small-town Babbitt, happy at being well-liked by everybody he met on the main street of Marion, Ohio. He gloried in flattering prestige as editor of the town newspaper, the Marion *Star,* which became a great success through his likable personality and the drive and assets of his aggressive wife, five years his elder. A playboy at heart, he had a wonderful time with his cronies at poker, drinking parties, and on the golf course. His good looks made him quite a favorite with ladies of not too high-priced virtue.

As a successful businessman and good mixer, he was inevitably drawn into politics and became a pillar of the local Republican party, popular and agreeable to everybody. His newspaper work had taught him the right vernacular for political speeches, and his self-confidence, born of his popularity, made him capable of stirring a receptive audience with high-sounding generalities that offended no one, proclaimed in a mellifluous voice.

At thirty-five Harding was chosen state senator, and four years later lieutenant governor. He was defeated for the governorship of Ohio in 1910 by a Democrat, but elected United States Senator by a great majority in 1915. In Washington he let his secretaries do most of his work, and took cues for his voting from the party regulars. With their coaching, he even voted for prohibition, in which he certainly did not believe. His vote did not alter his drinking habits. He continued to play poker and golf with the same gusto as he had in Marion, and also kept a young mistress, Nan Britton.

The First World War and its political implications hardly touched Senator Harding. He went on the usual senatorial jaunts across the country and abroad, without ever broadening his parochial horizon. The man from Main Street, Marion, Ohio, could never understand the lofty idealism of Wilson. For him the League of Nations was not a vital issue but a political football. Occasionally he was allowed to make some inconsequential speeches to a lethargic Senate, which Senator William G. McAdoo characterized as follows: "His speeches leave the impression of an army of pompous phrases moving over the landscape in search of an idea; sometimes these meandering words would actually capture a straggling thought and bear it triumphantly, a prisoner in their midst, until it died of servitude and overwork."

On October 22, 1919, Nan Britton gave birth to a girl whose paternity Harding never denied. Thereafter, for the rest of his life he was haunted by the specter that the evidence of his philandering might be used to smear him.

This was the man whom Harry M. Daugherty, his campaign manager, and Mrs. Harding maneuvered into the Presidency with the support of a senatorial clique and the notorious "Ohio Gang" bent on feathering their nest. Harding had no illusions about his own shortcomings. "I am a man of limited talents, from a small town. I do not seem to grasp that I am President," he told a friend shortly after his election.

In an off-the-record speech at the National Press Club banquet in Washington in 1922, Harding told an unusually revealing story about himself. His father, a blunt-spoken country doctor who had worked himself up from a veterinarian and possessed a good deal of horse sense, had said to him one day, "Warren, it's a good thing you weren't born a gal." "Why?" asked the youth. "Because you would be in the family way all the time. You can't say no."

True to his character Warren couldn't say no to the pressures of his selfish friends and his nagging wife when he permitted himself to be nominated candidate for the Presidency against his better judgment. A dark horse, he won on the tenth ballot after the leading candidates, Wood and Lawton, had become hopelessly deadlocked. The apparently colorless and safe Calvin Coolidge was chosen as his running mate by unanimous vote.

The presidential election was a landslide for the big, handsome Republican candidate who talked the language of the man in the street and sounded the clarion call for a return to "normalcy" from the unpopular war restrictions. His better qualified opponent, James Cox, the Democratic Governor of Ohio, never had a chance. Cox looked small and insignificant beside Harding, lackluster in the pale reflection of Wilson's starry ideals.

Thus, the third-rate legislator, soapbox orator, and tyro of a statesman, became the first member of the Senate to be elevated to the White House, though such former giants of the upper chamber as Webster, Calhoun, and Clay had been thwarted in their presidential ambitions.

The confinement and routine of the White House under the watchful eyes of his suspicious wife got on Harding's nerves. He was accustomed to roam at will through the streets of Marion or of Washington, visiting the gay night spots and secret hangouts. He looked for diversion in stiff poker games held twice a week in the executive mansion, and at least once a week in the house of a friend. On such occasions the choicest liquor flowed, provided abundantly by the Department of Internal Revenue.

One of his favorite boon companions was Charles R. Forbes, his court jester, whom he rewarded with the extremely profitable administration of the newly established Veterans Bureau. Forbes revealed that once, after a poker dinner, the President had a crying jag and sobbed how unhappy and empty his life was since he came to the White House.

Eventually the Drys got wind of the reek of liquor in the White House and their clamor forced the President to confine his drinking to his bedroom, which became his castle and his bar. His position as President also made it difficult for him to meet Nan Britton, to whom he seems to have been genuinely devoted. If we believe her own story, she occasionally managed to slip through a secret entrance into the White House to meet her lover under the very nose of the legitimate mistress of the house. To live dangerously like this was contrary to the nature of the middle-aged Harding, at heart a Philistine who wanted the easy way of life and no complications.

Harding's weakness of character, which got him into such sordid situations in his private life, made him also a misfit as President. His administration bred an epidemic of scandals, in corruption equaling Grant's administration. Several of his venal friends, whom he had injudiciously appointed to high government positions, went on a spree of fraud and plunder, unrestrained and even abetted by their incompetent chief. Their activities were too brazen to be hushed up for long and inevitably reflected on the President, who could not escape the responsibility and blame for the malfeasances of the rascals of his choice.

In February 1923 the Senate appointed a committee which exposed the corrupt practices of his pal Forbes, whose frauds cost the government $200 million. The Senate also started to investigate the chicaneries of another friend, Thomas W. Miller, who had stolen millions as custodian of alien property. Daugherty, Harding's Attorney General, was under well-founded suspicion of collusion with big-time racketeers and gangsters.

But the foulest stench of all came from the oil of Teapot Dome, one of several naval reserves which Harding, by his own executive order, had transferred from the Navy Department to the custody of his crooked friend Albert B. Fall, Secretary of the Interior, thereby committing an unconstitutional act. By the end of the second year of his term, the President found himself on the spot. Threats of exposure, impeachment, and disgrace converged on him from all sides. To add to his dismay, he lost consistently and heavily on the stock market, playing through a dummy.

As though to escape the inevitable day of judgment, Harding fled the heat of Washington to the coolness of Alaska and the West Coast on June 30, 1923. He was a sick man, mentally and physically, when he left the capital on his last journey—and found the only escape from dishonor left to him.

Before describing the course of Harding's last illness, which is the main theme of the last act of his tragedy, I must go back to his earlier medical history.

Shortly after his marriage, Warren Harding suffered from a mysterious disease, vaguely described as a digestive disorder, that in some strange way affected his nerves and his spirits. For some unknown reason he consulted neither his father nor any physician of note. For his secret ailment he dosed himself with a variety of nostrums, and eventually fell into the hands of a quack. His father at last sensed that something was radically wrong with his eldest son and gave him a thorough going over. According to his version, he cured Warren by putting him on a diet.

We do not know when the earliest manifestations of Harding's heart disease appeared. In January 1922 he was stricken with a serious sickness which was diagnosed as influenza, accompanied by digestive disorders and kidney symptoms. This episode perhaps represented an unrecognized attack of coronary thrombosis followed by myocardial infarction.

Thereafter the President became increasingly listless and easily exhausted. Physical effort and emotional stress occasionally brought on short periods of a strange pain in the middle of the chest, which made him momentarily stop in his tracks and remain quiet until the pain vanished after a few minutes. Like most people, Harding insisted upon interpreting this substernal pain as indigestion. But even the President's old-fashioned physician, Surgeon General Charles E. Sawyer, could not fail to discern these attacks as signs of angina pectoris. He also found that Harding was suffering from high blood pressure.

The seizures happened first on the golf course. The President had been a rain-or-shine golf enthusiast, insisting on playing through eighteen holes, undaunted by bad weather. Now, the attacks became more frequent and interfered with his game, particularly in cold weather—as is characteristic of angina pectoris. Even when it was warm, Harding was forced to stop at the end of nine holes, or even sooner, resting at intervals.

When Dr. Emmanuel Libmann met the President he must have based his snap diagnosis, mentioned earlier, on a casual observation of such intervals. He may have noticed that Harding, after briskly entering the room, would halt suddenly, stand rigid for a few minutes, his florid face blanching, then go on as if nothing had happened. Or, the doctor may have noted such abrupt pauses once or twice during an animated conversation.

Other signs of the deterioration of the President's heart condition was his shortness of breath on slight exertion or when in a recumbent position. For several months before his death he was unable to sleep without propping himself up with several pillows. We cannot surmise whether Harding sensed the seriousness of his ailment. Like many people who are moral cowards, he had physical courage and was not given to complaining.

His bad health added to the depression of his harassed mind. When left alone, the President would brood; feelings of guilt and self-reproach tortured him in his waking hours and disturbed his sleep at night. He sincerely tried to turn over a new leaf and cut down on his gay parties and drinking. He was seeing little of Nan Britton, and met her for the last time in January 1923, when he arranged for her to go to Europe and out of his life.

The President's effort to escape his troubles was doomed

from the start. On his stop at Kansas City he was approached by an elderly woman, veiled and furtive, who was secretly ushered up to the presidential suite, eluding the reporters. She was Mrs. Albert B. Fall, wife of the incriminated Secretary of the Interior. The President was closeted with her for nearly an hour. He emerged visibly shaken, his face pale, with a look of pain. Afterward, on the train, he muttered repeatedly a paraphrase of the classic complaint: "In this job I am not worried about my enemies; it is my friends that are keeping me awake nights." William Allen White saw him in Kansas City and noticed that "his lips were swollen blue, his eyes puffed, and his hand seemed stiff when I shook hands with him."

He continued his trip by train and boat to Alaska, then back to Seattle. On one of his stops a message arrived from Washington, D.C. by airplane. It was in code and its contents were never revealed. After reading it, Harding seemed to crumple in his chair. He was breathing hard, his pale face wearing the stunned expression of a fighter who had been hit a terrific body blow. Later he got up and walked aimlessly about the room, mumbling to himself. Time and again he would stop and buttonhole whoever happened to be near him . . . What should a President do when his friends played him false?

He finally asked for a drink; he needed it. The presidential party hadn't brought along any liquor, so firm had been Harding's resolve to mend his ways. A reporter brought him a bottle. But the liquor did not make him feel any better. Like his other pals, alcohol proved a false friend which let him down when he needed its solace most. At last, a sedative gave him a few hours of fitful sleep.

The boat trip back from Alaska did not refresh the President. He could not shake off the furies of worry and fear which pursued him relentlessly, giving him no rest at day and troubling his sleep as nightmares. He tried to forget himself by playing cards far into the night, and had to drug himself with sedatives to get some sleep. According to newspaper reports, which always represented the President to the public as a picture of health, he played a game of shuffleboard only four days before his fatal heart attack.

Harding was exhausted when he arrived in Seattle on July 27, 1923. It was an unusually sultry day, but he insisted on making a speech outdoors in the hot afternoon sun and attending a banquet in the evening. After a few restless hours in bed, in the early morning of July 28, he was suddenly awakened by an attack of pain in the lower chest and upper abdomen. It started like his previous seizures of angina pectoris. But this attack did not disappear after a few minutes like the other episodes. It continued and increased in severity. He became deathly pale with a bluish hue, and broke out in cold perspiration. The pulse rose to 120, respiration to 40. A distressing nausea and vomiting ensued. The gastric symptoms convinced Surgeon General Sawyer that this actually was an attack of acute indigestion.

In the President's party were two other doctors; the younger and better trained was Commander Joel T. Boone of the Navy Medical Corps; the other, Dr. Hubert Work, recently appointed Secretary of the Interior, who had been a practicing physician before he turned politician.

Dr. Boone examined the President and found the heart sounds feeble and the blood pressure at shock level. He disagreed with his elder colleague that this was "acute indigestion," and diagnosed the seizure as cardiac. Confidentially he advised some of the members of the President's party, among them Herbert Hoover, of the gravity of the outlook. The medical bulletins and official reports do not describe the details of treatment. Probably the President was given injections of morphine for his pain and stimulants for his heart.

After a few hours he rallied, and felt much better during the day. Apparently Dr. Sawyer permitted him to get up. In fact, no strict bed rest was enforced during the first three days. The Surgeon General went on record as calling the President's illness an "acute gastrointestinal attack," probably caused by "crabmeat-copper ptomaine poisoning." Because of his higher rank, Sawyer's diagnosis became official in the public medical bulletin.

At his own request, Harding was placed on his special train which was to take him back to Washington, D.C., with a few short stopovers. He was persuaded to remain in bed during the trip south. On Sunday, July 29, the party arrived at the San Francisco railroad station. The President remonstrated against being taken in a wheel chair to the automobile, and Dr. Sawyer permitted him to walk from the train to the car and also from the automobile to the elevator and to his hotel room. There, finally, he sank into bed.

The ill-timed physical effort aggravated Harding's condition. The chest pain and fever returned. The pulse started racing again. The breathing became faster and labored, and at times took the form of so-called Cheyne-Stokes respiration, characterized by alternating periods of acceleration and deceleration, and indicating a pronounced disturbance of the respiratory center of the brain caused by oxygen deficiency. Heart failure developed, producing stagnation of the pulmonary circulation, congestion of the lungs, and a copious cough—signs of pulmonary edema.

Two leading San Francisco physicians, Dr. Ray Lyman Wilbur of the Stanford Medical School and Dr. Charles Minor Cooper, a prominent heart specialist, were called into consultation. A blood count showed an increase of white blood cells; X-ray study of the chest showed an increase of the density of the lower lobes of both lungs. The laboratory and clinical findings were interpreted as signs of acute inflammation of the lungs, a so-called bronchopneumonia. This diagnosis was announced in the official bulletin, to which was added a second diagnosis: "Circulatory collapse."

At last bed rest was enforced and heart stimulants injected, which eased the labored breathing. Under this management Harding seemed to recover rapidly. An X-ray picture taken forty-eight hours later, showed the congestion of the lungs virtually cleared up. On the sixth day Harding was comfortable and in better spirits than he had been for a long time. Like any convalescent who has emerged from the throes of death, he felt happy and contented. The all-absorbing struggle for mere survival had made him temporarily forget the remoter dangers to his public life. Nothing mattered at the moment except to be alive and able to breathe again with ease.

On the afternoon of August 2, all perceptible symptoms of the sickness had disappeared. The doctors were overjoyed and gave out a very optimistic bulletin. At 7:30 P.M. the President was resting quietly, propped up in bed with Mrs. Harding reading to him from an article in the *Saturday Evening Post*. It was entitled "A Calm View of a Calm Man," in praise of the President for his poise and calmness in holding to his course unperturbed by the howling storm about him.

The two attending physicians, Sawyer and Boone, had momentarily left the bedside of their patient, whom they thought out of danger. The nurse was sitting in the adjacent room, completing her records. Suddenly a convulsive tremor passed over Harding's face. His body shuddered and sagged. Dropping the magazine, Mrs. Harding ran into the corridor shrieking, "Dr. Boone! Dr. Boone!" Within a few minutes the two doctors were bending over their patient. His face was calm and peaceful now. He was dead.

The doctors pleaded with Mrs. Harding to permit an autopsy. She could not be persuaded. In the absence of a definite postmortem diagnosis, the doctors had the impression that the unexpected death of the President had been caused by an unforeseen new complication—the bursting of a sclerotic blood vessel of the brain. They called it apoplexy. Lacking final proof, this diagnosis cannot be refuted with certainty.

It is more likely that the sudden death was caused by a complication of the unrecognized coronary thrombosis. The occurrence of the catastrophe on the sixth day in a patient who was permitted to walk around during the first three days, and suffering from high blood pressure, suggests a massive rupture of a softened infarct in the wall of the heart. It is noteworthy that one of his sisters died suddenly and unexpectedly in the same way.

Calvin Coolidge

(1872 – 1933)

CALVIN COOLIDGE held more elective offices than any other American President including John Quincy Adams, who topped all others in number of appointive offices and years in public service. Like John Quincy Adams, Coolidge was a New Englander and a Puritan, but unlike Adams, he did not excel as a statesman but as a politician.

Coolidge climbed the ladder of politics step by step, being elected successively to city councilman, state assemblyman, mayor, state senator, lieutenant governor, governor, and Vice-President of the United States, then fate accelerated his progress by catapulting him to the Presidency. His consistent ascent to the top has often been ascribed to "the Coolidge luck." But no man can win nineteen out of twenty elections in a democracy without possessing a special appeal for the voters, combined with an instinct for perfect timing and an unfailing sense of political expediency.

Coolidge was one of the greatest vote-getters in American political history, this despite his lack of the essential attributes commonly believed to be indispensable to a successful politician: imposing appearance, poise, oratory, and personal magnetism. Calvin Coolidge was a small, shy, awkward-looking man with a nasal voice and a handshake that lacked conviction.

Yet these apparent deficiencies in Coolidge became his greatest political assets. His boyishness and seeming helplessness had a certain appeal. His unprepossessing appearance and simple manner made him the hero of the man in the street, who could identify himself with this "Mr. Smith" who goes to Washington.

Other qualities that made Coolidge such a successful politician were his calculating caution, his patient readiness for any opportunity, and the gift of silence. Unlike some of the great Presidents who dared to explore new paths, the conservative New Englander preferred to stay on the safe and smooth road of conventionality. Steadfastly he believed in the American gospel of free enterprise and the unrestrained play of economic forces unhindered by government controls.

Coolidge made few mistakes because he tried no experiments and made few decisions. He created few enemies because he sidestepped most controversial issues; and attempts of his opponents to make him take sides he usually frustrated with a poker face and imperturbable silence.

What appeared to be the most daring action of his political career he took as Governor of Massachusetts when he assumed a fighting stance against the politically impotent American Federation of Labor on the occasion of the famous Boston police strike. He hurled at the labor leader, Samuel Gompers, the much publicized epigrammatic message, "There is no right to strike against the public safety by anybody, anywhere, at any time," that won the virtually unknown Massachusetts Governor national renown.

Closer examination shows that during the first riot-ridden days of the strike, the cautious Governor took shelter behind his wall of silence. Only after the mayor and the police commissioner had restored order and practically broken the strike did Coolidge emerge from hiding and take over as commander in chief of the National Guard; he gave the settlement the finishing touches, and got all the credit and glory.

In order to understand the man Coolidge in good health and ill, let us look at his ancestry and the environment in which he grew up. He was born in the little township of Plymouth, Vermont, of a family of substantial farmers. His grandfather and father were local politicians of some importance. His father ran a successful country store as a sideline, and in politics achieved the office of state senator; somewhere along the way he picked up the honorary title of colonel. The Coolidges were a tough-fibered, robust stock. Nine direct paternal ancestors averaged sixty-four years of age—high for their time. Over three centuries the average number of children per family dwindled from about nine to only two for the last three generations.

Calvin's ancestors, including his grandfather and father, were tall, rugged men. The son who was to become its most illustrious representative was the family's "ugly duckling" (and he never turned into a swan). He was a skinny boy with red hair, freckled skin, and a frightened look. Only on rare occasions when the child lifted his little face up to some person he knew and trusted would his keen blue eyes light up with animation.

In his appearance and build, Calvin bore a resemblance to his mother, from whom he inherited his delicate physical constitution. The hard farm life and the winter climate of Vermont was too strenuous for Mrs. Coolidge's frail body. Shortly after her marriage to John Calvin at the age of twenty-two, she took ill and was a partial invalid for the remaining seventeen years of her life, seemingly suffering from some form of tuberculosis.

Calvin Coolidge showed no symptoms of tuberculosis. His principal weakness was an allergic disposition which expressed itself during his youth in frequent sneezing, coughing, and a running nose. Possibly Calvin's well-known nasal twang became more pronounced by a chronic, allergic congestion of the mucosa obstructing the nasal passages. Even in the nasal chorus of his playmates, Calvin's quacking voice was something to make fun of and mimick.

As a country boy, Calvin was around horses from his early youth. He fell off an old mare when he was three years old and broke an arm, but it mended without trouble. His father again put him on horseback and showed him how to stay in the saddle.

Theodore Roosevelt, as already mentioned, was also a frail child, who suffered in his youth from an even more severe form of allergy—bronchial asthma—a condition which Coolidge developed later in his life. Unlike Teddy Roosevelt, who seemingly overcame his disheartening constitutional weakness by overcompensation, Coolidge, the product of different genetic heritage and environment, responded in a reverse manner to his feeling of inadequacy.

While Roosevelt steeled his body and became an outstanding athlete and extrovert, Coolidge early resigned himself to his inability to compete in strength with his father, or to become as tough and dexterous as the neighborhood lads. He never made any attempt to equal them in physical prowess, but he did try to become their superior in the mental gymnastics of linguistics and the art of legalistic discussion. At Amherst he distinguished himself as an effective speaker, by his simplicity and clarity of expression and an unexpected sense of dry impish humor.

Coolidge remained self-conscious and physically awkward all his life; he never overcame his timidity and aversion to ostentation. Although clever in all branches of farm work when he wasn't being watched, he was clumsy when he felt himself observed. His anxiety to avoid looking ridiculous kept him from joining in games or exercises requiring skill and grace. In his late twenties he took up skating and dancing to please his fiancée, but abandoned these social attempts when the victim of his attentions made a laughing remark about his efforts.

The only sport Calvin excelled in was horsemanship. A photograph of him in his forties shows him looking almost elegant in the English saddle. But he gave up this sport because, curiously enough, the farm boy seems to have been allergic to horse dander. The only outdoor pleasure Calvin enjoyed throughout his life was the solitary pastime of trout fishing, which he did in a leisurely and unsportsmanlike fashion with worms.

Calvin's mother died when he was twelve years old. She had received a serious injury caused by a runaway horse. The wound failed to heal and apparently brought on a flare-up of chronic tuberculosis. All his life Calvin remembered the melancholy day when he and his sister Abbey, three years younger, were called to the deathbed of their young mother to kneel and receive her last blessing. After they had buried her "in the blistering snows of March," the lonesome boy was despondent for several weeks. Gradually he came to lean on his father, a most kind and understanding parent who gave his son as much warmth and affection as could radiate through the insulation of his New England reserve.

During the years of Calvin's adolescence, a close relationship developed between him and his sister. He adored and admired Abbey for the qualities he lacked. She had a striking personality, accentuated by flaming red hair, charm, temperament, and an affectionate nature. Besides, she was precociously brilliant, receiving credentials to teach school at the age of thirteen.

In March 1890, Abbey was suddenly stricken with severe abdominal cramps and vomiting, symptoms that were diagnosed by the country doctors as "inflammation of the bowels," but unquestionably represented an attack of acute appendicitis. Probably the doctors, following the murderous practice of the time, dosed their luckless victim with laxatives, thus unknowingly contributing to the bursting of the appendix. Then, after having done their worst, the physicians stood helplessly by as general peritonitis developed. The lovely girl died within a week, only fifteen years old. Calvin sat at her bedside disconsolate, an impotent prayer on his lips.

In 1890 the majority of doctors, not only in Vermont but everywhere in the world, were still unacquainted with appendicitis, the inflammation of the vermiform process protruding from the blind pouch of the right colon. The little appendix is an evolutionary rudiment, the diminutive vestige of a large digestive organ of our grass-eating ancestors. As such, it is a neglected stepchild of nature and ready prey of bacterial invasions. Being narrow, the appendix is easily obstructed by inflammatory swelling, kinks, scars, and fecal concretions. If the intestinal contents become dammed up within the little pouch, they serve as a fertile soil for the pus-forming germs which can infiltrate and eventually destroy the thin wall.

According to the virulence of the particular bacteria and the individual resistance of the peritoneum of the patient, the infectious process of the appendix may either overcome the natural defenses and cause a spreading peritonitis which is usually fatal, or it may become arrested and imprisoned by the combative forces of the body. In the latter case, frequently, a localized abscess develops which may be spontaneously absorbed, resulting in either a temporary or a lasting recovery of the patient.

Before the turn of the century, acute appendicitis was one of the mysterious scourges of the world, although the pathology of appendicitis had been discovered and described as early as 1753 in Germany, and in 1812 in England. In 1886, Reginald Fitz of Harvard University gave a detailed account of the organic changes, signs, and symptoms associated with inflammation of the appendix, and advocated early surgery. A year later George Thomas Morton of Philadelphia performed the first successful appendectomy in the world, soon to be followed by a series of such operations by Charles McBurney of New York and John B. Murphy of Chicago.

Unfortunately, the teachings of Reginald Fitz had not reached the mountains of Vermont four years later. It took another ten years and thousands of victims until the rank and file of American doctors learned to recognize acute appendicitis and the necessity of early surgery.

The memory of the lost sister never faded, becoming superimposed on the idealized image of Calvin's mother. Understandably, as a man he could feel attracted only to a woman whom he could identify with his sister and his mother. Such a woman was Miss Anne Grace Goodhue, a schoolteacher, handsome, vivacious, and charming. After enduring several years of his awkward courtship, she finally consented to marry him in 1905, and apparently never regretted her choice. We do not know whether her decision was influenced by the secret confession her bashful suitor once made to her: that fate had pointed to the Presidency for him, though he was then a budding young assemblyman in the lower house of Massachusetts.

Grace Goodhue must have possessed an unusual measure of understanding and maternal instinct to marry a man with such an unfinished look. A Senator friend once said of him, "He's better than he looks." But in some respects Coolidge was not better than his immature features suggested. Some of his emotional reactions showed a level of immaturity that an average person of comparative age and background would have overcome. Even at the height of his political success he was unable to hide his discomfort when he was obliged to meet people he did not know well.

This fear of strangers, which survives to some degree in all of us, springs from the self-protective instinct of the infant to fear anything strange within the circle of his perception, particularly if it moves or makes sounds. Most adults learn to suppress and banish this fear into the twilight zone of the consciousness, along with other discomforting emotions.

In one of his rare confidential moods Coolidge once confessed to a close friend: "Do you know, I have never really grown up? It's a hard thing for me to play this game. In politics one must meet people, and that is not easy for me. . . . It's been hard for me all my life. When I was a little fellow, as long ago as I can remember, I would go into a panic if I heard stranger [*sic*] voices in the house. I felt I just couldn't meet the people and shake hands with them. Most of the visitors would sit with Mother and Father in the kitchen, and the hardest thing in the world was to have to go through the kitchen door and give them a greeting. I was almost ten before I realized that I couldn't go on that way, and by fighting hard, I used to manage to go through the old kitchen door back home, and it is not easy. . . ."

Coolidge also showed emotional immaturity in irrational temper tantrums, which sometimes shattered the dignity of the White House. The man who was inhibited in his relations with strangers gave vent to his aggression in a childlike manner toward underlings, members of his family, and close friends. Little things like the misplacement of an overcoat could kindle

violent outbursts of fury. Irving H. (Ike) Hoover, chief doorman, wrote in his book, *42 Years in the White House,* "Those
who saw Coolidge in a rage were simply startled. The older
employees about the White House who had known [Theodore]
Roosevelt, used to think he raved at times, but in his worst
temper he was calm compared to Coolidge."

Like a sleepy child, Coolidge was especially irritable in the
morning and snarled at his secretaries and friends at the slight-
est provocation. He was edgy because he hardly ever felt really
well and strong, but was always tired and easily exhausted.
Often his eyes were itching and burning, his nose running with
hayfever, and eventually he developed bronchial asthma.

In addition to horse dander, he seems to have been allergic
to house dust, to pollens, and to a variety of foods—among
them peanuts for which he had a special preference although
they often made him sick. Some of his worst allergic reactions
he experienced during his Vice-Presidency. The Senate floor
was covered with straw matting in which generations of house
dust had accumulated.

His lack of stamina forced Coolidge to economize his energy.
According to Ike Hoover, he worked fewer hours and took on
fewer tasks than any President the doorman had served under
in the White House. As President, Coolidge slept on an average of eleven hours a day, going to bed usually before 10 P.M.
He forced himself to get up at seven in the morning and was
at his desk at the stroke of nine. There he worked until 12:30,
took lunch, then a one- or two-hour nap. After this, he cleaned
off his desk and quit for the day.

Coolidge's long years in administrative positions had given
him unusual experience as an executive who knew how to delegate all the work he was not forced to do personally. Whereas
Harding's desk had always been piled high with unanswered
letters and unsigned documents in chaotic disorder, reflecting
the bewilderment of his untrained mind, Coolidge always left
his correspondence carefully sorted and disposed of at the end
of each day, his desk clean for the next morning's mail.

His habitual lassitude and lack of energy caused Coolidge to entrust to his Cabinet members most questions of policy making. Having little knowledge of the intricacies of high finance and economics, he took the easy way and left his shrewd Secretary of the Treasury, Andrew W. Mellon, a free hand in tackling most of the problems of the national economy and finance. He backed without questioning Mellon's reckless promotion of credit expansion, his encouragement of "buying on time," and his artificial stimulation of the stock market.

Strangely enough, during the last two years of Coolidge's administration, a few sincere Cassandras among the financial experts succeeded once in a while in penetrating the cordon of palace guard surrounding the President. They tried to awaken Coolidge to the imminent danger of an economic catastrophe which would involve not only the United States but the whole world, unless the prevailing financial practices were promptly changed. The longer they continued, the deeper the frantic buying and speculating public would be sucked into the quicksand of a depression.

But the tired President preferred to remain deaf to the dire warnings of the prophets of doom and to listen instead to the soporific bedtime stories of Uncle Andrew, who promised everlasting national prosperity through the magic of his financial genius.

Yet the keen nose of politician Coolidge could not be deceived forever from catching the scent that was in the air. By 1928 he could not help knowing that something was rotten behind the Potemkin villages of Andrew Mellon.

Coolidge realized that it was already too late to turn back and that any revelation of the real facts would precipitate the crisis. Like everyone who fears the humiliation of bankruptcy, he tried to hold off the day of reckoning. So he held his nose and supported Mellon in hiding the ugly specter behind a rosy smoke screen of promises and pep talks. And when the jittery stock market started to falter, the President broke his silence on one or two occasions to make encouraging public statements. He knew better, and this was one of the reasons he did not choose to run in 1928.

During the early summer of that year political friends made persistent attempts to make him change his mind about accepting the renomination "for the sake of the party and the nation." As usual on such occasions, Coolidge wasted no effort in answering, but sat in sphinxlike silence. Once when the visitors kept badgering the President, the faithful wife Grace Coolidge lost patience and suddenly piped up, "Papa thinks there will be a depression."

Several other reasons appear to have influenced Coolidge's decision not to run again. One he revealed in his autobiography. His ever-gnawing grief over the tragic death of his younger son Calvin, in 1924, made the glamor and prestige of the Presidency for him a vain and empty illusion.

The death of Calvin Coolidge, Jr., at the age of sixteen was caused by a "septicemia," the invasion and dissemination of bacteria throughout the blood stream. On July 1, 1924, the boy played a tennis match with his older brother John, on the White House grounds and in the course of it he developed a friction blister on a toe of his right foot. The blister broke and within a few hours an infection developed, manifesting itself in redness, swelling, and fever. The family physician, Dr. Edward Brown, called Commander Joel T. Boone into consultation. The foot was elevated and hot packs of bichloride of mercury applied. Under this treatment, the local inflammation soon subsided. However, symptoms of general blood poisoning appeared with alarming rapidity.

The bacteria invaded the blood stream directly through the open wound, bypassing the defenses of the lymphatic system which usually takes the brunt in such circumstances. Formerly, in cases of blood poisoning the victim was left to his own resources; then as a rule the forces of resistance of his body eventually became exhausted and he would succumb after some days or weeks of the unequal struggle. Only since the discovery of sulfa drugs and antibiotics did it become possible for the doctors to introduce powerful allies to fight a chemical warfare against the invading bacteria.

The physicians were powerless to offer young Calvin any effective aid in his desperate struggle for life. They gave him the best treatment known at the time, by employing continuous retention enemas and numerous intravenous infusions of saline solution. They made four cultures of the blood and one of the urine, finding in all of them an abundant growth of a virulent strain of *Staphylococcus albus,* a microorganism which in an attenuated and harmless form is a common inhabitant of the human skin. They vaccinated a blood donor with the dead bacteria, isolated from the cultures, and gave the patient transfusions of this blood containing some specific immunity factors. They also made intramuscular injections of a commercially produced staphylococcus antitoxin in horse serum.

In their desperation, the doctors even resorted to an intravenous infusion of the newly discovered antiseptic mercurochrome, to which miraculous bactericidal powers were attributed. All without avail. On the sixth day, severe pain, redness, and swelling developed on the shinbone of the left leg, opposite to the entrance focus of the infection on the right foot. It pointed to bacterial infiltration of the bone marrow, osteomyelitis, carried there by the blood stream from the heart.

The boy was taken to the Walter Reed Hospital. The famous surgeon John B. Deaver, and the eminent bacteriologist John Kolmer, both of Philadelphia, were hurriedly summoned. The failing patient was given a ten-minute anesthetic, and an opening was chiseled in the shinbone exposing the marrow cavity in order to release the infectious matter. No pus was found, but a profusion of deadly staphylococci. On the following day the boy developed the terminal complication of septicemia, abdominal distention and vomiting. During his last hours the delirious youth frantically implored his father to help him and make him well.

"When he went, the power and glory of the Presidency went with him," Calvin Coolidge wrote in his autobiography. It is little wonder that he, imbued with a Puritan guilt-consciousness, blamed himself for the death of his favorite son. The Father-God of the Puritan creed is the stern God of the Old Testament, the Lord Yahweh, who like his Latin counterpart, Jove, and other gods created in the image of man, is jealous of his celestial prerogatives. He will cast down in the dust a man who dares to climb too high toward heaven. And He will punish with the tears of remorse the mortal who usurps the divine privilege of tasting the sweet wine of success unmixed with the bitter gall of failure. Coolidge expresses this idea of heavenly retribution as follows: "I do not know why such a price was exacted for occupying the White House."

Another reason for Coolidge's decision not to seek re-election was his failing health. His allergic attacks occurred with increasing frequency. He had repeated spells of bronchial asthma which caused a thickening of the bronchial walls, distention of the lungs, and impairment of pulmonary circulation, thus straining the weakened heart.

There are indications that Coolidge, in addition, had developed arteriosclerotic narrowing of the coronary vessels. He suffered frequent spells of stomach upset, some of which may have been mild attacks of angina pectoris. The first severe attack of this kind occurred in May 1925 and could have represented a mild episode of coronary occlusion. It soon cleared up and the President made light of it.

There is reason to believe that Coolidge knew as early as 1928 that there was something wrong with his heart. Brigadier General Sherwood Cheney, who had been Coolidge's military aide, declared in 1938 that the President had been warned by his doctors of this weakness, and advised that he ought not to subject himself to the strain of another four years in the White House.

The most subtle influence in making up Coolidge's mind was the quiet but persistent pressure of his wife, who wished him to retire. Unknowingly she used the subliminal suggestion of a symbolic gesture to express to him, day by day, her feelings in this matter. A New England Penelope, more thrifty than her wasteful Greek prototype, she started as early as March 1925 to crochet a bedspread eight squares long and six squares wide, one square for each of the sixty-four weary months she had to wait for her hero to be freed from the toils of his term. Secretly she was looking forward to the day when he would safely return to his old fireside in Northampton and to her.

Even if his reasoning warned Coolidge not to run again, his craving for the power to which he was accustomed kept smoldering beneath the surface of his conscious decision. In spite of his sincere intention to leave the White House, there are numerous indications that his impulses were pulling him in the opposite direction; that deep in his heart he hoped that the Republican convention would become deadlocked and he would be drafted as the indispensable man.

Coolidge could not hide his jealousy of Herbert Hoover, his most likely successor, and called him "the miracle worker" and "the wonder boy." He seemed deeply wounded because his name was not even mentioned at the convention, and that his party had ignored him.

Retirement impaired the mainspring of Coolidge's life—politics was the passionate interest that had animated him for thirty-one years. It could not be replaced by the earthbound devotion for his wife. He was not versatile enough to have cultivated any absorbing hobby as a partial substitute for his vocation. He liked to solve crossword puzzles, and like many other Presidents, used to read detective stories. But these mild diversions could not fill the vacuum of leisure yawning at him after the abrupt change.

He started his autobiography, and for a while composed a dry newspaper column for a syndicate. Both were lucrative ventures. Yet he could never be really happy after his fickle mistress, politics, had taken him at his word and turned her back on him. He protested too much about how comfortable he felt in his retirement, but friends found him deeply resentful and feeling sorry for himself. In April 1932, Frederick C.

Nichols called upon Coolidge in his Northampton office and found him "quite embittered, and in obviously poor health." To Nichols he said, "I have been ignored and forgotten." And he compared his shabby office with his former White House surroundings.

Coolidge's hayfever did not improve, despite the Vermont climate. Come late summer, the strong smell of ragweed permeated the air of New England and filled it with the stinging pollen, heralding the opening of the worst of the hayfever seasons. Then Coolidge was troubled more than ever with sneezing, coughing, and suffocating attacks of asthma. The irritation of the respiratory tract was probably aggravated by his smoking several cigars a day, the only indulgence he permitted himself.

The former President's bitterness did not improve his physical resistance. His outlook was further darkened when he witnessed the ever-deepening inroads of the depression, that invaded Coolidge's remote little country town, bankrupting his neighbors and friends.

In the latter part of 1931 Coolidge's secretary observed his growing weariness. Sometimes the President took two naps a day instead of one. He suffered recurring attacks of shortness of breath, but he called them stomach trouble and took all kinds of digestive tablets, pounds of baking soda, and Enos Fruit Salts. He didn't have much confidence in his doctors and apparently never consulted a competent allergist.

Coolidge's favorite remedy always had been Aurora's liniment, which he used for headaches, bruises, and probably also rubbed on his chest for his asthma. It was an ill-smelling compound of pungent ingredients including ammonia and arnica, blended by Miss Aurora Pierce, Colonel Coolidge's old housekeeper who had bequeathed her secret formula to the grateful family. Unquestionably Miss Aurora was unaware of the fact that in brewing her malodorous mixture she conformed with the primitive belief that a medicine is the more effective the more repulsive it smells or tastes, since this increases its potency in driving away the evil spirits of the disease.

In the early summer of 1932 Coolidge went to Plymouth. There he had a severe attack of hayfever with asthma, which indicates that he was also sensitive to the pollen of the early grasses. His doctor felt that this attack left his heart in a weakened condition. People who had known him said he had aged so much that at sixty he seemed as old as his father had looked at seventy.

In spite of this, Coolidge promised to make two campaign addresses for Herbert Hoover, in New York and in Chicago. When he made his speech in New York he did not feel well, and at one point feared he couldn't finish. He sent word to Hoover that he had found the excitement and effort on that occasion more strain than he should rightly put on his heart. Hoover naturally asked him to forego the Chicago speech.

That autumn Mrs. Coolidge recalls that scarcely a night passed that Coolidge was not compelled to use a spray for difficulty in breathing. It is unlikely that all such spells of dyspnea from which Coolidge suffered in his later years were exclusively of allergic origin. We can assume that some were caused by heart failure and partially represented "cardiac asthma." It is also probable that his difficulty in breathing during the last months of his life was in part a manifestation of nocturnal dyspnea commonly occurring as a sequel of inadequate circulation, particularly in the lying position and was caused by coronary sclerosis.

In November 1932, Coolidge saw the Republican Party defeated in a Democratic landslide corresponding in vastness to the economic landslide which the voters blamed on the Republican administration. The downfall of his party deepened the former President's sadness. With the election of Franklin D. Roosevelt and the New Deal, Coolidge saw his world crumble before his eyes. He had nothing to live for any longer.

Suspecting that many foods contributed to his discomfort, he hardly dared to eat; he lost weight, and became more and more tired. Although he would not admit that he had heart trouble, Mrs. Coolidge noticed that he often surreptitiously took his pulse.

It was a fine winter day, January 5, 1933, in Northampton. Calvin Coolidge rose early but did not shave as usual before breakfast. He went downtown to his office at nine o'clock. After perhaps an hour there, he mumbled that he was not feeling well and was going home. At home he sat down awhile. Mrs. Coolidge had gone to Main Street for her daily shopping. Some household chore took Coolidge to the basement where he passed the handyman with a brusk, "Good morning, Robert," and then climbed two flights of stairs to reach his bedroom. It seems that at noon he remembered that he had not shaved. He went to the bathroom, took off his coat and got out his shaving kit.

When Mrs. Coolidge returned, she called out cheerily to him. There was no answer. She went upstairs, and there on the bathroom floor she found his lifeless body.

No postmortem was performed. It was the consensus of the doctors who had examined him over his last years that the silent Coolidge had died from some form of silent coronary occlusion.

Franklin Delano Roosevelt

(1882 – 1945)

Franklin D. Roosevelt's day of birth was almost a day of tragedy. The date was January 30, 1882, and the scene the country house on the family estate at Hyde Park overlooking the Hudson.

The delivery of the first-born of James and Sara Delano Roosevelt was difficult and prolonged. An overdose of chloroform administered to the mother almost asphyxiated the infant; he was born in a deathlike respiratory standstill, the skin blue, the body limp. Years later Sara Delano Roosevelt recalled: "I was given too much chloroform and it was nearly fatal to us both. As a matter of fact, the nurse said later she never expected the baby to be alive and was surprised that he was."

Apparently the most primitive and efficient method of resuscitation was used on the infant: mouth-to-mouth breathing. After minutes—an eternity—the air, rhythmically blown in and sucked out, expanded the collapsed lungs, cleared the narcotized respiratory center in the brain, and awakened the newborn infant. He heralded his entrance into the world with a cry of anger and bewilderment.

With careful nursing the ten-pound baby grew into a healthy and happy boy, unspoiled but overprotected by the parents as their first-born and only son. They did not expose him to the rough-and-tumble of school life until he was fourteen. Franklin's first teacher was his mother, who gave him the elements of grammar school. She was followed by private tutors who taught him French, Spanish and German, and awakened in him a life-long interest in natural history, geography and navigation.

The unfavorable consequences of the protective isolation in which Franklin was reared appeared in the succeeding years of his life. By being kept from contact with children outside his home environment he was sheltered from the barrage of disease germs and viruses through which most other children of his generation had to pass.

Among them were the viruses of anterior poliomyelitis—inflammation of the anterior part of the gray matter of the spine—viruses to which a certain percentage of humans are susceptible while others are not. These viruses subsist in excrements and sewerage, and during hot weather survive in dirt and dust, particularly in localities deficient in cleanliness and sanitation. Susceptible children born in such surroundings are prone to the infection at an early age. It was among such infants that the discoverers of poliomyelitis first discerned the pattern of the disease and therefore named it "infantile paralysis."

However, it seems that repeated ingestion of small amounts of the polio viruses—too minute to produce the actual disease—can effect in susceptible children a gradual active immunization, whereas susceptible children growing up in less contaminated surroundings and protected by too much cleanliness have less opportunity to acquire such an immunity. Consequently, they may catch the disease at any age if they happen to swallow a sufficient quantity of the virus with their food or drink.

Roosevelt's chief weakness from birth was the hypersensitivity of his respiratory tract, evidenced by sneezing, coughing and sore throat brought on by various factors. Among them were physiochemical stimuli, such as damp air, possibly smoking, and emotional upsets that produced changes in the mucus lining, making it vulnerable to the viruses of the common cold and secondary bacterial invaders.

Roosevelt's letters abound with complaints about colds and sore throats, often combined with sinus trouble, bronchitis and fever. He made his earliest entry in the lifelong list of colds in his first letter, written when he was five years old. Franklin had no other illnesses until he left the genteel bacterial milieu of his home for the jungle of germs pervading the outside world.

When he was eleven years old he had a frightening experience. His father had taken him to Superior, Wisconsin, to witness the launching of a large ore carrier. As the ship hit the water it raised a large wave that washed the boy over the pier into the bay. He was promptly pulled out. There is no record that he caught a cold as a result of the dunking.

In the happy surroundings of Hyde Park, Roosevelt grew up into a tall and handsome youth who enjoyed the healthful sports of hunting, fishing, horseback riding and, above all, sailing. At fourteen Roosevelt was sent to Groton, an exclusive prep school. Here the children's diseases he had escaped thus far caught up with him. In the complex jigsaw puzzle of his genes, arranged according to Mendelian law, he had apparently inherited almost no immunity against the disease germs and viruses to which he was to be exposed. In his first school year he contracted scarlet fever, followed soon after by mumps.

When he was sixteen it was a belated but the more severe attack of measles that prevented his running away from school to join the Navy in the Spanish-American War. In the manner of Alexandre Dumas, he and a friend had hired a bakery truck to smuggle them out of the campus during the night. The lowly measles was the villain that ambushed the two heroes on the eve of their venture. It nipped Roosevelt's coveted naval career in the bud by putting him to bed, sneezing and coughing, broken out in rose-colored spots, with eyes inflamed by the disease and downcast in disappointment. He did not dream then that his future would closely associate him with the Navy he loved, in the functions of Assistant Secretary and, eventually, Commander in Chief.

After four rather undistinguished years at Groton Roosevelt reluctantly entered Harvard in 1900. He still would have preferred a Navy career but his father persuaded him to take up the study of law. As a college student Franklin was the picture of a healthy young American, more than six feet tall, well built, slender, with a fair complexion and blond hair. His only defect was nearsightedness, for which he wore glasses. He played on the freshman football team and rowed on the freshman crew, although he never put his heart into competitive sports. He was more interested in English, writing and debating, and for his scholarship earned the Phi Betta Kappa key, like his fifth cousin Teddy Roosevelt before him. He graduated in 1904 and went to Columbia Law School. There, he spent three years and learned enough law to pass the New York bar but did not acquire the degree of L.L.B.

While Franklin was a senior at Harvard he fell in love with Eleanor Roosevelt, the daughter of his godfather Eliot, and won her consent to marry him. His dominating mother, whom he had not consulted, objected, and took him on a West Indies cruise for a cooling-off period. But young Roosevelt equaled his mother in determination and the marriage took place in 1905. President Theodore Roosevelt gave away the bride, who was his orphaned niece. In the first ten years of their marriage the young Roosevelts had five children—four sons and one daughter. One son born in 1909 died in infancy.

Franklin D. Roosevelt was up to now unaware of his particular genius that destined him to become a political leader. After practicing law in New York for only three years, he found himself carried into the main stream of politics, and was twenty-eight when the voters of his district elected him state senator.

In the fall of 1912 while running for his second term as state senator, Roosevelt contracted typhoid fever which took a severe but uncomplicated course of four or five weeks' fever and prostration, and a longer period for recuperation.

In March 1913 he accepted the post of Assistant Secretary of the Navy. During the same year he complained about stomach trouble; perhaps he was suffering from chronic recurrent appendicitis. This eventually culminated in a more severe attack necessitating an emergency operation in 1914. In 1915 he was troubled by an undefined type of backache called lumbago which had bothered him before, along with a succession of head colds and sinus attacks. A number of throat infections during

1916 and 1917 kept him in bed from two to four weeks at a time, and in August 1917 he had to spend several days in the hospital with a tonsillar abscess.

In the last summer of World War I an influenza epidemic, apparently originating in neutral Spain, reached the war theater in France and decimated the opposing armies. Roosevelt was then abroad on an inspection tour. On the return trip he caught the disease and developed an influenza pneumonitis which at the time carried a high mortality. He was so ill he had to be taken from the ship on a stretcher, but once at home recovered quickly. In 1919 his earlier nose and throat ailments again made his life miserable and in December he finally had his chronically infected tonsils cut out.

In the meantime Roosevelt's political star kept rising. As Assistant Secretary of the Navy he made such a name for himself that in 1920 the national Democratic convention nominated him candidate for Vice-President. Unlike his laconic opponent on the Republican ticket, Calvin Coolidge, Roosevelt made a number of campaign speeches and did not dodge controversial issues such as the lost cause of the League of Nations.

The Democratic defeat at the polls put him out of public office for the first time in ten years. The outcome neither disappointed nor discouraged him as it did some of his friends. He was still young and flexible, and felt that with Harding's election the national pendulum had swung from Washington to Wall Street. Without hesitation he joined Wall Street for a spell and took the job of vice-president of one of the largest bonding companies in the country. Emulating his indefatigable cousin Teddy, he also joined a new law firm, accepted innumerable speaking engagements, and accepted leadership in a dozen civic organizations—among them the Boy Scout Foundation of Greater New York, of which he was president.

Overworked and tired in the summer of 1921, he went with his family to his seaside cottage at Campobello, New Brunswick. His vacation was rudely interrupted by the news that a subcommittee of the Republican Senate had started investigation of a scandal in the Navy that had occurred during Roosevelt's appointment as Assistant Secretary. Without giving him an opportunity to defend himself the committee blamed him for negligence in office. He rushed to Washington and attempted to refute the wild accusations featured in blazing headlines. Burning with indignation because of the treatment by the committee, he left steaming Washington for the heat of New York. On July 27, he tried to forget his anger by visiting the New York Boy Scouts camp at Lake Kanowalke. He then returned to Campobello, where, on August 10, 1921, the virus of paralytic poliomyelitis struck him down and ended the first chapter of his brilliant career.

The incubation time of poliomyelitis supposedly lasts seven to twenty-one days, a period that would include his sojourn in New York and his exposure to the virus suspended in the street dust, or possibly carried by one of the Boy Scouts. On the morning of August 10, Roosevelt did not feel well but went with his children on a picnic, sailing and fishing, ignoring his indisposition. On the way home they all helped for several hours to extinguish a forest fire.

Covered with grime and perspiration, they dived into a freshwater lagoon, then took another swim in the frigid water of the Bay of Fundy near the cottage. During supper, Roosevelt felt chilly, a dull ache in his back. Believing he was having another attack of lumbago, he went upstairs to bed. A sudden teethchattering chill shook him. Extra blankets, hot drinks and hot-water bottles helped little. Almost the whole night he lay shivering and restless as the virus of the disease coursed through the blood stream, infiltrating the motor centers of his spine.

We cannot judge whether overwork and emotional strain to which Roosevelt had been subjected previously had increased his susceptibility to the virus, but it seems evident that the slight indisposition of August 10 was the beginning of the systemic stage of poliomyelitis that usually lasts some five days. It has been assumed that Roosevelt unwittingly aggravated the disease by exhausting his already sick body with strenuous exercise and shocking it with sudden lowering of the skin temperature. These catalytic factors accelerated the spread of the virus and telescoped the separate systemic and neurologic stages of the disease into one continuity.

Next morning the old family physician diagnosed the condition as a cold, disregarding the patient's complaints about an unusual weakness of his right knee. During the day this muscular weakness grew rapidly worse. When Roosevelt tried to get up in the afternoon he had the mortifying experience of feeling his knee double up under his weight. That evening the other knee began to fail and by the following morning had lost its strength. The patient was aching all over and had a fever of 102°.

Thoroughly alarmed, the family called in Dr. W. W. Keen, famous Philadelphia surgeon, who was vacationing nearby. He was the same Dr. Keen who had operated twenty-eight years before on Grover Cleveland. The elderly surgeon examined the patient and recognized that the paralysis was of spinal origin, but was unable to make the correct diagnosis. He gave a guarded prognosis concerning the possible duration of recovery and advised deep massage of the affected muscles.

Meanwhile the inflammatory process in the spine took its relentless course. By the end of the third day it had spread throughout the nerve centers controlling the muscles from the chest down. By-passing the musculature of the chest, it partially paralyzed the upper extremities, particularly the flexor muscles of the thumbs, making writing impossible. The bladder was also involved and had to be drained by catheterization; correlated was an atony of the rectum, interfering with control of the bowels. The fever continued for six to seven days, then abated, to recur in occasional spurts for several more weeks.

After two weeks the function of the bladder and rectum returned, followed briefly by the recovery of the upper extremities. However, the muscles from the hips down remained paralyzed and were exquisitely sensitive to touch for many weeks. It took as long as six months before the tenderness completely disappeared from the calves of the legs.

On August 25 Dr. Robert Lovett of Boston, expert on infantile paralysis, examined the patient and definitely established the diagnosis of epidemic poliomyelitis. In spite of the extensive nerve involvement, he believed that there was hope for an almost complete recovery. He stopped immediately the extremely painful massages as useless, if not harmful, and recommended relaxing hot baths instead. The helpless patient had to be handled like a baby, turned and bathed, his knees supported on pillows, his tender legs protected from blanket pressure by wire loops.

During the weeks of his deepest misery hardly a sound of complaint came from Roosevelt. He was too proud to reveal how wretched he felt and to accept the humiliation of pity. His attempt to make light of his condition is reflected in a note to a friend on September 16: "I have renewed my youth in a rather unpleasant manner by contracting what was fortunately a rather mild case of infantile paralysis." Years later he confessed that there were days when waves of utter despair overcame him and he thought that God had forsaken him.

In September Dr. Lovett entrusted the care of Roosevelt to Dr. George Draper of New York, who transferred him to the Presbyterian Hospital. Dr. Draper took a more pessimistic view of the chances of recovery; for a time he was even afraid that the lower back muscles, required for sitting up, would never regain their function. To his relief they showed some response in November; the patient could be placed in a wheel chair and taken to his home on East 65th Street.

In January 1922 a contraction of the flexor muscles at the back of the knees became noticeable and, simultaneously, a tendency of the right foot to drop. Some of the affected nerve centers had started to recover while others, damaged beyond repair, became absorbed and replaced by scar-lined cavities in the spine. Of the correlated paralyzed muscles some regained their tone while others atrophied, causing an imbalance between antagonistic muscle groups. The position of the knees and feet was corrected by plaster casts and, in February, these were replaced by heavy steel braces reaching from the hips to the attached shoes.

In order to be able to support himself on crutches Roosevelt started daily exercises of the muscles of his upper extremities, and in the spring of 1922 was able to sit on the floor and wrestle with his boys, holding his own by using his powerful shoulders and arms. Simultaneously, gentle exercises of the surviving muscles and muscle fibers of his pelvis, thighs and legs were started, systematically continued and extended.

In the summer of 1922 he took up swimming and other exercises in the warm water of an outdoor pool. He noticed that he could move his legs much better when their weight was balanced by the weight of the displaced water, and they could support his trunk while standing in deep water. In September 1924, Roosevelt went to Warm Springs, Georgia, and spent six weeks there. He fancied that the buoyancy of the warm mineral water put new life in his paralyzed legs. Wishing to share the benefit of the healing waters with fellow sufferers, he founded a nonprofit organization in which, over the years, he put a good deal of his fortune.

For seven years Roosevelt's single goal was to rebuild the muscles of his legs so that he could walk upright again. He succeeded in strengthening the surviving muscle fibers of his legs to the utmost and re-educating some auxiliary muscles, but most of the musculature lifting the feet was hopelessly atrophied and most of the thigh muscles that stretch the knees never regained their use.

With heavy braces locked at the knee joints he learned to keep his body upright and to carry and swing it forward with his arms, using the crutches as support and fulcrum. He also accomplished the feat of alternately lifting his legs from the hips and taking stiff-legged steps. Eventually, he was able to substitute a special cane for one of his crutches and the arm of one of his husky sons or an aide for support. To sit, he had to unlock the joints of his braces, then lock them again in pulling himself into an upright position.

Reading Roosevelt's optimistic notes during his years of

dauntless effort to rebuild muscles that were irreparably de-
nervated, one realizes that he refused to acknowledge his crippled condition—that he was only able to crawl without mechanical support. What he actually learned to do was to simulate the
walking movements; but he never could use his legs for walking.

When Roosevelt returned from the hospital, a bitter controversy about his future arose among his mother, his wife, and
his friends. Fastidious Sara Delano Roosevelt who had always
felt a distaste for the vulgar business of politics, wanted her son
to retire and live the life of a country gentleman at Hyde Park
as his father had done before him. There, he could indulge in
his hobbies of collecting stamps, ship models and the like. She
argued that at forty he had already done his bit for society and
had an honorable political career to look back on. On the other
side stood his wife, Eleanor, his devoted friend Louis McHenry
Howe, and his doctor, George Draper, who knew Roosevelt's
character and potentialities better than his mother and realized
that a life of leisure, away from the noise and excitement of
public life, was contrary to his nature. They insisted that in spite
of his handicap he should resume his activities in politics, law
and finance. Their encouragement was the spiritual crutch that
supported Roosevelt on his return to public life.

In 1924 Roosevelt acted as floor leader of the Democratic
convention at Madison Square Garden, and made his first political speech since his illness, nominating Al Smith as presidential
candidate. For this occasion he had practiced for weeks walking
unassisted, only with his braces and crutches, a measured distance to the lectern. Holding on to it with one hand, he was
able to speak standing up for some forty minutes. For the next
four years he remained in the political background, devoting
his time to law and business, but mainly to strengthening his
legs. At the same time he kept in close contact with the Democratic Party and the press, and his friends saw to it that his
name was kept before the public.

In 1928 he again nominated Al Smith as Democratic candidate for President. Smith begged him to run in his stead for

Governor of New York in order to keep the state Democratic. After long hesitation, Roosevelt accepted. He won the election, while Smith lost the state. Roosevelt had been reluctant to accept the governorship because it demanded too much of his time; he fancied that two more years of systematic exercise would restore his ability to walk. In 1930 he was re-elected Governor with such an enormous majority that his nomination as President on the Democratic ticket in 1932 was almost a foregone conclusion.

Much has been written about the influence of the crippling disease on the character of Roosevelt. Frances Perkins, an old friend of the family, wrote:

> Franklin Roosevelt underwent a spiritual transformation during the years of his illness.... The years of pain and suffering had purged the slightly arrogant attitude Roosevelt had displayed upon occasion before he was stricken. The man emerged completely warm hearted with humility of spirit and a deeper philosophy. Having been to the depths of trouble he understood the problems of people in trouble.... He never displayed the slightest bitterness about his misfortune.... He believed that Divine Providence had intervened to save him from total paralysis, despair and death.

Roosevelt had never lacked courage. His illness taught him to laugh at all obstacles and never to accept defeat. He reportedly said: "If you had spent two years in bed trying to wiggle your big toe, after that everything else would seem easy."

It seems of little consequence whether he succeeded in wiggling his big toe; what is important is that he never gave up trying. Even if he could never conquer his crippling disease physically—spiritually he triumphed over it. With the same mental attitude, as President he tackled the world-wide epidemic of the Great Depression which the economic determinists considered a natural phenomenon that must run its course like an eclipse of the sun, defying all human interference.

Roosevelt's political enemies maintained that he actually

never succeeded in overcoming the depression until the artificial stimulus of World War II revived the national economy. This may be true in the same sense that Roosevelt never really overcame the physical aspects of his illness. But, just as he conquered the terrifying concept of his own affliction, he succeeded as President in dispelling the demoralizing influence of the depression. His own courage renewed the courage of the people; his faith and his hope imbued them with faith and hope.

Two attempts were made to assassinate Roosevelt. One occurred during his first term as Governor, when a home-made time bomb was sent to him by mail. Rough handling of the package at the Albany post office set off the clockwork and the amateurish device was promptly rendered harmless.

More serious was the attempt on Roosevelt's life at Miami, Florida, in February 1932, a few weeks before his inauguration. It was made by the thirty-two-year-old Italian bricklayer, Giuseppe Zangara, a paranoiac like Czolgosz and Schrank before him. He also was small, unattractive, unmarried. Zangara's peculiarity was a chronic stomach ailment for which surgical exploration and a later autopsy revealed no organic explanation, although it was the center of his motivations and compulsions.

The early trauma of being forced to do hard labor as a child, while more fortunate children around him were playing games, instilled in him a gnawing envy and profound bitterness that were partially converted into cramps in the intestinal tract, the most responsive target of emotion. The stomach trouble grew up with him, always reminding him of his early deprivations. In adolescence he absorbed some Marxist and anarchist slogans, rationalizing that capitalistic exploitation was responsible for his affliction, and nursed a compulsion to kill the most prominent representatives of capitalist society, kings and presidents. Somewhere in Italy, in 1922, he bought a pistol, planning to assassinate King Victor Emmanuel III, but was unable to get close enough to him. Soon after he immigrated to the United States he toyed with the idea of shooting President Calvin Coolidge.

In 1931, an acute phase of schizophrenia completed Zangara's separation from reality. He gave up working and lived only for his ailing stomach and his plans for revenge on society. Because his stomach felt better in a warm climate he moved to Miami in the summer of 1932. In the winter of 1933 he conceived the plan to kill President Hoover in Washington, but hesitated because Washington was too cold for his stomach. Instead, Zangara decided to kill the President-elect when Roosevelt came to Miami for a short public address.

Zangara showed up at the public park hours early but still too late to get a front seat. Roosevelt arrived in an automobile and gave a short talk from the rear seat, the floodlight making him an outstanding target. However, the people in the first row towered over the small assassin, obstructing his view. His chance came when the crowd was breaking up. At the last minute, however, Roosevelt slid down in the seat, making himself a smaller target. This fortuitous move probably saved his life. He was not hit. One of the five bullets from the assassin's revolver mortally wounded Mayor Anton Cermak of Chicago, the others inflicted minor wounds on four bystanders. Immediately after the shooting the FBI, fearing more than one man was involved in the plot, wanted to spirit Roosevelt away. But he insisted on getting his bleeding friend Cermak to the hospital in the car, holding him in his strong arms all the way.

During his twelve years in the White House Roosevelt was under the constant care of the Surgeon General of the Navy, Dr. Ross T. McIntyre, an eye, nose and throat specialist. During the first year as President he had more than his usual quota of head colds and sinus trouble, which Dr. McIntyre attributed to the newly installed air-conditioning at the White House, the high humidity in Washington, and the complete change of living conditions. Roosevelt was particularly troubled by his sinuses after days of high tension, but much less during vacations. It is reported that for months his daily afternoon routine consisted in sinus treatments after a swim and a rubdown.

In 1934 Roosevelt had a prolonged influenza-like respiratory infection. The President's blood pressure during the summer of 1937 showed a slight rise; simultaneously he gained weight and had to go on a diet. In the fall of the same year he had a severe intestinal virus attack, followed by an abscess of a molar, which had to be extracted.

It is reported that in the late summer of 1938 Roosevelt had the first of a series of "little strokes." One of these, it is said, occurred while he was visiting his son at the Mayo Clinic. The manifestations of such little strokes are described as attacks of dizziness or fainting, often associated with temporary one-sided numbness and muscular weakness, unilateral blurring of vision or transitory blindness, frequently also a temporary inability to talk. A concomitant complaint, hard to evaluate, may be headache. Characteristically, little strokes are of short duration and leave no evidence of residual cerebral damage.

They are assumed to be caused by a temporary insufficiency of blood supply to a cerebral area, based on arteriosclerotic occlusion of a vessel segment feeding the brain, combined with temporary failure of a compensatory mechanism. If the anemia of a brain area lasts beyond a few minutes, the "little" becomes a full-blown stroke, resulting in destruction of the gray matter involved. Such destructive episodes are mainly due to obstruction of a sclerotic artery by blood clots, either formed locally or carried there from another source, or by rupture of and hemorrhage from a vessel within the brain.

Following Roosevelt's trip to Cairo and Teheran in December 1943, his health suffered a marked decline. He had another influenza-like attack of two weeks' duration and lost about ten pounds. Several doctors were called in consultation. All refused to talk for publication, but intimated to some of their colleagues that the President had symptoms of cerebral arteriosclerosis with vascular cerebral insufficiency. In the spring of 1944 the President developed a severe bronchitis that gave the appearance of bronchopneumonia. He was seriously ill. He recovered slowly and incompletely, and his coughing persisted. In June 1944, an examining physician is said to have given his private opinion that the President had only a fifty-fifty chance to outlast his third term.

Shortly after Roosevelt's death Walter Lippmann contended in his syndicated column that the Democratic delegates who voted for Roosevelt in Chicago in July 1944 were fully aware that he was desperately ill, and were really voting for Truman as President. This startling statement unquestionably is an exaggeration of the known facts. Rumors were going around (though never substantiated) that the President had suffered a coronary thrombosis and had a cancer of the prostate. The cerebral arteriosclerosis from which he was suffering has an unpredictable prognosis and duration, as the example of other Presidents has shown. Roosevelt himself certainly never knew how ill he was.

In the fall of 1944 Roosevelt again had a series of upper respiratory colds. An inveterate smoker, he cut his daily quota of cigarettes from two packages daily to less than one. About the same time, his increasing weariness overcame his pride and he discarded his heavy painful braces, giving up the pretense of walking. His last address to Congress he made sitting in a wheel chair.

In October 1944 a whispering campaign about the President's precarious health seemed to diminish his chances for re-election to a fourth term. Some of his political advisers urged him to quiet these rumors by making a public appearance. A chilling rain was falling on the day set. Against the strenuous objections of his family, Roosevelt went through with the plan, riding bareheaded in an open automobile through the streets of New York.

It has often been claimed that the President's cerebral deterioration at Yalta in February 1945 was responsible for agreements which caused the international neurosis of the cold war. The fact is, not the pledges given at Yalta, but the breaking of them, generated an atmosphere of international distrust and hostility. And there is no remedy against international amorality and broken pledges. In the pictures taken at Yalta the President looked haggard and worn; death seemed to be written on his face. About March 1, 1945, a full-time bodyguard was assigned to Vice-President Truman.

It has been reported that Roosevelt had a definite stroke in the latter part of March 1945 at Hyde Park, but recovered quickly. If this is true is it difficult to understand why his physician permitted him to travel by train on March 30 to Warm Springs, or why he did not accompany him on the trip.

On the morning of April 12, 1945, in the "Little White House," Roosevelt was preparing a speech to be delivered over the radio two days later. Dr. McIntyre talked by phone with the doctor in charge of the President at Warm Springs. He was assured that the patient was in excellent condition. During the noon hour the President sat in his leather chair looking over some state papers; Margaret Suckley, a cousin, was crocheting in a chair nearby. Elizabeth Shoumatoff, an artist, was sitting opposite him making sketches for a new portrait. About one o'clock Roosevelt suddenly looked up and said: "I have a terrific headache." He raised his left hand to his head, pressed it to his temple and ran it to his forehead—then slumped in his chair. He never regained consciousness, and expired at 3:35 P.M. No autopsy was performed. "Massive cerebral hemorrhage" was given as the cause of death. This diagnosis seems to be substantiated by the severity and rapidity of the cerebral catastrophe.

INDEX